Cooperative Extension

ES–93

Herbaceous Perennials Production

A GUIDE FROM PROPAGATION TO MARKETING

Written by

Leonard P. Perry
Professor
University of Vermont Extension System

Northeast Regional Agricultural Engineering Service
Cooperative Extension
152 Riley-Robb Hall
Ithaca, New York 14853-5701

NRAES–93
July 1998

©1998 by the Northeast Regional Agricultural Engineering Service
All rights reserved. Inquiries invited.

ISBN 0-935817-29-8

Library of Congress Cataloging-in-Publication Data

Perry, Leonard P.
    Herbaceous perennials production : a guide from propagation to
marketing / written by Leonard P. Perry.
        p.   cm. -- (NRAES : 93)
    Includes bibliographical references.
    ISBN 0-935817-29-8 (pbk.)
    1. Perennials. 2. Floriculture. I. Title. II. Series: NRAES (Series) ; 93.
SB434.P4755   1998
635.9'32'068--DC21   98-18961
                                                            CIP

Requests to reprint parts of this publication should be sent to NRAES. In your request, please state which parts of the publication you would like to reprint and describe how you intend to use the reprinted material. Contact NRAES if you have any questions.

Northeast Regional Agricultural Engineering Service (NRAES)
Cooperative Extension, 152 Riley-Robb Hall
Ithaca, New York 14853-5701
Phone: (607) 255-7654 • Fax: (607) 254-8770 • E-mail: NRAES@CORNELL.EDU

About the Author

Dr. Leonard Perry has been growing perennials in the United States for twenty-eight years, first in the South and later in the North. He has an undergraduate degree from Auburn University and graduate degrees from Cornell University. Dr. Perry has spent summers working in industry and at Longwood Gardens in Kennett Square, Pennsylvania. He has been with the cooperative extension system at the University of Vermont since 1981, working directly with the industry and region and touring perennial gardens and nurseries worldwide. Research during his tenure in Vermont has focused primarily on herbaceous perennials and has covered all aspects of perennial culture, particularly overwintering and hardiness. At grower programs in the United States and Canada, Dr. Perry has shared what he has learned from industry and research, and this publication collects that information for the first time.

Table of Contents

Table of Contents

Table of Contents

Table of Contents

Table of Contents

Table of Contents

List of Figures

List of Tables

List of Tables

Introduction

Herbaceous perennials are unique landscape plants. Like annuals, they can be accent elements in the landscape. Unlike annuals, most perennials die back to the ground each fall and emerge again the next spring from a perennating structure — a part of the plant that can survive the winter, such as a fleshy root or rhizome. Some perennials are evergreen.

Perennials are inexpensive to install and maintain when their cost is projected over their life spans, which is two or more years. Some gardeners have mistakenly looked to perennials for a "quick-fix," no-maintenance alternative to annuals. In fact, labor is required to stake, disbud, divide, and generally maintain perennials. Another common misconception of consumers is that perennials are substitutes for annuals; however, most perennials have a shorter blooming period than annuals.

In an herbaceous perennial planting, the composition of foliar textures, flower types, colors, and plant sizes can change dramatically during a single season. Subtle tones and textures of foliage assume a greater importance in perennial plantings than in annual plantings. Seasonal change is provided by "exotic" species (nonnative or tropical species, such as the large-leaved *Gunnera)* and by native species. Native species are defined differently by many, but they generally include wildflowers such as the spring-flowering trilliums or the fall-flowering asters.

Perennial groupings often combine plants of many origins and habitats — for example, a grouping in a shady location could contain rhododendrons from the Pacific Northwest, *Astilbe* cultivars from Germany, England

primroses, and new *Epimedium* varieties from China. The diversity of perennial species adds complexity to perennial gardening and a challenge to production.

After almost two decades of growth, herbaceous perennial production and sales are still strong and likely to remain so. Worth an estimated U.S.$1.37 billion in retail sales in 1993 in the United States and Canada (Rhodus, 1994), this crop continues to increase in popularity and sales and is a key income or growth area for many firms, especially during recessionary times. When home gardeners have less income, they tend to use perennials to add color and structure to borders and foundations rather than costlier shrubs.

In a survey of firms that sell perennials among other crops, Canadian firms responded that perennials accounted for gross sales of 43% (up 74% from 1992); firms in the northeastern United States reported that perennials accounted for gross sales of 33% (up 27% from 1992) (Rhodus, 1994). According to an article in *Greenhouse Management and Production*, a 1994 survey of bedding plant growers found that 77% of the firms surveyed sold perennials, and 74% reported an increase in sales over the previous year. However, according to the same article, sales are up but prices are not (Behe and Walker, 1995).

While gardeners looking to perennials as a no-maintenance alternative to annuals are reverting back to easier-to-care-for annuals, others have become "hooked" by the rich diversity of herbaceous perennials and the ability to specialize in groups or genera. Perennials are also being purchased as a less expensive ingredient for borders than shrubs and trees.

About This Book

A lot of cultural and varietal information about herbaceous perennials can be found in popular references (see "Recommended Reading and Other Sources of Information" beginning on page 203). This publication presents pertinent information from such references, along with research-based information about commercial production, all in one convenient place. The goal in writing this book was to discuss items specifically relevant to production. The focus is on nursery and greenhouse production of field or container perennials, but the greenhouse plug and bedding plant methods of perennial production are covered as well. Many topics, such as botany, greenhouse engineering, soils, pests, and marketing, are covered in more depth in other sources.

This reference should be a valuable source of information for most perennial growers, especially those who are new to the industry. It will also be of interest to people who are thinking about getting involved in the industry and students who may be contemplating a career in the perennial industry.

The extensive appendixes on propagation and pests, which were compiled from many of the most complete references available, should prove useful to all who grow perennials, whether they grow them commercially or at home. A glossary of terms is included beginning on page 196 to help readers who may be unfamiliar with some of the terminology used in the book.

CHAPTER 1

Starting a Business

Many people like to grow flowers or grow them well, so they think they could do it for a living. However, making the transition from hobby to vocation involves learning about all aspects of business, including money management and marketing. Some growers need good people management skills and an awareness of government regulations (both federal and state) that must be followed when hiring and serving people — the Americans with Disabilities Act, for example.

This chapter contains a few tips and answers to frequently asked questions to get you thinking about what it entails to start a business. If you are considering growing or selling perennials or using them in a service (as in the case of landscaping), you first need to make sure you really want to do it as a business and not merely as a hobby. Having a successful full-time business often requires a total commitment of resources and time from you and any close family members.

An alternative to having your own business is working in one owned by someone else. Advantages to this are that you do not have to worry as much about cash flow, especially during off months; you do not have the liabilities and stresses involved; and you do not have to work as wholeheartedly for the business.

On the other hand, when you own your own business, you do the decision making, you choose which plants to grow, you control your working hours, and, in good times, you reap the rewards. A key issue in having your own business is having a cooperative partner or family.

What Can I Expect to Earn?

Your earnings will vary depending on your market, drive, desire to earn, abilities, resources, and other factors. In general, the industry as a whole has grown about 10–20% per year (in increased income over the previous year) during this past decade. In fact, the industry has grown most of this century. Some segments vary; for instance, the landscape industry is more closely tied to growth in the housing industry.

People need plants. When times are tough, they tend to buy smaller and less expensive plants — perennials versus shrubs, for instance, or a few bedding plants. When times are better, they buy larger and more expensive plants and do those bigger landscape projects they have been dreaming about. Of course, the market in your area may vary greatly depending on whether you are selling to a permanent population or summer homeowners, to a rural population or an urban one, or to other demographic groups. As with many similar businesses, it often takes five to seven years to show a profit.

Will I Need to Work Full-Time?

Many get into the business part-time — for instance, they will start off with a spring bedding plant or summer cut flower business, both of which are adaptable to a perennial business. Often people combine a perennial business with another agricultural business (for example, a dairy farm or sugar maple plantation) or even another nonagricultural business (for example, sales or a medical practice).

Those who do work full-time in the industry in the northern states and Canadian provinces often put in sixty- to eighty-hour weeks or more for a six- to nine-month period, and then take a few months off in winter. During the "winter break," some growers work ski areas or plow snow, engage in other occupations such as crafts and specialty foods, get ready for spring, take their vacation, or attend meetings. Overall, a grower in the business full-time works at least forty hours a week when their hours worked are figured over the whole year.

Is There a Market for Perennials in My Area? How Can I Find a Niche?

It depends on your interests. You should love what you do in order to do it well and make it a success. Firms have shown time and again that even though a market seems to be saturated, success is possible — either by doing something better than others and taking market share away from them or by expanding the market. Creating a "niche" market — specializing in a product that few or no other businesses carry — is one key way of expanding the market. For example, you could specialize in a certain genus of perennials like *Hosta*, a certain type of landscaping such as night lighting, or a certain category of plants such as those that attract wildlife.

Niche markets also provide a way to compete with mass marketers. **You cannot compete with mass marketers on price** — you have to offer products that they and others do not. As a small business, you can change products quickly, and you should do so as soon as others take on your current specialty products. As a small business, you can also offer a broader product line — a wider selection of species or cultivars or even a line of plant-related products such as specialty fertilizers and tools.

Perhaps the most important goal should be **top-quality service**. Good service is perhaps the most endangered aspect of the current retail and service industry. To ensure that you are offering your best, learn all you can — read all you can, take courses, join professional organizations, attend meetings, and become certified if a certification program is available in your state. Many states offer certification programs for professional horticulturists based on an experience requirement, knowledge requirement, or both. Many programs require applicants to complete an exam and keep up-to-date with new information.

I've Decided on a Perennial Business — What Now?

You will need to make some contacts to register your business and obtain any necessary licenses and permits. Some important contacts to make when starting a business include:

- Secretary of State — to register a trade name
- State Department of Taxes — to obtain a tax number and filing forms
- State Department of Agriculture / Plant Industry — to obtain a state certification listing and inspection and to obtain pesticide training (this is good to have even if you do not plan to use pesticides)
- Town — to register your business, obtain building and other permits, and pay any town fees
- Bank — to get a possible loan (you will need a business plan — talk to the bank about this) and open a business account
- Grower or Trade Association (state, regional, and national) — to learn about newsletters, meetings, suppliers, certification programs, and buying programs
- Trade groups and societies (see list beginning on page 207)
- Other agencies, depending on your business — for example, you may need a commercial pesticide license or truck permits

You will also need to consider how you will get the funds needed to start your business, what type of business you want to have, what you will sell, whether you will grow your own plants or buy them from a producer, and how you will price your products and services. These issues are discussed in more detail in the sections that follow.

Where Can I Get Help with Financing and Business Decisions?

When you own your own business, the two most important people in your life (outside of your family) may be your accountant and your banker. An accountant can advise you on what type of business to have (a sole proprietorship is the most common and simplest), how to set up and maintain a record-keeping system, how to file financial and tax reports, and how to analyze these reports to make sound business decisions. In addition to basic accounting services, a certified public accountant (CPA) can provide audits and management advice. A record-keeping system is crucial for decision making, helpful in dealing with the Internal Revenue

Service (IRS), and important when approaching banks for a loan.

Most businesses, both new and established, require loans from banks. Short-term loans, also known as lines of credit, usually have terms of six to twelve months and are used to get through periods of low cash flow. Long-term loans, also known as fixed-asset loans, provide extra funds for equipment purchases and capital improvements (for example, adding a greenhouse) and usually correspond to the depreciation or life of the equipment or facility.

To get a loan from a bank, you are usually required to have a personal financial statement and résumé; two years of income or pro forma financial statements (if the business is not new) on a monthly or quarterly basis; projections for income, fixed and variable expenses, and cash flow; specifics about how the loan will be used; a listing of collateral such as equipment, buildings, or property; and at least 20% capital investment in cash or equity from you. An accountant can help assemble this presentation. In addition to loans, banks often provide other services such as business analysis, credit card services, and even payroll services.

What Kind of Business Should I Have?

Whether you should be a retailer, wholesaler, or both ultimately depends on you and your personality. If you would rather spend your time producing plants, have other time commitments and priorities, or have a small customer base, then wholesale may be the best choice. On the other hand, if you like dealing with and helping people and you have lots of time and a large enough customer base nearby, then retail may be a good choice. Retail operations vary from businesses that offer many plants and products other than perennials to specialty businesses that develop a wide presence, perhaps through the use of mail-order catalogs. People will often drive long distances to visit such specialty businesses.

Which Perennials Should I Sell?

Deciding from among the thousands of available perennials can be a formidable task. If you have many other aspects to your business, such as bedding plants, holiday crops, or farm produce, you may need to keep the perennial selection simple and include only basic and popular varieties (see "Selection" on page 85 in chapter 11). If perennials are a large component or the sole component of your business, you will need to offer a broader range and include the newest cultivars. You should join appropriate specialized societies for your primary crops

for information about and sources of new cultivars (see societies listing on page 207). A large wholesale grower in the Northeast estimated that 40% of their varieties account for 70% of their sales, and the other 30% of sales comes from varieties that give their selection depth and make their business attractive to customers.

If I Grow My Own Plants, Should I Grow Them in the Field or in Containers?

This is obviously not an issue if you are selling plants that you bought from a producer. In this case, you will have higher up-front costs to buy the plants but less production costs, as you will hopefully move the plants out quickly. However, if you do grow your own, the decision of whether to grow them in the field or in containers will depend in part on whether you have a site or need to buy one. It will also depend on the soil type at the site, as field-grown perennials need good soil (see chapter 9, which begins on page 62). Container production requires containers, media, and perhaps other items such as irrigation, so up-front costs are a bit higher. But container production is often more controllable and convenient than field production (see chapter 8, which begins on page 48). Field production is usually better suited to smaller growers who grow for a retail market, while container production can be suitable for either retail or wholesale.

If you grow container perennials, the size or sizes of plants you grow will depend on what market segment you are growing for. For instance, consumers may prefer a range of sizes — from small 4-inch pots to 1-gallon pots. A 1-quart size is common. Landscapers may require larger sizes — 1- to 3-gallon pots.

You must also decide whether to propagate plants yourself from stock plants. Propagating and growing your own plants usually involves overwintering or vernalizing plants, which may require additional facilities and the ability to control the environment in the facility (see chapters 3 and 5).

How Do I Price My Plants?

This is crucial, as prices determine your profit and therefore your ability to remain in business. Pricing is one of the least understood production principles. Most growers' strategy is to charge the same prices they charged the previous year, plus "a little" such as 5%. Or they relate their prices to what their competition charges with no clear idea of what their actual costs are. Pricing based on costs is often difficult, as different perennials may be produced differently — for example, they can be produced from seeds, cuttings, or divisions (see chapter 5).

Pricing based only on costs of production may not yield the best possible return, however, as a high demand for a particular perennial may justify that a higher price be charged for that perennial than for other perennials in lower demand. This is often the case with specialty perennials, new ones, or ones in short supply.

Pricing based solely on market demand is not advisable, either. If your costs of production are high, and the demand and return from sales of some particular perennials are low, then you might actually be losing money on those plants.

The best approach to pricing is to figure your costs of production, then decide what additional amount you need to earn to make production of a particular perennial worthwhile. Finally, factor in what the market will bear or pay. For instance, say you produce a certain yellow yarrow at a cost of $2 per plant, and you figure you need to make $4 per plant. If there are already many of these plants in your market area, then you may not be able to sell many at the price you need to charge. On the other hand, if you have a new pastel color of yarrow that no one else has locally, you may be able to make even more profit per plant and sell out rapidly.

Some retailers use an average price for all types of plants. Others use a couple of prices — one for the common perennials and a higher one for the more unusual perennials. Still others differentiate prices by color labels in pots, each color denoting a different price (figure 1-1); a legend explaining the label colors and corresponding prices is posted throughout the sales area.

One problem with labels is that they can fall out of or be removed from pots. If this is a problem, you can staple labels to pots, although this is an extra labor step and therefore an additional expense. Some growers avoid

these problems by pricing by pot color (each color pot denoting a different price), or more commonly by size of pot (in which case, the different pot sizes are attached to a sign and their prices are listed next to them).

There are many models for accurately and completely figuring costs (Taylor et al, 1986; Taylor et al, 1990; Perry et al, 1987). Cost calculations can be done simply with computer programs designed for the purpose; such programs can be expensive, however. Simple spreadsheet programs are a less expensive alternative to ready-made programs, but you have to set them up. A general guide to figuring costs is shown in table 1-1. Of course, costs will vary depending on your location, your scale of production, the market in your area, the species of plants being sold, and many other factors. The table serves only as an example of a simple way to figure costs.

Where Do I Get More Information?

For a free packet of information about starting and operating a nursery, contact the government agency ATTRA (Appropriate Technology Transfer for Rural Areas) at 800-346-9140. Once you have made the necessary and legally required local contacts, contact your state cooperative extension service for answers to specific questions about growing perennials in your state. In addition to extension specialists in production, they will likely have pest management specialists and plant diagnostic clinics or a soil-testing service. Also see the lists of recommended readings, societies, and other contacts at the end of this book beginning on page 203.

Table 1-1. A simplified guide to pricing perennials (for wholesale, plants in 1-quart containers)

Budget item	Cost (U.S.$)
Direct Costs	
1-quart container	0.13
Average plant cost (purchased large plug, division)	0.40
Potting mix, fertilizer, labels	0.10
Labor (for potting, moving, watering, and loading)	0.72
Weeding, herbicides	0.10
TOTAL DIRECT COSTS	1.45
Overhead (Indirect) Costs[1]	
35% of direct costs	0.51
TOTAL COSTS	1.96
Profit	
20% of costs	0.39
Selling Price	2.35

[1] Overhead here includes such items as utilities, property-related costs, and marketing.

Figure 1-1. Color label system for pricing perennials

CHAPTER 2

Species and Their Characteristics

Perennials are most often classified by their hardiness (see discussion beginning on page 10). They have also been classified by their growth habit (such as "tall" or "front of border") or culture (such as "shade-loving"). Many bulbs, ornamental grasses, and herbs are herbaceous perennials, but they usually are not included in perennial classifications, even though they are frequently incorporated into plantings with perennials. Biennials — those perennials that generally live for only two years — usually are included (see table 2-1 on page 8). Most biennials bloom the second year; many self-sow, giving the effect of true perennials.

Most herbaceous perennials die back to the ground each winter. A few have foliage that usually remains evergreen (see table 2-2 on page 8). Because of their persistent, green foliage, these plants tend to be much more sensitive to artificial storage conditions and susceptible to diseases during storage and overwintering. Some perennials bloom the first year (see table 2-3 on page 9).

Taxonomy and Nomenclature

Taxonomy is the science of naming organisms in a way that reflects their natural relationships. Perennials are classified taxonomically by their growth and flowering characteristics into a hierarchy of families (such as Asteraceae or Compositae), genera (such as *Aster)*, species (such as *novae-angliae)*, and often cultivars, which are designated by single quotation marks (such as 'Patricia Ballard'). Simply speaking, cultivars are "cultivated varieties" — similar plants arising from and/or maintained in cultivation. Cultivar and family names are not italicized; genera and species names are.

Nomenclature refers to the international system of standardized names for plants. Common names often vary geographically, whereas Latin-based scientific names do not. Common names are useful, as many consumers are turned off by Latin names that they do not understand. But even though common names are often more easily remembered by consumers, they often lead to confusion because several plants may share the same common name. For example, the genera *Crinum, Hymenocallis*, and *Lycoris* are all commonly referred to as spider lily. For this reason, common names are often merely a marketing tool and should always be accompanied by a scientific name. This point is also specified in the standards developed by the Perennial Plant Association (see next section). Perennial names have gotten even more confusing with the advent of trademarked names. Even scientific names are hotly debated by taxonomists and change periodically. For sources of more information on taxonomy and nomenclature, see the list of recommended reading beginning on page 203 at the end of this book.

For years the authority for scientific names has been *Hortus Third* by Liberty Hyde Bailey, but it is quite a few years old now and contains few perennial cultivars. Of the various other sources of names, the one proposed most recently by the Perennial Plant Association as a standard is the Dutch *Namelist (Naamlijst van Vaste Planten)*, which is updated periodically. This reference, however, is very hard to find in the United States. *The Plant Finder*, a British publication, is updated yearly and has quite a few taxonomic authorities as contributors, so it is quite useful as a name reference as well as a source list. It is the most widely used plant reference in the

Table 2-1. Biennials

Scientific name	Common name
Adlumia fungosa	Climbing Fumitory
Alcea rosea	Hollyhock
Anagallis monellii	Blue Pimpernel
Anchusa capensis	Alkanet, Bugloss
Anthriscus sp. (some)	Cow Parsley
Arabis sp. (some)	Rockcress
Atropa sp.	Deadly Nightshade
Bellis sp.	Daisy
Campanula medium	Canterbury Bells
Campanula pyramidalis	Chimney Bellflower
Campanula rapunculus	Rampion
Campanula thyrsoides	Bellflower
Campanula sp. (some)	Bellflower
Cheiranthus (Erysimum) sp.	Wallflower
Chelidonium majus	Greater Celandine
Cynoglossum sp. (some)	Hound's Tongue
Digitalis sp. (some)	Foxglove
Dipsacus sp.	Teasel
Echium sp. (some)	Viper's Bugloss
Eremurus sp.	Foxtail Lily
Erysimum: see Cheiranthus	–
Eschscholzia californica	California Poppy
Glaucium sp. (some)	Horned Poppy
Hesperis sp.	Rocket
Hyoscyamus sp. (some)	Henbane
Ipomopsis sp. (some)	Skyrocket
Isatis sp.	Woad
Lunaria sp.	Honesty, Money Plant
Lychnis coronaria	Rose Campion
Matthiola sp.	Stock
Michauxia (Mindium) campanuloides	–
Myosotis sp.	Forget-Me-Not
Oenothera sp. (some)	Evening Primrose
Onopordon (Onopordum) sp. (some)	Thistle
Onosma pyramidale	–
Orostachys sp.	–
Papaver nudicaule	Iceland Poppy
Phacelia bipinnatifida	Scorpion Weed
Ratibida columnifera	Prairie Coneflower
Reseda sp. (some)	Mignonette
Silybum sp.	Holy Thistle
Smyrnium sp.	Black Lovage
Solenanthus apenninus	–
Symphyandra armena	Ring Bellflower
Trachystemon (Ptilostemon) afer	–
Urospermum sp. (some)	–
Verbascum sp.	Mullein
Viola sp.	Pansy, Johnny Jump Up

Note: Some species are grown as annuals or short-lived perennials.

Table 2-2. Evergreen perennials

Scientific name	Common name
Achillea sp. (some)	Yarrow
Aethionema sp.	Stone Cress
Ajuga sp.	Bugleweed
Arabis sp.	Rockcress
Armeria sp.	Thrift, Sea Pink
Asarum sp.	Ginger
Aubrietia sp.	Aubretia
Aurinia sp.	Basket-of-Gold
Bergenia sp.	Heartleaf Saxifrage
Campanula sp.	Bellflower
Coreopsis sp. (some)	Tickseed
Dianthus sp.	Pinks
Digitalis sp.	Foxglove
Erigeron sp.	Fleabane
Ferns (some)	Ferns
Gaillardia sp. (some)	Blanket Flower
Galax sp.	Coltsfoot
Gaultheria procumbens	Wintergreen
Geum sp.	Avens
Helleborus sp.	Hellebore
Hemerocallis (in mild climates)	Daylily
Heuchera sp.	Coral Bells
Iberis sp.	Candytuft
Iris, bearded	German Iris
Kniphofia sp.	Torch Lily
Linum sp.	Flax
Liriope sp.	Lilyturf
Lobelia sp. (some)	–
Mitchella sp.	Partridge Berry
Penstemon sp. (some)	Beardtongue
Perovskia sp.	Russian Sage
Phlox subulata	Moss Phlox
Polystichum sp.	Holly Ferns
Potentilla sp.	Cinquefoil
Rosemarinus officinalis sp.	Rosemary
Sagina subulata	Pearlwort
Santolina sp.	Lavender Cotton
Saponaria sp. (some)	Soapwort
Sempervivum sp.	Houseleek
Shortia sp.	–
Teucrium sp.	Germander
Tiarella sp.	Foamflower
Vinca sp.	Periwinkle
Yucca sp.	–

Note: Some species may be evergreen, others not. Some genera may be evergreen only in mild climates, such as USDA hardiness zones 8 and 9 (see figure 2-1 on page 11).

Table 2-3. Species for first-year flowering (species without a cold requirement for flowering)

Scientific name	Common name
Achillea ptarmica	Sneezewort
Anchusa sp.	Alkanet, Bugloss
Anemone x hybrida	Windflower
Aster novae-angliae	New England Aster
Aster novi-belgii	New York Aster
Callirhoe sp.	Poppy Mallow
Campanula carpatica	Tussock Bellflower
Catananche caerulea	Cupid's Dart
Commelina sp.	Dayflower
Coreopsis lanceolata	Lanceleaf Tickseed
Coreopsis verticillata	Threadleaf Tickseed
Delphinium elatum	Delphinium
Dendranthema x grandiflorum	Chrysanthemum
Glaucium sp.	Horned Poppy
Gypsophila paniculata	Baby's Breath
Helenium autumnale	Sneezeweed
Heliopsis sp.	Oxeye Daisy
Lychnis x arkwrightii	Arkwright's Campion
Lychnis coronaria, Oculata group	Rose Campion
Nierembergia sp.	Cupflower
Osteospermum sp.	Star of the Veldt
Petrocoptis sp.	Catchfly
Phlox paniculata	Border, Garden Phlox
Phlox subulata	Moss Phlox
Physostegia virginiana	Obedient Plant
Rudbeckia fulgida	Black-Eyed Susan
Sagina subulata	Pearlwort
Salvia x superba	Hybrid Sage
Sedum spectabile	Showy Sedum, Ice Plant
Solidago sp.	Goldenrod
Veronica sp.	Speedwell
Viola tricolor	Johnny Jump Up
Viscaria: see Lychnis coronaria	–

United Kingdom and, with a CD-ROM version now available that contains many other resources and world plant lists, is quickly becoming a worldwide standard. A problem with this reference, though, is that some cultivars of North American origin are not in it. The *Andersen Horticultural Library's Source List of Plants and Seeds* from the Landscape Arboretum of the University of Minnesota is issued every few years (the latest in 1996). While it is not primarily a taxonomic reference, it is useful for locating cultivars and names not found elsewhere. The British *Index Hortensis* is another useful reference for names, especially the names of authors of plant names, but it has not been updated regularly. The

> **Useful References on Perennial Names**
> (See the recommended reading section beginning on page 203 for complete citations.)
>
> • *The Plant Finder* (British)
>
> • *Naamlijst van Vaste Planten* (the Dutch *Namelist*)
>
> • *New Royal Horticulture Society Dictionary of Gardening*
>
> • *Andersen Horticultural Library's Source List of Plants and Seeds*

New Royal Horticulture Society Dictionary of Gardening, which was updated in 1992, gives much botanical and cultural information as well as name information. (See the recommended reading section beginning on page 203 for complete citations of books mentioned in this paragraph.)

A practical problem is that with so many perennials available and many new ones added yearly, it is often necessary to check several references or even catalogs to find a plant name and any sort of description. Sometimes the names and even descriptions vary among publications, in which case the name or description common to the most publications should be used if no information to the contrary is available. This is the approach taken in this publication. Nomenclature throughout this publication has been based first on *The Plant Finder*, then the Dutch *Namelist*, then the *New Royal Horticulture Society Dictionary of Gardening*, and finally, if no information was found in any of those sources, the *Andersen Horticultural Library's Source List of Plants and Seeds*. Where discrepancies among sources occurred, the same order of authority was used.

Standards

The Perennial Plant Association has developed standards "to facilitate and promote uniformity and understanding of terms, definitions, and procedures within the perennial industry." The *American Standards for Perennial Plants* is a standardized system of describing and sizing perennials in production for use by nurseries, landscapers, educators, and the public (see the recommended reading section beginning on page 203). In addition to containing extensive sections on perennials for landscape plantings, preplanting, installation, and maintenance, this reference gives standards for plant grades for seven major perennials and perennials in general.

Grades are classes or designations of plants based on factors such as size and number of growing points or buds. The glossary of terms in the standards includes:

1. *Astilbe* — "Eye" is the correct term to describe an *Astilbe* division.

2. *Dicentra* (Bleeding Heart) — "Eye" is the correct term to describe a *Dicentra* division.

3. *Hemerocallis* (Daylily) — "Fan" is the correct term to describe a daylily division. "Eye" is incorrect.

4. *Hosta (Funkia)* — "Eye" is the correct term to describe a *Hosta* division.

5. *Iris* — "Fan" is the correct term to describe an *Iris* division.

6. *Papaver orientale* (Oriental Poppy) — Designate whether the plants were propagated from seed or root cuttings.

7. *Paeonia* (Peony) — "Eye" is the correct term to describe a *Paeonia* division. All eyes counted must be flowering eyes and/or large nonflowering eyes on heavy roots. Small "eye" buds shall not be counted.

8. Perennials in general — Designate whether they are bare-root, field-grown, or propagated vegetatively or from seed.

In addition to these definitions of terms, standards for plant size per pot size are given. For perennials in general, these are:

1. Liners or plugs (smallest size): 1-quart size

2. Field-grown transplants: 2-quart to 1-gallon size

3. Heavy field-grown transplants (grown one full season before harvesting): 2-quart to 2-gallon size

Transplants and seedlings or liners are defined in the standards as:

1. Transplant: a rooted seedling or rooted cutting that has been transplanted at least once.

2. Seedling or liner: a plant grown from seed and grown in a plug, flat, or field bed.

Hardiness

An often misunderstood topic, hardiness is deserving of special discussion. It is an often oversimplified topic. Without taking into account all the possible factors involved, the question of whether or not a plant is hardy may be wrongly answered, which will result in disappointment for the grower or customer if the plant dies or does not bloom.

Hardiness is genetic. That is why some plants are hardier than others and why some cultivars of the same plant are hardier than others. Some cultivars may have been bred or selected to be hardier clones. To confuse the matter further, plants can adapt or change genetically over time in response to their climate; that is why a species growing in a southern location may not be as hardy as the same species growing in a northern location. This should be a consideration when buying plants or ordering them through the mail.

Roots, stems, and leaf and flower buds are usually hardy to different temperatures. This explains why many perennials die to the ground in winter but produce new shoots the following spring — their roots can survive the winter cold but their aboveground parts cannot. It is also why forsythia often have leaves but no flowers; the flower buds, being less hardy than the leaf buds, are killed by cold. If flowers appear only to a particular height on a plant, then it is easy to figure the depth of snow cover that protected the flower buds during the killing cold.

Hardiness is a function of location in a different sense as well. Some plants are hardy but only to a certain temperature. For example, a plant such as *Salvia* or beard tongue *(Penstemon)* may be a perennial in a southern or warm climate but only an annual if moved to a colder climate. Keep this in mind when books or articles, especially those from other countries, categorize a plant as an annual or perennial.

Most discussions about hardiness make reference to hardiness zones. These are geographic zones that are shown on maps and that share the same range of average annual minimum winter temperatures. Few references discuss hardiness zones in terms of heat — in other words, how high a temperature a particular plant can endure. Maples, lilacs, and many of our herbaceous perennials cannot take the heat of hot climates or need a certain amount of cold to bloom properly.

There are at least three hardiness maps in gardening publications: one from the Arnold Arboretum in Boston, Massachusetts; one from the U.S. Department of Agriculture (USDA) that was used prior to 1990 and based on data from about 1930–1960; and a revised USDA map that has been used since 1990 and was based on more recent data from 1974–1986 (figure 2-1). The various zones on these maps are labeled by number, and the same number zone represents different temperature ranges on the USDA and Arnold maps. The zone numbers are the same on the USDA maps — only the locations of zones have changed on the new version.

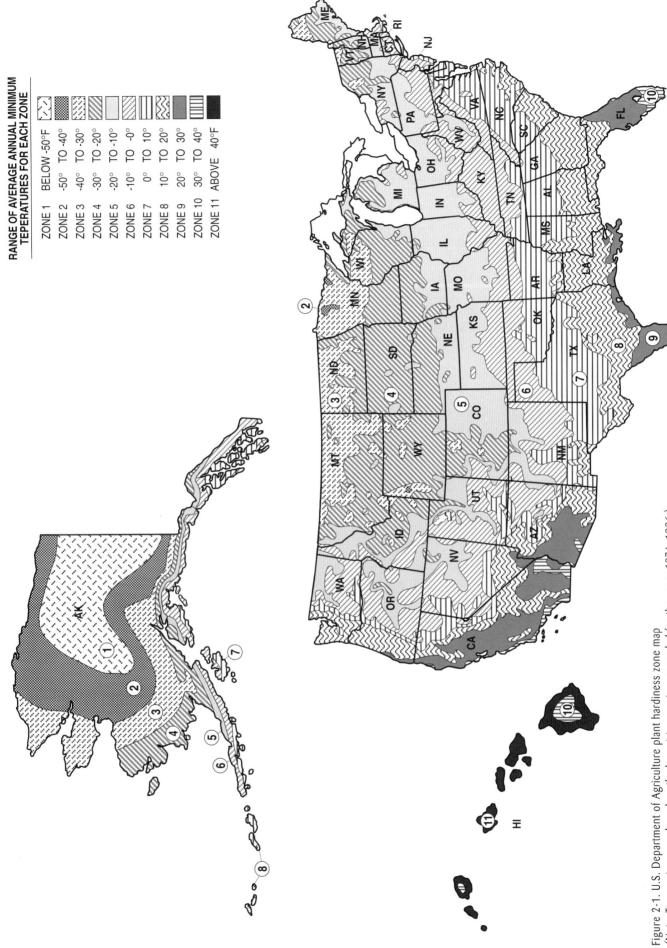

RANGE OF AVERAGE ANNUAL MINIMUM
TEPERATURES FOR EACH ZONE

ZONE 1   BELOW -50°F
ZONE 2   -50° TO -40°
ZONE 3   -40° TO -30°
ZONE 4   -30° TO -20°
ZONE 5   -20° TO -10°
ZONE 6   -10° TO -0°
ZONE 7   0° TO 10°
ZONE 8   10° TO 20°
ZONE 9   20° TO 30°
ZONE 10   30° TO 40°
ZONE 11   ABOVE 40°F

Figure 2-1. U.S. Department of Agriculture plant hardiness zone map
(*Note*: Temperatures are based on the lowest temperature recorded for the years 1974–1986.)

According to the revised USDA map, most areas have become colder. Another recent map divides the country and classifies plants by climate zones, taking factors such as growing season and rainfall into account in addition to temperature (see the *National Garden Book* in "Publications from Other Sources" in the recommended reading section, page 204). An interactive USDA hardiness map called "What's Your Zone?" can be found on the Internet. The user enters a zip code, and the computer comes up with the corresponding hardiness zone. The map can be accessed through the Garden Escape web site at WWW.GARDEN.COM.

The hardiness zones on these maps represent averages. This means that even though a plant is listed as being hardy in a particular zone, an unusually cold year may come along in that zone and kill the plant. If a plant is listed as hardy in a zone or two colder than yours, it is likely to be hardy in your zone. On the other hand, a plant listed for one or two zones warmer than your zone may also grow in a site within your zone under certain conditions.

Conditions that determine whether a plant will survive in a particular site are collectively known as the microclimate. These conditions include soil type, exposure to sun and wind, and other factors such as ground slope and the proximity of the site to buildings. After determining the zone in which a site is located, or macroclimate, you should consider the microclimate.

If a soil is heavy, wet, of low pH or low fertility, or for any other reason not suited to a plant, it can cause stress that may result in winter injury. On the other hand, if a soil is too fertile, the plant may grow late into the season and not harden off properly; this, too, may result in winter injury or lack of hardiness. Amendments such as compost or peat moss can be used to improve poor soils.

Mulches can be used to moderate soil temperatures. They are especially useful on exposed sites, where protective snow cover may blow off. Mulches keep soil from getting as cold in the winter, which may help prevent root injury. Winter winds, which usually come from the North and West, can cause evergreens to dry out, resulting in winter injury as leaf burn. Using a protected site, or shielding plants with a burlap screen in an exposed one, helps prevent this. Sites exposed to early morning sun in winter may result in "frost cracking" of bark on some woody perennials, especially young ones. Frost cracking results from the rapid heating of frozen bark by the sun. Burlap screens can help prevent it as well.

If a plant is growing near a building, it may be in a warmer hardiness zone. This may be because of heat loss from the building or the sun's heat being absorbed by the building.

Slope can make a site seem like it is located farther in the direction in which it faces, perhaps by several hundred miles for steep slopes. In other words, a steep southern-facing slope may be a whole hardiness zone or two warmer than adjacent level areas. This is important to consider if a site is on a hill or in a valley. A hillside may also have airflow down it, which results in less chance of frost.

By this point, hardiness may seem like a totally confusing concept, but it need not be. Just keep the hardiness zones and their limitations in mind when choosing or recommending a plant. Keep the microclimate factors in mind when selecting a planting location. Nothing can guarantee a plant's hardiness, as Mother Nature cannot be predicted, but careful consideration of the factors discussed should result in minimal loss of plants from winter injury.

Potentially Harmful Perennials

A subject of increasing concern lately is the harmful nature and potential toxicity of certain perennials. Whether you are propagating and growing perennials, installing them, or retailing them, it is important to know — for your own safety and that of your customers — which perennials may cause problems. This is especially important if your part of the country seems more prone to liability lawsuits. Warnings about the harmful nature of some perennials are increasingly seen in mail-order catalogs. The Horticultural Trades Association (HTA) in the United Kingdom has even begun requiring that warnings appear on certain perennial labels and point-of-purchase sales materials.

Table 2-4 lists the major perennials that are found in the literature on poisonous plants. Many of the plants are also poisonous to animals. Some, in whole or in part or in some altered form, may be poisonous to animals but not to humans or vice versa (for example, hops, when boiled, is poisonous to dogs). This fact should be kept in mind when reading books on poisonous plants. With so many perennials available, it is likely that some perennials not in table 2-4 are toxic in some degree. It is also likely that some persons will have a reaction to certain plants while others will not. Some species or cultivars of a genus may be toxic and not others. Some perennials listed in the table may have the *potential* to cause

Table 2-4. Potentially harmful perennials

Scientific name, common name	Toxicity[1]	Scientific name, common name	Toxicity[1]
Achillea millefolium, Yarrow	Skin irritant in sunlight	*Echium*, Viper's Bugloss	Skin irritant (HTA)
Aconitum, Monkshood	CAUTION toxic if eaten (HTA)	*Erigeron*, Fleabane	Skin irritant
Actaea, Baneberry	Harmful if eaten/skin and eye irritant (berries, roots)	*Euphorbia*, Spurge (not poinsettia)	Harmful if eaten/skin and eye irritant (HTA)
Adonis, Pheasant's Eye	Toxic if eaten		
Agrimonia, Agrimony	Skin irritant in sunlight	*Gaillardia*, Blanket Flower	Skin irritant
Agrostemma githago, Corn-Cockle	Harmful if eaten (HTA)	*Galanthus*, Snowdrop	Harmful if eaten (bulb)
Allium, Onions, Garlic	Skin irritant	*Gloriosa superba*, Gloriosa Lily	CAUTION toxic if eaten (HTA)
Alstroemeria, Peruvian Lily	May cause skin allergy (HTA)	*Hedera*, English Ivy	Harmful if eaten/may cause skin allergy (HTA)
Amaryllis, Belladonna Lily	Harmful if eaten (bulbs)		
Ammi majus, Bishop's Weed	Skin irritant in sunlight	*Helenium*, Sneezeweed	Skin irritant
Anthemis cotula, Dog Fennel	Skin irritant in sunlight	*Helleborus*, Hellebore	Harmful if eaten (HTA)
Aquilegia, Columbine	Harmful if eaten (HTA)	*Heracleum*, Hogweed	Skin irritant in sunlight
Arisaema, Jack-in-the-Pulpit	Harmful if eaten	*Humulus*, Hops	Skin irritant
		Hyacinthus, Hyacinth	Skin irritant (HTA)
		Hymenocallis, Spider Lily	Harmful if eaten (bulbs)
Artemisia, Mugwort	Skin irritant	*Hyoscyamus*, Henbane	CAUTION toxic if eaten (HTA)
Arum, Wild Ginger	CAUTION toxic if eaten/skin and eye irritant (HTA)	*Hypericum perforatum*, St. John's Wort	Harmful if eaten (HTA)
Aster, Aster, Daisy	Skin irritant	*Iris*, Iris	Harmful if eaten (HTA)
Atropa, Deadly Nightshade	CAUTION toxic if eaten (HTA)	*Lactuca*, Lettuce	Skin irritant
Baptisia, False Indigo	Harmful if eaten	*Lobelia*, Cardinal Flower	Harmful if eaten
Calla palustris, Water Arum	Harmful if eaten	*Lobelia tupa*, Devil's Tobacco	Harmful if eaten/skin and eye irritant (HTA)
Caltha, Marsh Marigold	Harmful if eaten (HTA)	*Lupinus*, Lupine	Harmful if eaten (HTA)
Caulophyllum thalictroides, Blue Cohosh	Harmful if eaten (berries, roots)	*Lycoris*, Spider Lily	Harmful if eaten (bulbs)
Chelidonium majus, Swallow Wort	Toxic if eaten	*Narcissus*, Daffodil	Harmful if eaten/skin irritant
Cicuta, Water Hemlock	Harmful if eaten	*Oenanthe crocata*, Water Dropwort	Toxic if eaten
Clematis, Virgin's Bower	Harmful if eaten	*Ornithogalum*, Star-of-Bethlehem	Harmful if eaten (HTA)
Colchicum, Autumn Crocus	CAUTION toxic if eaten (HTA)		
Colocasia esculenta, Elephant Ears	Harmful if eaten	*Pastinaca sativa*, Parsnip	Skin irritant in sunlight
Convallaria majalis, Lily of the Valley	CAUTION toxic if eaten (HTA)	*Phacelia*, Stinging Phacelia	Skin irritant
		Physalis, Lantern Plant	Toxic if eaten (esp. to children)
		Phytolacca, Pokeweed	CAUTION toxic if eaten (HTA)
Crinum, Spider Lily	Harmful if eaten (bulbs)	*Podophyllum peltatum*, May Apple	Skin irritant, toxic if eaten (except fruit)
Cypripedium, Lady's Slipper	Skin irritant		
Daucus carota, Queen Anne's Lace	Skin irritant in sunlight	*Polygonatum*, Solomon's Seal	Harmful if eaten (HTA)
Delphinium, Larkspur	Harmful if eaten (HTA)		
Dendranthema, Mum (not pot mums)	May cause skin allergy (HTA)	*Primula farinosa*, Birdseye Primrose	Skin irritant
Dicentra spectabilis, Bleeding Heart	Skin irritant	*Primula obconica*, Primrose	CAUTION may cause skin allergy (HTA)
Dictamnus albus, Gas Plant	CAUTION skin irritant in sunlight (HTA)	*Pulsatilla*, Pasque Flower	Harmful if eaten
Digitalis, Foxglove	CAUTION toxic if eaten (HTA)	*Ranunculus*, Buttercup	Harmful if eaten/skin and eye irritant

See footnotes on next page.

continued on next page

Table 2-4. Potentially harmful perennials *(continued from previous page)*

Scientific name, common name	Toxicity[1]	Scientific name, common name	Toxicity[1]
Rheum, Rhubarb	Harmful if eaten (uncooked leaves)	*Spigelia*, Pinkroot	Toxic if eaten
Rudbeckia hirta, Black-Eyed Susan	Skin irritant	*Symplocarpus foetidus*, Skunk Cabbage	Harmful if eaten (leaves)
Ruta, Rue	CAUTION severely toxic to skin in sunlight (HTA)	*Tanacetum vulgare*, Tansy	Skin irritant
		Tulipa, Tulip	Skin irritant (HTA)
Sambucus, Elderberry	Harmful if eaten (except cooked ripe fruit)	*Veratrum*, False Hellebore	CAUTION toxic if eaten (HTA)
Scilla, Squill	Harmful if eaten (HTA)	*Zantedeschia aethiopica*, Calla	Harmful if eaten (leaves)
Senecio, Groundsel	Toxic if eaten	*Zephyranthes atamasco*, Atamasco Lily	Harmful if eaten (bulbs)
Solanum, Nightshade	CAUTION toxic if eaten (HTA)	*Zigadenus*, Death Camus	Toxic if eaten

Sources: American Medical Association Handbook of Poisonous and Injurious Plants, 1985, American Medical Association, Chicago, Illinois; *Human Poisoning from Native and Cultivated Plants*, Second Edition, 1974, Duke University Press, Durham, North Carolina; *Poisonous Plants of the United States and Canada*, 1964, Prentice Hall; *Poisonous Plants of the United States*, 1961, MacMillan; *Poisonous Plants in Britain and Ireland*, 1996, interactive CD-ROM available from Direct Media, 10 Market Street, Lewes, United Kingdom BN7 2NB; and *The Plant Finder*, 1997, interactive CD-ROM also available from Direct Media.

Note: Harmful means here causing any abnormal bodily reaction, from a mild skin rash to death. This table lists the major perennials that are found in selected literature on poisonous plants for humans (see source note). Many of the plants are also poisonous to animals. Some, in whole or in part or in some altered form, may be poisonous to animals but not to humans or vice versa (for example, when boiled, hops is poisonous to dogs). With so many perennials available, it is likely that some perennials not in this table are toxic in some degree. It is also likely that some persons will have a reaction to certain plants while others will not. Some species or cultivars of a genus may be toxic and not others. Some perennials listed may have the *potential* to cause toxicities, even though no poisonings have been reported or an improbable amount of the plant or plant parts would have to be ingested to be harmful or toxic.

[1] HTA = labeling required by the Horticultural Trades Association, United Kingdom. "Skin irritant in sunlight" may be seen in references as "photodermititis". "Skin irritant" generally refers to any skin reaction. Plant parts noted in parentheses may be particularly harmful.

toxicities, even though no poisonings have been reported or an improbable amount of the plant or plant parts would have to be ingested to be harmful or toxic. Of course, there are other plants such as herbaceous weeds, annuals, tropical houseplants, and woody plants that are toxic, and these can be found in the references listed in the sidebar at right. Every business should have a reference on poisonous plants, especially if serving the public, and **the number of the nearest poison control center should be clearly posted on the premises.**

Invasive Perennials

One disadvantage of some perennials is that they are invasive — they spread where you do not want them and are difficult to control and keep in bounds. They may spread by roots, as in the case of mints, or by seeds, as in the case of purple loosestrife. Those that spread by roots can be useful in a confined situation or in rough areas such as slopes to control erosion. In perennial beds, the root spreaders can kill less vigorous species and take over most the bed. Perennials that spread by seeds may

Useful References on Poisonous Plants

- *American Medical Association Handbook of Poisonous and Injurious Plants*, 1985, American Medical Association, Chicago, Illinois

- *Human Poisoning from Native and Cultivated Plants*, 2nd ed., 1974, James Hardin and Jay Arena, Duke University Press, Durham, North Carolina

- *Poisonous Plants of the United States*, 1961, W. C. Muenscher, MacMillan

- *Poisonous Plants of the United States and Canada*, 1964, John Kingsbury, Prentice Hall

- *Poisonous Plants in Britain and Ireland*, 1996, interactive CD-ROM available from Direct Media, 10 Market Street, Lewes BN7 2NB United Kingdom

- *The Plant Finder*, 1997, Horticultural Trades Association listing, interactive CD-ROM available from Direct Media, same address as above

be useful in creating a "wildflower" effect, but some, such as purple loosestrife, colonize wet areas, eventually destroying them and the wetland wildlife habitats. For this reason, purple loosestrife and other perennials that behave similarly are banned from sale in many states.

The term "invasive" is relative. Some consider any plant that spreads at all to be invasive. Others define an invasive perennial as one that not only spreads but is quite vigorous and difficult to control. Perennials that spread but still remain controllable with yearly cultivating or dividing can be termed either "spreading" or "aggressive," depending on how fast they spread.

The invasive nature of perennials is also relative. Many perennials are not hardy in areas that are either too cold or too hot, and therefore they are not perennials or problems in those areas. Or they may be hardy but not quite as vigorous in some areas. Some perennials, especially the root spreaders, may be less invasive or not invasive depending on factors such as culture and soil type. Perennials that invade by seed may not be a problem in northern areas if the short growing season keeps them from going to seed (this is the case with some silver grasses).

Besides cultivating around them, dividing them, and weeding out their seedlings, root-spreading perennials may be controlled by planting them in containers either in or on the ground. If putting the container in the ground, make sure the plant's roots do not exit the drain holes or go over the top of the container. To keep these perennials from year to year, you may need to divide and repot them annually to keep them from dying out.

Systemic herbicides may also be used to control invasives. Herbicides may need to be applied several times to provide control. Herbicides that act by burning back foliage (such as some of the organic ones) are not very effective with vigorous perennials, because the plants merely resprout from the roots. When using any herbicide, be sure to read and follow all label directions.

Table 2-5 on page 16 lists some of the perennials that are commonly considered invasive in some areas of the world. Some perennials that "self-sow" once they go to seed may be included in the table as well. Some species or cultivars of a perennial may be invasive while others are not, so just because a genus is listed in the table, do not assume all its members are invasive. If a genus is listed, consider its listing a "red flag", and check closer into that particular genus of perennials.

Table 2-5. Potentially invasive perennials

Scientific name	Common name	Scientific name	Common name
Adenophora liliifolia	Ladybells	*Lychnis coronaria*	Rose Campion
Aegopodium	Goutweed	*Lysimachia*	Loosestrife
Ajuga	Bugleweed	*Lythrum*	Purple Loosestrife
Alcea	Hollyhock	*Macleaya*	Plume Poppy
Allium tuberosum	Garlic Chives	*Mentha*	Mint
Anemone x *hybrida*	Hybrid Windflowers	*Miscanthus*	Silver Grass
Angelica	Archangel	*Monarda*	Bee Balm
Artemisia ludoviciana and cultivars	Western Mugwort	*Oenothera*	Evening Primrose
Arundinaria	Bamboo	*Ornithogalum umbellatum*	Star-of-Bethlehem
Aster (certain species, such as *ericoides*)	Aster	*Oxalis*	Wood Sorrel
Borago	Borage	*Persicaria virginiana* 'Painter's Palette'	Persicaria
Campanula punctata	Bellflower	*Phalaris arundinaceae* var. *picta*	Ribbon Grass
Campanula rapunculoides	Creeping Bellflower	*Phlox paniculata*	Garden Phlox
Campanula takesimana	Korean Bellflower	*Physostegia*	Obedient Plant
Carpobrotus	Hottentot Fig	*Polygonum*	Knotweed
Centaurea montana	Mountain Bluet	*Rehmania*	Rehmannia
Convallaria	Lily of the Valley	*Sedum* (some species)	Stonecrop
Cymbalaria muralis	Kenilworth Ivy	*Sinobambusa*	Bamboo
Elymus	Lyme Grass	*Spartinia*	Cordgrass
Euphorbia amygdaloides var. *robbiae*	Euphorbia	*Stachys byzantina*	Lamb's Ears
Filipendula rubra 'Venusta'	Queen-of-the-Prairie	*Symphytum*	Comfrey
Fragaria	Strawberry	*Tanacetum*	Tansy
Freesia	Freesia	*Tovara* (see *Persicaria*)	
Helianthus	Perennial Sunflower	*Tradescantia*	Spiderwort
Houttuynia	Chameleon Plant	*Tropaeolum peregrinum*	Canary-Bird Vine
Hypericum calycinum	Creeping St. John's Wort	*Verbena* cultivars (such as 'Homestead Purple')	Perennial Verbena
Lamium maculatum	Dead Nettle	*Vinca minor*	Periwinkle
Leucanthemum vulgare	Ox-Eye Daisy	*Viola*	Pansy, Johnny Jump Up, Violets

This table was based on suggestions by members of a perennial e-mail list on the Internet, trials with perennials in Vermont, and various articles and books. (For information on the e-mail list and more information on perennials, consult "Perry's Perennial Pages" at <http://www.uvm.edu/~pass/perry/>.) Some perennials that "self-sow" once they go to seed may be included in the table. Some species or cultivars of a perennial may be invasive while others are not; just because a genus is listed, do not assume all species, cultivars, and varieties (var.) are invasive. If a genus is listed, consider its listing a "red flag," and look closer into that particular genus of perennials.

CHAPTER 3

Engineering a Production Facility

Many perennial businesses began as a hobby but evolved over time into a full-time business. Frequently, very little thought or planning goes into this expansion, which results in poor placement of structures and an inefficient layout of growing areas. If you are thinking about starting a perennial nursery or expanding an existing operation, consider the factors discussed below.

Site Selection

Before contacting a real estate agent to locate a site, you will need a clear definition of (1) the type of business you will have — wholesale, retail, or both; and (2) the type of production system you want — seedlings, liners, bulbs, or container-grown or field-grown plants. Knowing this information will help you design and size your facility. Listed below in order of importance are some factors to consider when choosing a site.

Adequate Land

A minimum of 5 acres is needed to allow for structures, a growing area, access in the form of public roads and work aisles, parking, and buffers. The availability of additional vacant land adjacent to the site is desirable for expansion as the business grows. The soil type should provide good drainage.

Adequate Water

The amount of water needed depends on many factors including climate, the irrigation system to be employed, and the crop. The water supply should be adequate to meet peak load demands. Have the water quality tested for suspended solids, pH, electrical conductivity (salts), total dissolved solids, alkalinity, and hardness.

Orientation

Shelter belts or windbreaks to the North can provide wind protection (figure 3-1 on page 18). This is useful in reducing transpiration, water loss (and therefore watering needs if growing outdoors), and heat loss from greenhouses during cold months.

Good solar access is needed throughout the day and year so plants get enough light energy for photosynthesis. In greenhouses, an east-west orientation gives the most solar gain; however, plants on the north side will get less light. A north-south orientation gives the most uniform light but less solar gain (figure 3-2 on page 18). Unless perennials are being produced and forced during the winter, when the most solar gain is needed, uniform light may be more important and therefore a north-south orientation would be preferred.

Topography

A site that has a gentle slope to the South will have increased solar gain and allow drainage of rain and run-off. A fairly level site with a 1–2% slope reduces site preparation costs.

Location of Markets

An evaluation of potential markets for the crops to be grown is crucial. With wholesale nurseries, a produc-

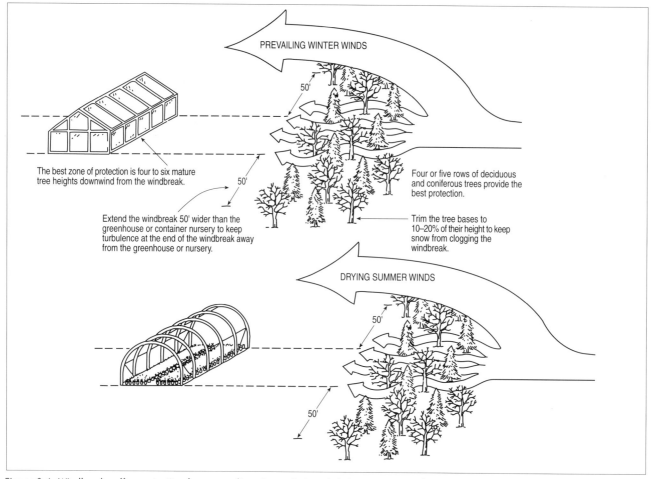

PREVAILING WINTER WINDS

The best zone of protection is four to six mature tree heights downwind from the windbreak.

Extend the windbreak 50' wider than the greenhouse or container nursery to keep turbulence at the end of the windbreak away from the greenhouse or nursery.

Four or five rows of deciduous and coniferous trees provide the best protection.

Trim the tree bases to 10–20% of their height to keep snow from clogging the windbreak.

DRYING SUMMER WINDS

Figure 3-1. Windbreaks offer protection from prevailing winter winds and drying summer winds

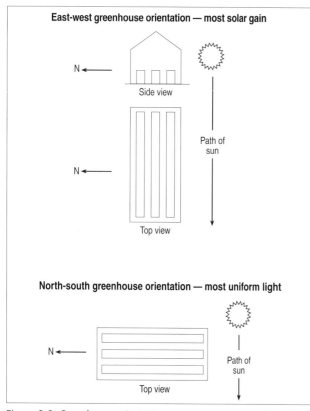

East-west greenhouse orientation — most solar gain

Side view

Path of sun

Top view

North-south greenhouse orientation — most uniform light

Path of sun

Top view

Figure 3-2. Greenhouse orientation: east-west versus north-south (Adapted from Langhans, 1990)

tion site that is far away from markets means high delivery costs. With retail nurseries, the location of customers in relation to the nursery is important.

Seasonal Labor Supply

Like many other agricultural businesses, perennial production has seasonal labor needs, such as for spring transplanting and sales or summer potting. The nursery's location should be evaluated with respect to the size and skill level of the labor pool from which the business can draw.

Road Accessibility

For wholesale operations, good access to the interstate highway system can improve shipping. For retail operations, a location on a heavily traveled road will improve visibility of the business.

Utilities

The cost of providing electricity and telephone service to the site should be considered. Where extensive greenhouse operations are to be installed, the type and availability of fuel may be a concern. Single or few greenhouses used for overwintering may require only single heaters in each house with a propane gas tank outside. A more extensive greenhouse range that is also used for plant propagation, forcing, and perhaps other crops such as bedding plants may need a central heating system and may allow the grower the benefit of quantity discounts on fuel.

Regulations

Federal, state, and local regulations may restrict what can be done on a particular site and affect the length of time it takes to get approval to build. Zoning, building, and wetlands regulations should be checked before purchasing a site.

Site Layout

Facilities Master Plan

Perennial nurseries must be laid out in a way that facilitates the safe flow of people, materials, and plants among the various work areas. A facilities master plan (figure 3-3) provides a framework for orderly construction of a perennial nursery, is important to ensure efficient movement of materials and personnel, and should be based on a sound business plan. When developing the master plan, it is best to plan on paper and look at several different layouts. Figure 3-4 shows some common arrangements of greenhouse buildings.

Planning should start with a survey of any existing facilities. This will help in evaluating the benefits and constraints of the site and establishing where new fa-

cilities should be built. One good arrangement is to plan a core area where the propagation and production greenhouses, the headhouse, storage facilities, and parking are located. Production areas should be located nearby for efficient plant movement and shipping. If the operation is strictly retail, sales areas should be located near the entrance and parking. If it is strictly wholesale, then the loading dock should be central along with the headhouse, where orders are assembled and from which production emanates to various areas. If the operation is both wholesale and retail, it may be useful to separate the wholesale and retail areas of the business for ease of pricing and production and to keep customers from pro-

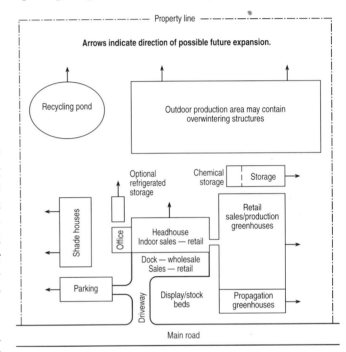

Figure 3-3. Sample perennial facilities master plan (Adapted from Bartok, Connecticut Perennials Shortcourse proceedings, March 1996)

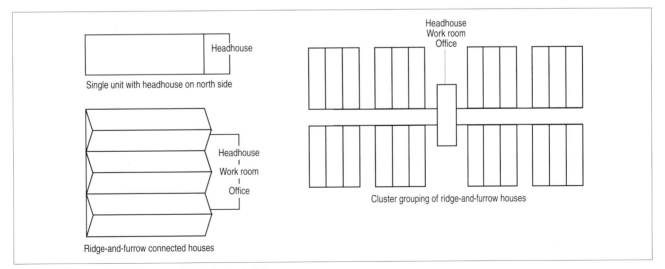

Figure 3-4. Common arrangements of greenhouse buildings

duction areas. Many growers have yielded to retail customers' desires to visit production areas, whether the business is retail or retail in combination with wholesale. Expansion space should be planned for all areas.

Nursery Production Areas

Prime space should be allocated for plant production areas, including growing beds, shade areas, and overwintering structures. Long rows for field production may be easier to cultivate by tractor. Good light and drainage and a close proximity to water are needed.

Production areas should be laid out in rectangular blocks of 1,000–2,000 square feet (figure 3-5). Within each block, 6- to 8-foot-wide beds are placed adjacent to 2-foot-wide walkways. For containers, an arrangement with shorter walkways across the block is generally preferred over one with walkways that run the length of the block. This results in less walking time to place or remove the plants, which in turn means less labor cost.

Place roadways between blocks to facilitate transporting and maintaining the plants. Roads should be 15–20 feet wide to allow movement of tractor/trailer units or trucks. Narrower roadways may be acceptable if only garden tractors and carts are to be used. Main access roads should be 25–30 feet wide to allow two-way traffic. Placing gravel or stone on the road surface will minimize road maintenance.

Production beds should be crowned 3–4% from the center to the edges to aid in the removal of runoff water. Drainage ditches along the edges of roadways will carry runoff away from the production area. Ditches should be sloped toward a lower area. Calculations should be made to ensure that culverts downstream will be able to handle the added runoff.

Production beds can be constructed of underlying soil if the soil has good drainage and physical properties. If the soil is poor, then gravel or stone should be used as a base.

Container bed surfaces are frequently covered with a weed barrier to reduce weed growth (figure 3-6). Weed barriers are made of tightly woven plastic materials that keep light from penetrating (which prevents weeds from germinating) but allow water to pass (which prevents puddling).

Propagation Areas

Seed germination and most propagation are done in greenhouses. Hotbeds may also be used, especially in

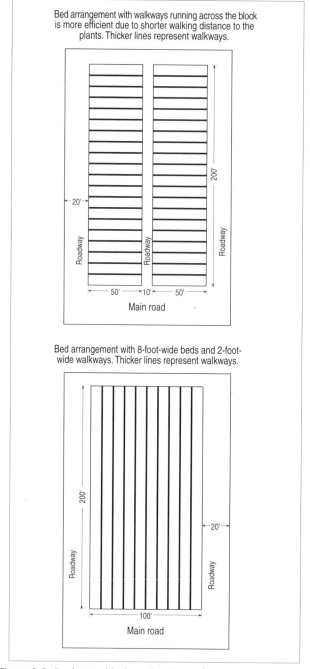

Figure 3-5. Production blocks and walkways (Adapted from Bartok, Connecticut Perennials Shortcourse proceedings, March 1996)

small operations, as they are much less expensive than a propagation greenhouse. Outdoor beds may be necessary for some varieties of perennials. Freestanding greenhouses (those not connected to other greenhouses or buildings) allow growers to maintain different temperature and humidity levels in different houses. Gutter-connected houses (those connected at a common gutter with no wall in between them) make better use of land area and are more efficient. A calculation should be made of the maximum growing space needed during the year.

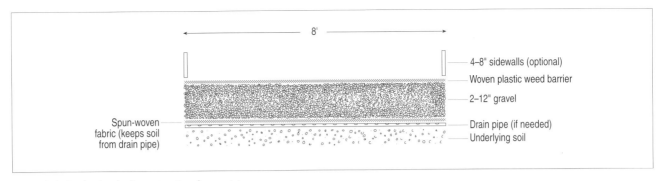

Figure 3-6. Production bed construction for containers

Propagation greenhouses should be located in the core area adjacent or attached to a headhouse. This allows for frequent checking of the seedlings and efficient flow of materials to the transplanting area.

Good environmental control is necessary to get top-quality seedlings. Root zone heating is essential. Several stages of fan ventilation should be installed to provide cooling throughout the year. Shade is needed during the summer. See chapter 5 for more information.

Production Greenhouses

To speed production and to meet seasonal demands for plants, some growers are erecting greenhouses with environmental control systems. With environmental control, production time is reduced and plants with color can be produced for the spring gardening season.

Production can occur on benches or on the floor. Movable benches increase space utilization (figure 3-7). Bottom-heat systems speed plant growth. A complete heating and fan ventilation system in production greenhouses will yield the best results. See chapter 8 for more information.

The following references cover greenhouses, their construction, and environmental control systems more in-depth (complete citations can be found in the recommended reading section beginning on page 203):

- *Greenhouse Management: A Guide to Structures, Environmental Control, Materials Handling, Crop Programming, and Business Analysis,* 3rd Edition, written by Robert W. Langhans

- *Greenhouse Engineering,* NRAES–33, written by Robert A. Aldrich and John W. Bartok, Jr.

- *Greenhouse Systems: Automation, Culture, and Environment,* NRAES–72, a conference proceedings

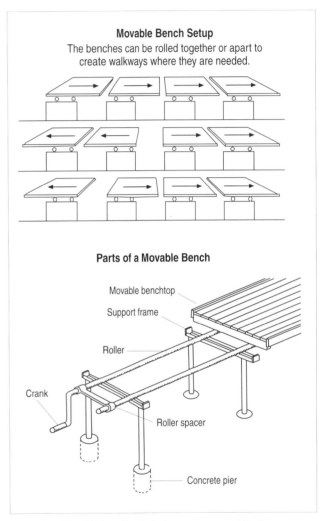

Figure 3-7. Movable benches help increase space utilization

The Headhouse

If the operation will contain more than a couple of greenhouses, a headhouse should be considered. Besides providing an area for potting, transplanting, shipping, and storage, the headhouse is an excellent place for the support facilities needed to run an efficient business — for example, employee restrooms and a break room. The headhouse can also serve to tie the greenhouses together, thus providing indoor access to production and propagation areas, which is nice to have during inclement weather.

Parking

Good all-weather vehicular access to greenhouses, the headhouse, and storage buildings should be provided. Parking for employees and customers that is convenient to the core area is desirable.

The number of parking spaces for a retail operation may have to meet zoning codes, and a paved surface is usually required. Other parking areas and driveways can be unpaved. Alternative surfaces include bank-run gravel, pea stone, crushed stone, or trap rock. Driveways and parking areas should slope to provide drainage. Swales (runoff ditches or holding areas for surface water) or underground piping is necessary to carry water away from the area. Swales should be grass and slope at least ¼ inch per foot.

Storage

An area for storage of materials (including soil mix, containers, chemicals, and equipment) is needed. Indoor storage for some items is desirable for access and to prevent deterioration from weather. Storage can be in the headhouse or a separate building. An outdoor storage area is usually provided for the growing mix.

Space for an equipment storage shed with a shop for maintenance should be planned. A clear-span pole building is a low-cost option.

Pesticide storage and handling activities should be separate from other production activities. The storage facility should be self-contained so that no chemicals can be spilled where they might contaminate the environment. See *On-Farm Agrichemical Handling Facilities,* NRAES–78, for further discussion and suggestions (see "Publications from NRAES" in the recommended reading section beginning on page 203 for a complete citation).

Expansion

Space for expansion should be allowed for all activities, as perennial businesses tend to grow when they are successful. A five-year plan that allows for a doubling or tripling of the size of the business will ensure an efficient operation. Utilities should also be designed with growth in mind.

Other Considerations

Other considerations for customers include safe access to and from main roads at times of peak traffic. Road signs should be attractive, visible, and lighted at night. There are often local and state codes that must be followed for signs. A public restroom is usually appreciated by customers and viewed by some as a necessity.

CHAPTER 4

Production Systems and Schedules

Herbaceous perennials have historically been grown in fields on sandy loam soils or loamy sands. Field production opportunities remain in areas with well-drained land where winter temperatures are moderated by snow cover. However, containerized production of perennials has greatly expanded in recent years to become the norm.

There are many reasons for this, the major ones being reduced handling and labor costs, easier weed management, quicker turnover, and an expanded season. With containerized production, growers can send finished plants to market all year, in bloom or in full growth during summer. Prior to pot culture, the market was restricted to spring and fall — the best times when most plants could be dug.

Before determining a production system, a grower should answer the following questions:

1. What is the market/who are the buyers? Growers often attempt to produce too many sizes of containers or too many varieties of plants. Keep in mind that landscapers often want larger plants, price-sensitive consumers want smaller plants, and collectors seek out the unusual (see "Selection" section on page 85).

2. When will the plants be grown and sold? This will vary with who the buyers are and other aspects of the operation. If bedding plants are produced in addition to perennials, then perennials may be produced or forced with them as bedding plants, or produced as larger plants later when more time is available for production and plants are desired to supplement the bedding plant season.

3. How much time is available to produce the plants? This will also vary with the type of operation and other aspects — for example, whether the operation produces strictly perennials or is diversified many ways.

Herbaceous perennial production may be viewed from five starting points.

1. Small plugs — These usually number 375 per tray; are started from seeds; are planted either individually in quart-size or smaller pots or in groups of three to four plugs per 1–2-gallon pot; and are planted September through October in order to vernalize the plants, which completes the juvenile phase of growth for bloom the next season (see chapter 12). Those that bloom in one year can be sown January through March.

2. Mid-sized plugs — These usually number 70–125 per tray, are started from seeds, and are planted in fall into 4-inch, quart, or gallon pots.

3. Mid-sized vernalized plugs/cells — These usually number 50–70 per tray (sometimes 36); are started from seeds or vegetative propagation; are species that complete their juvenile phase early in life; and, having already received vernalization elsewhere, are planted into 4-inch, quart, or gallon pots January through March for bloom and sales that season. If started in summer, they are often fall transplanted and then must be vernalized.

4. Bare roots — Roots are received in fall to plant and vernalize, or in spring already vernalized and ready to plant and grow to flower. These are usually large and go into 1–3-gallon pots.

5. Large field-grown plugs — These are a combination of the above. They receive vernalization in the field over winter and are ready to plant and grow on in spring in 1-gallon or larger pots, depending on the end point desired.

Six herbaceous perennial time-based or season-based production strategies are commonly employed to provide the consumer with a range of product sizes and prices: spring bedding plant production; spring production from bare-root plants and plugs; winter production from bare-root plants; production and overwintering of purchased small plants, rooted cuttings, or small divisions; start-to-finish production in containers; and field production. Some growers use a combination of these strategies, depending on their facilities, abilities, and desires, and on the needs of individual species.

Spring Bedding Plant Production

A common system for containerized production of perennials is to vegetatively propagate the species, sow seeds, or buy small or mid-size plugs in spring, and then sell small 4-inch or pack plants with annual bedding plants that same season. Some species may even flower the first year when produced as a flatted bedding plant (table 2-3 on page 9). However, since most do not flower the first year (unless they are vernalized), color labels or point-of-purchase materials are crucial for their spring sales (see "Information" section on page 83).

Some species require specific day length conditions to flower (see chapter 12). Other species must undergo a cold period (vernalization or overwintering) to flower. Some of these species have a juvenile stage and must be grown for at least six months before cold treatment will be effective (for example, *Aurinia saxatilis* and *Lupinus* species). Others need at least three months before cold treatment is effective (for example, *Aquilegia* hybrids and *Leucanthemum* x *superbum*).

Strategies to attempt flowering of these species the season they are planted are based on:

1. The type of environmental requirement needed to promote flowering.

2. The rate of growth of the species and the minimal size required to end juvenility before stimulating the plants with flower-inducing environmental conditions. (In other words, how old the plants must be or how many leaves the plants must unfold before being subjected to forcing conditions.)

3. The rate at which the species develops flower buds in the spring.

Spring Production from Bare-Root Plants and Plugs

Planting one-year-old (for some species, two-year-old), field-grown, bare-root plants; mid-sized vernalized plugs; or large field-grown plugs is the least complex and a common production method. While the cost to the producer for plants is high and potting is at an already busy season, there is no overwintering overhead, less heat is needed, and less labor costs are incurred (such as for watering and spraying). These plants are not sufficiently established for early spring sales and are sold in May or later. Most producers purchase plants since they have no facilities to properly store or overwinter them. A few specialty growers may produce some plants in the field and spring dig after natural overwintering and vernalization.

Winter Production from Bare-Root Plants

Planting one-year-old, bare-root, field-grown plants in 1- to 3-gallon containers in September to early October, establishing their root system in the fall, and overwintering them in protective structures for spring sales involves purchasing less costly plants, but the costs of overwintering and plant losses are incurred. This system does avoid potting during a busy spring, and plants bloom the year after potting. With the exception of some specialty producers who do some field production, most producers purchase the plants.

Production and Overwintering of Purchased Small Plants, Rooted Cuttings, or Small Divisions

Planting cuttings, divisions, small plants, or plugs in 4-inch to 1-gallon containers in late summer to early fall after the busy period; growing the plants for the remainder of the season; and overwintering the salable-sized plants for spring sales requires skill in growing and overwintering perennial species. Insufficient rooting prior to storage and overwintering may cause the plants to die. Because the plants are purchased when small, costs are controlled to a greater extent by the finished plant producer.

Start-to-Finish Perennial Production in Containers

This approach involves sowing seeds, planting plugs, or vegetatively propagating each species, usually in late spring to mid summer. Seedlings or small plants are transplanted to containers, perhaps with a second transplanting from flats to a finishing container. Transplants are grown on to a salable size and overwintered prior to spring sales.

The advantage of this method is that the producer controls the seed or cutting source of the plants. This is important for some to guarantee trueness of cultivars, and for others to ensure pest-free plants.

Not all species are suited to the same method of production, since overwintering (cold treatment) is necessary for only some species (see chapter 12). Many species propagated January through March may achieve flowering size the first season in the garden.

Field Production

Growers in areas with well-drained, sandy soils and either a mild climate or heavy snow cover can successfully produce perennials by either sowing seeds directly in the ground or transplanting small plants or divisions to a field. Some growers prefer field production if they are producing perennials with large divisions, such as daylilies and iris, or if their soil is fertile and abundant. Some growers believe that field production generates healthier plants, or they simply prefer growing plants in the field rather than in pots with soilless media.

Some small growers custom dig their field-grown plants and sell them wrapped in newspaper or a bag directly to the customer. Most growers dig and pot plants in the spring for sales through the season. Initial costs are lower for field production than for containers (there are no pots or media to buy), but weed control is more of a problem and requires labor. Other disadvantages are that labor to dig may be costly, growth and culture is dependent on the weather, and soil is depleted as it is sold along with plants. A few producers grow plants in field soil covered with a hoophouse or Quonset greenhouse to provide more control of environmental conditions such as wind, rainfall, and temperature.

CHAPTER 5

Propagation

Herbaceous perennials are a highly diverse group of plants. Propagation methods vary from seeds to stem cuttings, root cuttings, division, or tissue culture. Appendix A, which begins on page 94, lists the different propagation techniques for various perennials and the time of year the techniques are performed. Actual dates and procedures vary with work load, production scheme, and market.

For many (but not all) perennial selections, seed sowing is an inferior method of propagation. The best cultivars often are not "true" from seeds; that is, seedlings are not genetically identical to the parent and are less attractive. However, large numbers of plants can be produced easily and economically by this method, so it remains a very popular means of supplying inexpensive perennials to the mass market. Seeds can also be used to provide or maintain a genetically diverse population of plants for revegetation or for native, woodland, or meadow habitats.

Discriminating customers will often insist on vegetatively propagated material from nurseries that supply uniform, genetically superior cultivars. Seed-propagated plants may need to be selected for suitable characteristics, then vegetatively propagated to achieve a uniform product. Propagation of uniform, high-quality perennials can be highly technical. Some firms specialize in only propagation. One large East Coast wholesale producer ranks top cutting, division, and seed propagation as equally good methods of propagation, with division being the preferred or only method used for most cultivars. Tissue culture and root cuttings are important, too, but ranked lower.

In addition to being propagated in the spring, most perennials can be divided in the early fall, potted, and overwintered in protective structures. They also can be divided and field grown. Seeds sown in early to mid summer after the busy spring season will produce plants that are large enough by fall to require only minimal winter protection. If seeds are germinated in the fall, then the seedlings must be held in a heated greenhouse over winter since they will be unable to withstand severe freezing. Seeds of many perennial species can be sown November through December in plugs and grown in a low-temperature greenhouse until spring; this method often provides adequate cold (vernalization) for bloom that year.

Propagation Media

Many growing mixes are suitable for perennial germination and production. They fall into two basic categories: peat-lite mixes, which contain no soil, and soil mixes, which contain 20–33% soil. Most commercially bagged mixes contain no soil. Once a satisfactory mix is chosen, that mix should be used for all or most species and kept in use until a better mix is found through actual tests in the nursery. Media used for production often contain bark, sand, or other coarse ingredients, so they are unsuitable in most cases for propagation.

Media should provide plants with support, water, fertility, and microorganisms. Media consist of about half solids, and the other half is split about equally between liquids (water) and gases (air) by volume. Usually less than half of the solids is inorganic with the majority organic in nature. The space in media that holds water and gases is referred to as "porosity." The water porosity and air porosity are key to good plant growth. An imbalance can cause pots to continually dry out or stay too wet (see "Measuring Media Porosities" on page 50).

Media Components

Peat moss is the remains of dead plants. It takes one year's growth of sphagnum moss to produce 1 millimeter of compressed peat. Other peats are more decomposed and often less desirable. Peat moss is very acidic, with a pH of 3–5. With 70–80% porosity, it is mainly air and water. A good peat moss may be 20% air and 50% water.

Vermiculite is gray, expanded mica ore that was heated to 1,800°F in its creation. It is graded in three sizes: #2, which is for pots; #3, which is for bedding plants; and #4, which is for seeds. The larger the number, the smaller the particle size. Vermiculite is easily compressed, which destroys its porosity, so it should not be compacted. When totally wet, it will hold 500% of its weight in water. It can provide some potassium, magnesium, calcium, cation exchange capacity, and buffering (ability to prevent large nutrient imbalances).

Perlite consists of white granules that are formed when volcanic silicate ore is heated to 1,400°F. It does not compress, adds aeration, and improves drainage. Problems with perlite are that it is dusty (so moisten it before using), and it floats to the surface of media over time with watering. It has few nutrients and a neutral pH.

Sand can be added to media in small amounts (perhaps less than 10%) for porosity and weight. Sand consists of finely ground stones and is generally alkaline. Sand from limestone should never be used, as it may change the pH. Sharp sands (those that are flat, mined, and white) are best. Ocean sands high in salts are worst. Sand is often a large component in media for vegetative propagation. It can have 10% air and 30% water porosity, or about 40% total porosity.

Media for Germinating Seeds

Common media for germination are equal parts sand and peat moss by volume or a peat-lite medium (peat and vermiculite or perlite, or both). Some perennials from specialized habitats or those with propagules (such as spores from ferns) may require other media such as sphagnum peat moss.

The peat-lite formula is given in table 5-1. In addition to the major components, starter nutrients and a wetting agent are included. The latter amendment assists the medium, which is often quite hydrophobic, in absorbing water. In the formulation and handling of these mixes, the goal is to maintain nutrient levels as listed in table 5-2 on page 28. Usually enough nutrients are contained in the medium for this stage of growth, which has little demand.

Media for Vegetative Propagation (Cuttings)

Media for vegetative propagation should have even greater porosity and moisture retention than container media. This is often achieved by adding peat moss, per-

Table 5-1. Peat-lite mix for sowing perennials

Ingredient	For one cubic yard[1]	For one bushel[2]
Sphagnum peat moss[3]	0.5 cu yd (13 bu)	0.5 bu
Vermiculite[3] (#3 for seed germination, #2 or #3 for transplanting)	0.5 cu yd (13 bu)	0.5 bu
Dolomitic limestone	5 lbs	104 gm (5 Tbsp)
20% Superphosphate OR Treble superphosphate	1 lb 0.5 lb	20.5 gm (1.2 Tbsp) 10.25 gm (0.6 Tbsp)
Gypsum	2 lbs	41 gm (2.5 Tbsp)
Calcium nitrate	0.5 lb	10.25 gm (1.2 Tbsp)
Potassium nitrate	0.5 lb	10.25 gm (1.2 Tbsp)
Aqua Gro[4] Liquid OR Granular	3 oz 1 lb	4 ml (0.5 tsp) 26 gm (2 Tbsp)
Trace Elements: Fl 503 OR Fl 555 OR Esmigram OR Perk OR Micromax	2 oz 2 oz 4 lbs 4 lbs 1.5 lbs	2.5 gm (0.25 tsp) 2.5 gm (0.25 tsp) 81 gm (4 Tbsp) 81 gm (4 Tbsp) 31 gm (1.7 Tbsp)

[1] 1 cubic yard (cu yd) = 27 cubic feet (cu ft) or 22 bushels (bu)

[2] Tbsp = level tablespoonful; tsp = level teaspoonful

[3] Due to a 15–20% shrinkage that occurs in mixing, use an additional 2 bushels each of peat moss and vermiculite to obtain a full cubic yard of mix.

[4] Aqua Gro is a wetting agent.

Table 5-2. Nutrient levels for propagation and growing media

Component	Soil mix	Peat-lite mix
Modified Spurway Extract (ppm)		
Nitrate	30–50	30–50
Phosphorus	4–6	4–6
Potassium	25–35	25–35
Calcium	150+	150+
1 Soil:2 Water or Equivalent Extract		
pH	5.8–6.8	5.5–6.0
Maximum soluble salts (Siemens x 10^{-5})	125	175

lite, vermiculite, or a combination of these. Traditionally, peat moss has been combined with sand. When experimenting with different combinations, start with equal proportions of ingredients by volume.

Media are quite varied for vegetative propagation and can include sand, sand and peat (in equal volumes), perlite, or perlite and vermiculite (in equal volumes). A "gritty" medium may have equal parts sand, peat, and pea gravel and may be useful for such plants as alpines. A "loamy" medium may have equal parts loamy soil, peat moss, and either perlite or vermiculite (or a combination of the two) and may be used for woodland native plants.

Peat moss is basically a nonrenewable resource in Europe and (according to some) in North America, so some nurseries have begun using a fine, composted bark as a substitute. (In North America, many claim more peat moss is being produced than is being harvested, particularly in Canada.) A typical mix might contain by volume five parts composted bark, five parts peat moss, three parts sand, and two parts perlite. A thin layer of sand may be used over the soil; sand dries out quickly, thus reducing the chance of problems such as damping-off and fungus gnats. If nutrients are not included in the medium, add half-strength liquid fertilizer once rooting begins (see chapter 7).

Nutrients

Nutrients are generally available to plant roots in the form of ions — elements with either a positive or negative charge. Often roots cannot distinguish between elements with similar charges, and so they absorb too much of one nutrient at the expense of another; this creates a nutrient imbalance and potential growth problems (table 5-3). It is important to avoid excesses of nutrients (table 5-4).

Macroelements are those elements needed in large amounts by plants. Nitrogen, phosphorus, and potassium are all macroelements.

Nitrogen

Nitrogen (N), one of the most important elements, is the first element percentage listed on a fertilizer bag. It is easily altered in the soil and plant into other forms. Plants absorb nitrogen in either nitrate (NO_3) or ammonium (NH_4) form. It is part of amino acids that form proteins, including the green pigment chlorophyll, and it is key to many plant functions, such as forming enzymes. An excess of nitrogen prolongs vegetative growth, retards maturity, and increases succulence. A nitrogen deficiency stunts growth and produces an overall yellowing, starting with the lower leaves. Elements whose deficiencies affect lower leaves first are said to be "mobile" — they are moved by the plant from the less important lower leaves to the more crucial new leaves and growing points, flowers, or fruiting structures.

Phosphorus

Phosphorus (P) is needed in smaller amounts than nitrogen or potassium. It is the second element listed in a fertilizer analysis (it is actually listed as percent phosphate). It is absorbed by the plant as phosphate ions (phosphorus and oxygen combined as P_2O_4) and is key for cell division and thus growth, flowering, setting seeds, developing roots, and carrying out photosynthesis — the process by which plants use sunlight to produce sugars and starches to live on from carbon dioxide and water. An excess of phosphorus causes iron deficiency. A deficiency stunts growth and turns leaves darker green, then purple, starting with the lower ones first.

Table 5-3. Element excesses that cause deficiencies

Nutrient in excess	Resulting deficiency
N	K
NH₄	Ca, Cu
K	N, Ca, Mg
P	Cu, Fe, Zn
Ca	Mg, B
Mg	Ca, K
Na	K, Ca, Mg
Mn	Fe, Mo
Zn	Mn, Fe
Cu	Mn, Fe, Mo
Mo	Cu

B = boron, Ca = calcium, Cu = copper, Fe = iron, K = potassium, Mg = magnesium, Mn = manganese, Mo = molybdenum, N = nitrogen, Na = sodium, NH₄ = ammonium, P = phosphorus, Zn = zinc

Table 5-4. Symptoms of nutrient excesses and deficiencies

Element	Excess	Deficiency
Boron	Marginal leaf burn, older leaves develop symptoms first	Growth stops, younger buds and leaves die, terminal side shoots form
Calcium	Iron and micronutrient chlorosis	Buds fail to develop, terminal ones fail first
Chlorine	Marginal burn, lower leaves show symptoms first	Stunt and dieback, older growth first
Copper	Interveinal yellowing of lower leaves	Growth stops, younger buds and leaves die, terminal side shoots form
Iron	Insignificant	Interveinal yellowing of lower leaves
Magnesium	Tip or marginal burn along leaves, lower leaves affected first	Interveinal yellowing, lower leaves affected first
Manganese	Interveinal yellowing of lower leaves	Fine network of green veins in yellow leaves, younger leaves affected first
Molybdenum	Growth stops, younger buds and leaves die, terminal side shoots form	Yellowing, first of lower leaves; distorted growth
Nitrogen	Prolongs vegetative growth, retards maturity, increases succulence	Stunts growth, yellowing overall with lower leaves yellowing first
Phosphorus	Iron deficiency	Stunts growth and leaves, lower leaves turn dark green then purple
Potassium	Magnesium deficiency, salt burn on leaf edges	Tip or marginal burn along leaves, lower leaves affected first
Sulfur	Marginal salt burn of leaves and roots	Retards growth, uniform yellowing except for leaf tips
Zinc	Interveinal yellowing of lower leaves	Stunted growth, seeds fail to form

Note: Symptoms will vary with some species and cultivars.

Potassium

Potassium (K) is the third element listed in a fertilizer analysis (as percent potassium oxide, K_2O). It usually exists in adequate to high levels in the soil, but the amount available to plants is less than the amount in the soil, because potassium sometimes exists in a form not readily taken up by plants. However, a plant will absorb more potassium than it needs, which is referred to as luxury consumption. The excess potassium can keep the plant from absorbing magnesium, and so a magnesium deficiency can result. This situation can be corrected by reducing the amount of potassium in the soil — increasing magnesium levels will not help.

Potassium is important for the movement and use of sugars by the plant and for operation of the stomates (leaf openings used for gas exchange). As was stated earlier, an excess causes magnesium deficiency or salt burn on leaf edges. Salt burn causes a yellowing then browning of the leaves, which is a reflection of damage to roots caused by excess salts drying moisture out of the roots. A deficiency is intensified if ammonium nitrogen is used and will result in a tip or marginal burn along leaves, with the lower leaves being affected first.

Secondary Macroelements

In addition to the three primary macroelements needed by plants are three secondary macroelements:

- Calcium (Ca) is important in growing tips and flowers. It is a component of salts in plant sap and is used in cell walls and cell sap. An excess of calcium causes a nutrient imbalance with iron and micronutrient chlorosis. A deficiency causes buds to fail to develop, with terminal buds affected first. (Calcium is an immobile element, which means it fails to move within the plant.)

- Magnesium (Mg) is a constituent of chlorophyll — the green pigment in plants — and in enzyme systems that help a plant function. An excess may induce potassium deficiency. A deficiency causes interveinal yellowing with lower leaves affected first.

- Sulfur (S) is usually absorbed as sulfate and changed to its elemental form inside the plant. It is a constituent of proteins and enzymes. An excess causes a salt burn of the roots, which is evidenced by browning root tips. A deficiency retards growth and causes uniform yellowing on all plant parts but the tips.

Microelements

In addition to the macroelements are the microelements, which are often called trace elements. They are needed by plants only in small amounts.

- Iron (Fe) is important for enzyme systems and the formation of chlorophyll. A deficiency causes interveinal yellowing of younger leaves (it is immobile).

- Boron (B) is needed for protein synthesis and movement of water and sugars. A deficiency causes growth to stop, and younger buds and leaves die.

- Manganese (Mn) is needed for enzyme systems and to oxidize iron, so an excess results in iron deficiency. A deficiency of manganese results in a fine network of green veins on leaves with the rest of the leaves yellow; younger leaves are affected first (manganese is immobile).

- Zinc (Zn) is important for enzymes. A deficiency stunts growth and causes seed formation to fail.

- Molybdenum (Mo) is important for the enzyme system involved in nitrate metabolism. A deficiency of molybdenum is similar to a nitrogen deficiency; it causes a yellowing starting with the lower leaves and distorts growth.

- Chlorine (Cl) is important for photosynthesis and oxygen production. An excess causes salt burn, first of the lower leaves. A deficiency causes stunted plants and dieback (it is immobile).

- Copper (Cu) deficiency is sometimes found in conjunction with peat and organic soils.

Temperature

An air temperature of 70–80°F and uniform moisture are preferred for propagation. The media temperature will often be 10–15°F cooler. After the seeds have germinated, the flats should be removed to a cooler environment. A 55°F night temperature and 65°F day temperature produce high-quality transplants that are not soft or spindly in growth. Flats should be placed on an open mesh or similar bench to "air prune" roots (prevent root growth out the bottom of the plug cells).

Bottom heat is preferred for seed germination and rooting cuttings and is most important fall through spring when the temperature of the growing mix may drop below 70°F. Bottom heat is provided by several methods, including steam or hot water pipes or tubes, hot air, and electric heating cables or mats (figure 5-1). Most seeds germinate best and cuttings root best when the growing medium temperature is 70–80°F. (See appendix B on page 145 for requirements of specific plants.) A few species prefer slightly cooler temperatures. A constant 60°F temperature is recommended for some crops. A root zone temperature of 65–70°F and night air temperature of 50–55°F is often recommended depending on the time of year. Bottom heating can be adjusted to provide different temperatures for each bench or area.

If only one greenhouse is available for propagation, maintaining cool temperatures for growth of more mature and older crops can be a problem. Usually one end of the greenhouse is cooler than the other and can be adapted to the needs of older crops.

Watering

Proper application of water is critical to successful seed germination and subsequent growth of the seedlings and to rooting of cuttings. Because seeds are so easily disturbed by overhead watering, the need for watering during the germination process should be eliminated by creating conditions that will keep the seed flat sufficiently moist and prevent water loss. One method of doing this is to cover the containers with a white plastic sheet or place them in plastic bags after irrigation. This method is also effective with cuttings. Use of white plastic reduces the chance of the seeds being overheated by bright sunlight during late March and early April. If clear plastic is used, a special effort should be made to

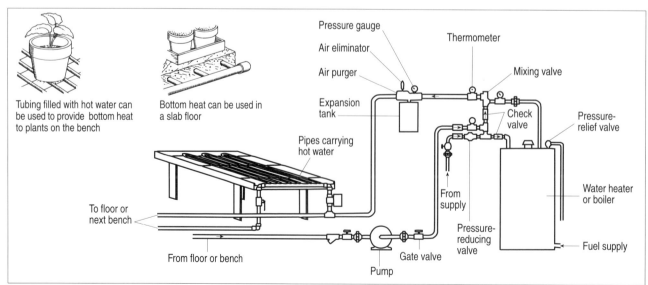

Figure 5-1. Types of bottom heat and piping schematic for bottom heat system

provide shade to the flats as needed to prevent injury. A layer of cheesecloth over the plastic is effective in preventing excess temperature increase.

Regardless of the type of covering material used, it is important to remove the covering upon germination or as cuttings root. Diseases such as *Botrytis* may quickly develop when ventilation is restricted and condensation exists on the plant surface for six to eight hours.

Many growers prefer to use low-pressure, intermittent mist (figure 5-2). Proper control of the misting cycle is important to prevent overwatering. Other growers use a fog system, either a commercial one for greenhouses or a home humidifier placed in a small white plastic tent. Mist systems are simpler and less expensive than commercial fog systems, but they leach more nutrients from leaves and media, do not contribute to general cooling of the house, and use more water. Fog provides more consistent humidity but does not cool the soil as mist does. Misting or fogging frequency is gradually reduced until propagules are finally upright and established. Regardless of which system is used, cool and moist conditions at night coupled with a fluctuation to warm days can lead to powdery mildew disease.

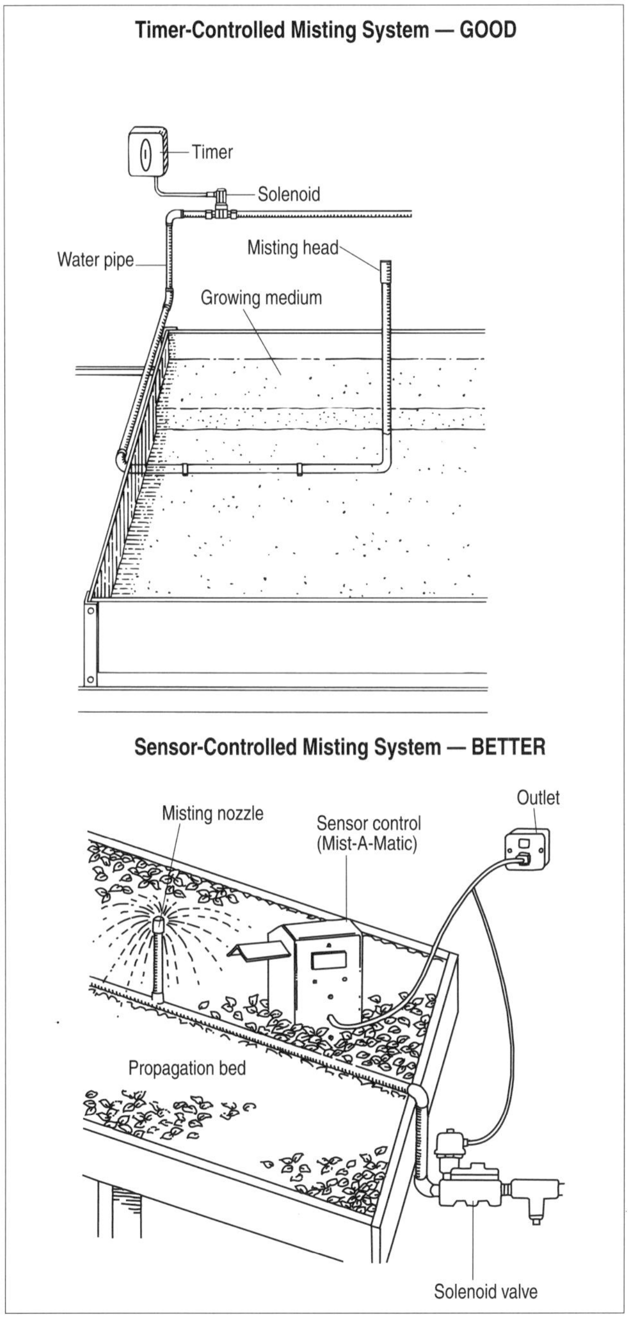

When plastic covering, low-pressure mist, or fog is not used, watering should be accomplished via fine-mist spray nozzles or "roses" to avoid dislodging the seeds and cuttings (figure 5-3). Several types of nozzles are on the market. For rooting cuttings in late fall through early spring, hand misting three times daily may be sufficient.

In many regions, growing medium pH is too high because high-pH ingredients are used or because the irrigation water pH is too alkaline. To counteract these reactions, incorporate finely ground sulfur into the medium before planting or acidify the irrigation water (figure 5-4). For information about acidifying water, contact your state cooperative extension specialist, nursery or greenhouse products supplier, or a water-testing lab;

Timer-Controlled Misting System — GOOD

Sensor-Controlled Misting System — BETTER

Figure 5-2. Two types of misting systems: the system at top is controlled by a timer, the system at bottom is controlled by an electronic Mist-A-Matic sensor (*Note:* The Mist-A-Matic is available from most greenhouse suppliers.)

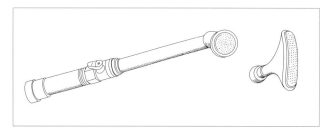

Figure 5-3. Waterers used for hand watering

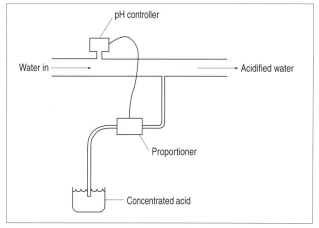

Figure 5-4. pH controller in the water line

they should be able to provide more details and sources of equipment. Actual rates of acidification are determined through testing of the growing mix and water.

Propagation from Seed

Production of high-quality transplants from seed is possible only when the best seed is used. Buying poor-quality seed or saving old seed can result in significant dollar losses on the final product. In a three-year study at the University of Vermont (Perry and Bove, 1985), seed characteristics of several perennial cultivars were compared. Seeds for each cultivar were obtained fresh from several sources, and it was found that the only real difference among sources was seed cost, not quality. This cost difference may reflect differences in marketing and customer service and in the quality of the packaging.

Once seeds are obtained, they should be stored under conditions that will maintain their viability. Storage temperatures of 32–40°F and a relative humidity of less than 50% will maintain the viability of most seeds for at least one year. Storing seeds in the refrigerator in a closed jar containing an absorbent, such as silica gel or corn meal, works well. Do not store seeds under extremely warm or humid conditions, as viability may be drastically reduced.

The germination percentage of seed is affected by many other factors. Preharvest conditions over which the grower has little control, such as the fertility of and stresses on the seed parent, are the greatest influence. As a result of these conditions and the genetic variability of species, germination percentages may vary widely. Improved methods of cleaning and sorting seeds to reduce the number of immature and poor seeds have improved the germination percentages reported on seed packets.

Seeds of herbaceous perennial species can often be handled like those of annuals. For some species, fresh seed should be sown (such as with *Baptisia);* for others, freezing or cold storage is required to break seed dormancy (such as with *Aconitum);* for others, scarification (abrading the seed coat) may be required for rapid germination (such as with *Lupinus).* Much of the available germination information from books, catalogs, and other publications is compiled in appendix B, which begins on page 145.

Sowing to Seed Flats, Market Packs, or Cell Packs

Seeds may be either broadcast into seed flats or planted in rows. Sowing in rows reduces the chance of damping-off disease destroying an entire flat of seedlings. Sowing in rows also speeds up the transplanting process, as the seedlings are less difficult to separate.

When sowing in rows, a mechanical vibrator makes the job easy. Several types of vibrating seeders are available. Some growers have adapted old electric razors to provide more uniform movement to the unit. For fine and medium-size seeds, sow ten to fifteen seeds per inch of row. Large seeds are sown so that they slightly overlap each other. Space rows about 1½ inches apart. Seeds requiring light for germination should not be covered with medium after sowing. Fine seeds that do not require light need not be covered, either; they will fall into the crevices of the medium and be covered upon watering. Non-light-requiring coarse seeds should be covered to a depth of twice their thickness. Use the same medium for covering as for planting, or cover with fine vermiculite. Some growers prefer to sift a small amount of sphagnum moss (not peat moss) over the seeds.

Most growers oversow seeds in order to ensure enough seedlings, as many perennials have low or erratic germination compared to annuals. So it is advisable to sow more seeds than the number of plants needed for transplanting and to transplant more seedlings than the number of plants needed for sale.

A study at the University of Vermont showed that the traditional method of sowing in rows, then transplanting to a market pack was the most expensive method of seed propagation (table 5-5). With high germination percentages, sowing to plugs and then transplanting to the final container is least expensive.

Table 5-5. Cost comparison, per seedling, for five propagation methods with five germination percentages (1997 costs)

| Method[1] | Germination percentage | | | | |
	100%	90%	70%	50%	30%
C	$0.26	$0.28	$0.32	$0.50	$0.82
P	0.10	0.12	0.16	0.22	0.32
P–C	0.22	0.22	0.24	0.26	0.34
MP–C	0.26	0.26	0.28	0.32	0.40
MP–MP	1.20	1.20	1.22	1.26	1.34

Source: Adapted from Duarte and Perry, 1987

[1] Propagation methods are as follows: C (1206 cell), P (273 plug), P–C (plug to cell), MP–C (market pack to cell), MP–MP (market pack to market pack).

When using plugs is either not an option (such as when a source cannot be found or a business is unable to produce its own) or inadvisable due to stress at transplanting (such as too hot and dry field conditions), then sowing to market packs and transplanting to cells is best (especially if a low germination percentage occurs). Plugs are actually a type of cell, and the terms are often used interchangeably with perennials, although traditionally plugs refer to very small cells — fifty to three hundred or more per 11-by-22-by-3/4-inch tray. Seventy plugs per tray is common for perennials.

Direct Seeding for Plugs

The introduction of seeders that sow one to several seeds per tray location is revolutionizing the propagation-from-seed industry. The procedures used for plug seeding vary with the type of machine employed; however, certain conditions are required regardless of the seeding machine used (see next chapter on plug production).

After sowing, the fine mix should be thoroughly wetted and kept moist. The small volume of mix in each cell makes the seedlings especially vulnerable to rapid drying and quick death.

Inexpensive seed species are sown with two or three seeds per cell to avoid skips from poor germination. The labor saved in eliminating the transplanting operation more than pays for the extra seeds required. Direct sowing, as described, is usually done over a period of several weeks.

Extremely precise control of the growing mix nutrient content, moisture application, and the growing mix and air temperatures are necessary for success with this system (see next chapter on plug production). As a result, growers planning to go into plug seeding should obtain as much information as possible on all plug seeders available, and then gain at least one year's experience before committing themselves completely to this method of growing. Information on the various seeders may be obtained from equipment suppliers.

Seedling Storage

Seedlings of some perennial species can be held in refrigerated storage with fluorescent lighting for periods of up to six weeks. Storage is useful when too many seed flats are ready for transplanting at one time. Not all herbaceous perennial seedlings can be stored successfully. Trials are essential before adopting this practice to avoid potentially severe losses of varieties.

If perennial seedlings must be stored, try the following procedure:

1. When seedlings have reached the proper transplanting stage, water containers thoroughly. Allow excess water to drain and place containers in polyethylene bags large enough to permit closing with a twist tie or rubber band.

2. Place bagged containers in a 35–40°F refrigerator. Place fluorescent lamps (the same ones used for germinating) 12 inches above the seedling flats and light them for fourteen hours daily. If plants are dormant, they may be stored in the dark for several months at 28–32°F. Cycling temperatures (alternating between high and low, warm and cold) can lead to condensation on plant surfaces, which in turn may promote the development of *Botrytis*.

3. If plants are stored for two weeks or less, they can be used immediately from the cooler. Allow them to warm to room temperature. If they are stored two to four weeks, then place containers in a cool location (55–60°F) for twenty-four hours before use to allow them to resume growth. Allow dormant plants to resume growth at these temperatures before using them.

Storing seedlings is not a substitute for planning; only healthy seedlings should be stored. Storage is a tool to be used in properly managed perennial production.

Vegetative Methods of Propagation

A key to most types of cuttings is a good, sharp propagator's knife. As one propagator put it, "Your knife is your life." Hand clippers can be used for small amounts of cuttings or for removing larger stems from stock plants. But knives are often easier on your hands and the plants, and they are easy to keep sharp. A propagator's knife is different from a standard jackknife in that it has a straight edge that is easily sharpened, and it is not made from stainless steel, which cannot keep a sharp edge. Carbon steel knives are perhaps best, but they will rust and so must be wiped off after use and stored dry.

Knives should be sharpened on fine whetstones, not power machines that can ruin their temper. Apply oil or water to the whetstone. *Push* the knife edge on the whetstone *toward* the cutting edge, not away from it. Do not drag the knife backwards.

Increasingly, choice new perennials are being patented or otherwise protected from propagation; royalties are paid to the originator. These royalties are used to support breeding and development efforts and should be respected.

Stem Cuttings

Stem cuttings are a highly desirable means of vegetative propagation for many species. For optimum results, use stock plants that are healthy, well-watered, adequately fertilized, and free of insects and disease. Stock plants (such as *Campanula lactiflora)* may be grown in the greenhouse and forced for cutting material for more cuttings and sometimes better rooting. Often cuttings taken from vegetative growth forced in a greenhouse will root better than cuttings taken from plants growing outdoors; this is because plants growing outdoors may not be as succulent (that is, they may be woody) or conducive to forming roots, or they may be preparing to flower instead of root.

A day length conducive to vegetative growth (not flowering) is best; this is usually the opposite of the day length required to force flowering. For example, if short days are needed to flower, then long days are needed for vegetative growth. The best time of day to take cuttings is in the morning or on cool and cloudy days when cuttings will not lose moisture as quickly.

As was stated earlier, cuttings are best taken when plants are in a stage of active vegetative growth prior to or following flowering. Growers learn this stage by examining the plants and becoming familiar with their life and growth cycles. By constantly taking cuttings and removing flower buds, growers can keep many plants in the vegetative stage for a long period of time. The best time to take cuttings is when they will root well and when the grower has a chance to produce them and provide appropriate care (see table 5-6 and appendix A on page 94).

If necessary, cuttings can be taken when plants are more mature, but this procedure often requires the use of rooting hormones, which are not required for soft tissue cuttings. If hormone is required, one of the weaker formulations available [such as 1,000 ppm indole butyric acid (IBA)] is usually sufficient. Rooting of many species may be enhanced by dipping stem bases in IBA talc (such as 0.5–1% IBA). Dips in liquid formulations of rooting hormone are also successful.

Perennial stem cuttings can be grouped into several types. Tip or terminal cuttings are for plants such as

Table 5-6. Requirements for stem cuttings of some perennials

Name	Comment
Achillea, Yarrow	SF
Anthemis, Marguerite Daisy	S
Artemesia, Wormwood	SF
Aster, Aster	S
Boltonia, False Aster	S
Ceratostigma, Leadwort	S
Chelone, Turtlehead	S
Chrysanthemum, Chrysanthemum	S
Coreopsis, Tickseed	SF
Dianthus, Pinks	S
Dicentra, Bleeding Heart	S
Eupatorium, Joe-Pye Weed	S
Gaura, Gaura	S
Geranium, Geranium	SR
Gypsophila, Baby's Breath	SFR
Iberis, Candy Tuft	SFR
Lavandula, Lavender	SF
Lysimachia, Loosestrife	S
Lythrum, Loosestrife	S
Monarda, Bee Balm	SF
Perovskia, Russian Sage	SF
Phlox carolina, Phlox	S
Phlox divaricata, Phlox	SF
Phlox maculata, Garden Phlox	SF
Phlox paniculata, Garden Phlox	S
Phlox stolonifera, Creeping Phlox	SF
Phlox subulata, Moss Phlox	SF
Physostegia, Obedient Plant	S
Potentilla fruiticosa, Cinquefoil	SFR
Salvia, Sage	SF
Sedum, Stonecrop	S
Solidago, Goldenrod	S
Veronica longifolia, Speedwell	S

Source: Adapted from Van Hees and Hendricks, 1987
Key: S = take cuttings in spring to early summer; F = take cuttings in late summer to fall; R = the use of rooting hormone is suggested

Amsonia, Euphorbia, and *Phlox subulata.* They should be cut just below a node, allowing three nodes on average per cutting. Stem, leaf node, or internodal cuttings from a section of stem root at leaf nodes and are some of the easiest cuttings to root and sometimes even root in just water. They are suitable for plants such as *Agastache, Ajuga, Chelone, Clematis,* and *Lamium.* A few plants, such as *Galax, Sedum, Ramonda,* and *Shortia,* may be taken as leaf cuttings (a leaf with small section of stem attached).

Cuttings taken at the base of the plant where plant parts join the roots are called "basal" cuttings. If several roots are attached, they are referred to as "heel" or "rooted" cuttings. Basal cuttings are taken early in the season as plants sprout and are made with such perennials as *Achillea, Aster novi-belgii, Armeria, Coreopsis verticillata* 'Moonbeam', *Delphinium, Dryas,* and *Geranium.* Basal cuttings are the most reliable method for cultivars of *Heliopsis, Stokesia,* and *Veronica gentianoides* and about the only method for *Salvia* 'May Night'. Spring-flowering plants, such as *Pulmonaria* (lungwort), may be taken as basal cuttings after flowering or in early fall. Some plants, such as fall-flowering *Sedum,* may be taken as basal cuttings in the spring or stem cuttings in summer. Succulent cuttings (such as from *Sedum)* should be allowed to air dry for a couple of hours before sticking and should not be placed under mist in order to prevent root or stem rot.

Rhizome Cuttings

Rhizome cuttings are a special type of stem cutting. Rhizomes of plants such as *Bergenia, Dicentra eximia,* and *Darmera* are cut into 1- to 2-inch sections, each with a dormant bud, and treated with a fungicide before being laid horizontally onto a moist propagation medium. The cuttings are covered with $1/2$ inch of soil to keep them from drying out and are kept moist.

Root Cuttings

Root cuttings will form adventitious shoots with plants such as *Crambe, Erodium, Eryngium, Gaillardia, Ligularia,* and *Phlox paniculata.* Root cuttings of plants that have thin roots, such as *Anemone japonica, Macleaya,* and *Symphytum,* should be placed horizontally like rhizome cuttings. Root cuttings should not be confused with cuttings from plants with underground stems such as *Coronilla, Ceratostigma,* and *Monarda.* Although root cuttings are useful for most members of the Borage family, such as *Brunnera,* they cannot be used for many variegated cultivars of the same species, as only green-leaved plants result; the same is true of variegated cultivars of phlox.

Root cuttings are useful to make up more plants than would otherwise be possible, to propagate plants that produce poor seed or have hard-to-root stem cuttings, and to get propagation done during the slow winter months. The shoot that results from a root cutting comes from different tissue than that from a stem cutting. Root cuttings are also slower to make and grow, and they are a dirty method compared to cuttings from aboveground parts, because soil or growing medium must be washed from the roots before taking cuttings.

Take 2- to 4-inch cuttings, usually between $1/8$ and $1/4$ inch thick, from large, established stock plants. Some growers take cuttings as small as 1 inch long. Root cuttings are best taken during the mid dormancy period, often in November through March. They are not as successful when taken during periods of active growth. Only about one-third of the stock plant root system may be removed at any one time if vigorous stock is to be maintained.

Cuttings may be treated with a fungicidal dust or dip to minimize rotting and are stuck proximal end (top end) up or laid flat on moist propagation medium until roots and shoots develop. Many layers of medium and cuttings can be placed in a deep flat. Cuttings can also be bundled a dozen or so per bundle, placed upright in cell flats, and placed in a shaded but highly humid chamber in a greenhouse until rooting begins. Rooting hormones should *not* be used, as they help only stem tissue to root. Water the flats sparingly during winter, keeping soil moist but not wet as root cuttings easily rot.

Division

Division is a very common propagation method for herbaceous perennials. Gardeners multiply most species by this means, but not into as many divisions as growers. Commercial propagators pull offsets containing root initials (buds on crowns that will form new roots) from species such as *Hemerocallis, Heuchera sanguinea,* or *Leucanthemum* x *superbum,* and divide the crowns of several other species.

Before dividing plants, remove as much soil as possible and cut back any foliage. Early spring or early fall is often the best time to divide most plants. Exceptions to this are iris, peonies, and poppies, which should be divided in late summer.

It is often easier on a plant and less stressful for subsequent regrowth if the plant is pulled apart rather than cut apart through its foliage and roots. However, some woody perennials, such as *Astilbe* and *Epimedium,* will need to be cut apart with a knife. Plants should be broken or cut into halves, then quarters to avoid ripping or breaking, which often happens when a grower tries to pull a small division off a larger one. Manually dividing plants using a rocking motion and the balls of your thumbs as pivots works best. For large clumps, use two spading forks back-to-back instead of a hatchet or spade. Rock the forks back and forth against and then away from each other to pry the divisions apart (figure 5-5 on page 36).

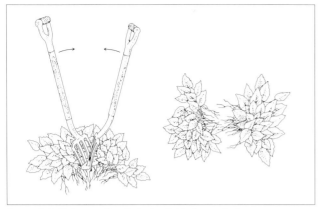

Figure 5-5. Using spading forks to divide large plants

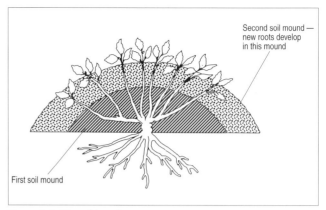

Figure 5-6. Mound layering

The size of the division will vary with the number of plants needed, the type of plant, the size of the pot, and other factors. *Astilbe* hybrids may have one eye per quart pot or three per gallon pot. Eyes should be at or just below the soil surface after watering. Peonies usually have a minimum of three eyes, and eyes should be an inch below the soil surface. In a study at the University of Connecticut (Brand, 1996b), large divisions of vigorous grasses such as *Panicum virgatum* and *Pennisetum alopecuroides* potted in 2-gallon (Classic 600) containers grew too large for the containers, resulting in water and nutrient stress. Large divisions of *Miscanthus sinensis* cultivars resulted in more tillers (offshoots, side shoots from grasses) and larger plants without stress. Large divisions of *Calamagrostis* 'Karl Foerster' had more than double the number of flowers, making the plants more marketable.

A unique division variant for *Hosta* called "Rossing" or "Rossizing" (after its inventor Henry Ross from Ohio) involves cutting deep into the crown in early spring with a knife, with several cuts being required for large crowns. The plant is not disturbed again until the following late summer, when each of the sections will hopefully have formed strong buds and are ready to divide. Two or more years may be saved on the growth of a mature plant by using this method.

Layering

Layering is a method more commonly used with woody species and less commonly used with herbaceous species. It involves mounding soil up around the base of certain perennials (such as *Phlomis)* to allow roots to develop from covered stems (figure 5-6). The initial layer of soil is added when shoots are young and short; as shoots grow, more soil is added. The rooted stems are then removed and potted. Other loose material, such as sawdust or well-rotted compost, can be used instead of soil.

For perennials with runners or stems along the ground (such as some *Verbena)*, the stems may be pegged or pinned to the ground with wire, pegs, or even heavy objects such as stones to encourage stem/ground contact. Allow the stems or runners to root before cutting them from the mother or stock plant. Others perennials (such as some *Lobelia)* can have their stems laid horizontally on rooting media under mist.

Grafting

Grafting is a method used for only a few species, such as tree peonies and in the past some *Gypsophila*, in order to propagate desirable clones of plants that do not root readily or produce seed. A scion (budded stem) of the desired plant is inserted into a vigorous rootstock of another plant. This is similar to the procedure used with woody plants. The rootstock may be merely a plant crown, such as the large tuberous roots of herbaceous peonies. The graft union is waxed or wrapped with parafilm to prevent desiccation, then placed in moist peat moss in a plastic bag at 70°F. Once the union is formed, the plant is put in the field with the union several inches below the soil surface so the scion can form roots. Once the scion has an established root system (in about two to three years), the plant is lifted and the original herbaceous peony rootstock removed. Otherwise, the rootstock will enlarge and may lift the entire plant above the soil.

Tissue Culture

Tissue culture is still a relatively new method of propagation for perennials. It is especially valuable for vegetatively propagating improved selections of hard-to-root species such as *Gypsophila*, slow-to-propagate species such as *Hosta*, or new selections of which rapid multiplication is desirable such as *Heuchera* and *Pulmonaria*.

Many species, especially those with variegated foliage, may not reproduce true from tissue culture. Some colors such as red-flowered *Astilbe* may not reproduce either. Tissue culture is often a last resort for propagation, as it requires special facilities and techniques and is expensive.

Plants produced in tissue culture usually need gradual acclimation from test tube to greenhouse to outdoors. Some varieties may mutate in tissue culture, creating chimeras, or plants with tissues representing more than one genetic type. This may happen with flowers (such as daylilies) or with foliage (such as hostas) and may not be apparent until plants are several years old or mature. A retailer buying in such tissue-cultured small plants would have to grow all plants on to mature size or flowering in order to assure trueness to type. The Perennial Plant Association standards require that plants propagated from tissue culture be labeled as such (see *American Standards for Perennial Plants* in the recommended reading section beginning on page 203).

A unique method of propagation described by one grower as "goo" is a cross between tissue culture and cuttings, and it is useful for very finely textured small plants such as *Thymus* and *Arenaria balearica*. In this method, plants are trimmed with scissors, the cuttings are mixed with a tapioca starch mixture to become "gooey", and then the mixture is blended in a food processor. The resulting "goo" is then squeezed onto the top of soil in cells (in a manner similar to squeezing cake frosting out of a tube), where the plant parts root and grow.

CHAPTER 6

Plug Production

Perennial growers, especially those who also produce bedding plants, are beginning to produce plug perennials that can be propagated effectively from seed. Relatively inexpensive seeders are available for producing plugs — even to small growers. Most plugs are transplanted manually, as only larger growers are able to afford transplanting equipment. There are many similarities between annual and perennial plugs in general cultural stages and requirements. The following overview of plug production is adapted in part from a presentation by Karlovich (IQDHO, 1994) and articles by Aylsworth (1995) and Yantorno (1997).

The advantages to plug production are that (1) plug seedlings are often easy to transplant, are easier to handle than cuttings, and are less labor-intensive than cuttings; (2) perennial seed is relatively inexpensive compared to the cost of making cuttings; and (3) it fits better into many firms' production practices. For instance, some small bedding plant growers do not have a mist system or similar rooting system for cuttings.

Other advantages to the final grower or retailer are that the erratic nature of some perennials in germination and growth has already been dealt with by the plug producer; decisions about what to grow have already been made by the plug producer; and the cold or vernalization period that many perennials need to flower is provided by many plug producers. For some varieties, perennial plugs can often be ready for sale or even in bloom only six weeks from the time they are acquired from the producer and planted.

Advantages of Perennial Plugs

- Easy to handle and transplant
- Often more cost-effective than vegetative propagation
- Fit well into many firms' production practices
- Erratic or poor germination is dealt with by the plug grower
- Often plugs have already received a cold treatment for flowering
- Often a short time from transplanting to sale

Perennial plugs differ from annual plugs and present challenges (especially for the producer) in several important respects. Challenges of perennial plugs include:

- There are few or no specialty seed products (such as pelleted seed) available with perennials, which often makes their seeds harder to handle.

- Perennials have received little attention from breeders and seed companies, so there are fewer selections (especially varieties) of perennials than annuals, and they often have poorer seed quality.

- Dormancy is often a bigger problem with perennial seeds than with annual seeds.

- There is less fine-tuned information on perennial germination and culture, and there are many more perennials to learn about than annuals. Multiple sowings can help make up for poor germination. For some perennials, poor germination may be 75%; for others, 75% may be good germination — it all depends on the species and cultivar.

- Many favorite perennials, especially cultivars, are not available from seed.
- Perennial seeds, as mentioned in a previous section, often are not genetically pure and therefore often yield a range of plant variations. Annuals, on the other hand, are often highly hybridized and therefore genetically pure.

Preproduction

A key to successful plug production is attention to details that may not be as crucial with vegetative or pot production. The medium should be just moist — not too wet, not too dry. Trays should be filled completely and uniformly with a medium that is uniformly moist throughout. Some growers have a filling machine made specifically for plug trays, while other growers adapt other types of filling machines for plug trays. There are many seeders available, and the cost of a seeder does not necessarily correlate with its quality — a seeder works only as well as the person operating it. Knowledge of how to best operate a seeder usually comes with experience. Growers often have one or two trained people who are totally responsible for plug seeding.

There are several sizes of plug trays and therefore many sizes of plug cells. The 128-count tray, which is often sold as a 125, takes longer to finish (grow plants to maturity) than a 72-count tray, which is often sold as a 70. This is because, with more plants per flat, the plants are smaller and so take more time to grow once they are transplanted. But the seedlings from the 128-cell tray will be less expensive to purchase initially. Larger sizes with 50 or even 36 cells per tray are sometimes seen.

Some varieties will be better adapted to one size over another. For example, if plants are propagated vegetatively, the larger trays are usually used to allow proper rooting. Larger plugs are useful for a fast-cropped 4-inch pot (which takes several weeks) or for overwintering plants as a large plug. Depending on the variety, one to three large plugs should be used for a 1-gallon pot: for example, one plug would be used for poppy or three plugs for creeping phlox.

Stages

Five production stages that have been identified for annual plugs can apply to perennials as well. Each stage has different cultural procedures in order to produce the optimal plugs.

- *Stage 1* is from sowing until radicle (embryonic root) emergence.

- *Stage 2* is from radicle emergence until the first true leaf develops. The goal of the plug producer in this stage is to provide the proper conditions so a root system will develop from the radicle.
- *Stage 3* is from development of the first true leaf until the product is large enough to ship.
- *Stage 4* is a toning stage prior to shipping in which the plugs are held to toughen the plants. This stage usually lasts a week.
- *Stage 5* is the storage of transplantable plugs.

Factors Influencing Plugs

Water

Water is the single most important factor in the germination process and plug production. Too much or too little water can disrupt the entire germination process. Growers tend to err on the wet side during stage 1, because seeds dry out quickly due to their large surface-area-to-volume ratio. If they do dry out, germination is delayed or stopped. Seeds need very little water to germinate. Most seeds absorb all the water they need to germinate within eight hours after being placed in contact with water.

The ideal method is to provide the seed with enough water to germinate without any delay and to maintain the medium in a moist but not saturated condition so that when the radicle emerges, it can immediately grow into the medium. A germination chamber can be used, in which humidity is kept at 90–95% and plugs are checked for need of hand watering at least twice daily.

Long-term and consistent success with plug production demands high-quality water (table 6-1). Water should be tested at least twice yearly to check for changes

Table 6-1. Water quality analysis for plug production

Acceptable levels of various elements and other factors. All values are parts per million (ppm) unless stated otherwise.		
NO_3 <10	Na <50	Cl <140
NH_4 <10	P <30	Mg 10–50
K <100	S <100	Ca 25–150
Fe <4	Mn <2	Zn <1
B <0.5	Cu <0.2	Mo <0.1
F <1		

Alkalinity: 40–120 milligrams/liter $CaCO_3$

Electrical conductivity (EC): <1.5milliSiemens/centimeter

Source: IQDHO, 1994

in quality. Contact your local greenhouse product supplier or cooperative extension specialist for lab addresses.

Temperature

Next to water, temperature is the second most important factor in plug production. In general, temperature is much easier to control than other factors. Soil temperature, not air temperature, is what should be maintained. This is generally done through the use of hot water that provides bottom heat via small tubes on which flats are placed (see figure 5-1 on page 30). In stage 1, most annual and perennial seeds will germinate best at a soil temperature of 65–85°F, depending on the species. With the widespread use of germination chambers, most growers can maintain one or more of these temperatures. It is not necessary to have a germination chamber, especially if a whole greenhouse or isolated section of one can be dedicated to plug germination. Uniform germination is one of the first characteristics lost when germinating at the wrong temperature, either too high or too low. For stage 2, maintain most perennials at a soil temperature of 70–75°F.

Two additional aspects of temperature that are important are the temperature's effect on evapotranspiration and relative humidity. In this regard, shading, fog, or both are valuable tools to help control temperature and drying.

Once produced, the larger plugs (such as 50, 75, or 125 cells per flat or tray) are often "cooled" to 35–40°F for ten to twelve weeks. This is done for overall better growth upon transplanting and to help ensure flowering the first year for retail customers. This cold is necessary for many spring-flowering varieties, and it helps summer-flowering varieties reach a mature stage sooner, in which they will respond to long days for flowering. Cooling often begins when plugs are about eight weeks old and is done gradually in 3–5°F increments. Logically, this is done in fall, when cool temperatures are easier to maintain. Aim to reach the target temperature around mid November.

If plugs are not vernalized prior to transplanting into final pots, they should be held for four to six weeks or until they are well-rooted and the crown is well-developed. This is best done at 55–60°F nights and 60–65°F days. If light conditions are low, then provide supplemental high-intensity discharge (HID) lighting for sixteen-hour days. After four to six weeks, the temperature can be lowered to a constant 35–40°F for ten weeks of hardening and vernalization (see chapter 12 for more information on forcing).

Chemicals

When using a medium that has a nutrient already incorporated — a precharged mix — no additional fertilizer is needed for stages 1 and 2. For stages 3 and 4, fertilizer can be used in conjunction with water and temperature management to control plant growth. Toned plug growth is achieved primarily by using nitrate-based complete fertilizers. Ammonia sources of nitrogen should be used for quick growth and cosmetic greening, but they can easily lead to stretch (plugs that are too tall). Avoiding high salts (over 100 milliSiemens per centimeter in the North, over 200 milliSiemens per centimeter in the South and West) also helps prevent stretch.

The rate at which to fertilize is highly variable, depending on the use of the plug. Although most perennial plugs tolerate less fertility than annuals, they do not tolerate extremes of nutrient deficiencies as well as annuals. In general, fertilize at 100–200 ppm nitrogen at the frequency that will give the desired growth and plant quality. During the first two weeks of stage 3, the 250-size plug might get 50–100 ppm of 20-10-20 fertilizer twice weekly. That may then be increased to 150 ppm. The larger plugs may start with 150 ppm weekly during the second week of stage 3. Locations in the South or West with predominantly bright, sunny days may use 350–800 ppm nitrate nitrogen and have tolerable salt levels of 150–225 milliSiemens per centimeter. During stage 4, these rates may be applied as needed or eliminated prior to cooling.

Growth regulators are often used as a last resort, especially since most are labeled for only a couple dozen perennials out of the thousands available. With the proper use of water, temperature, and fertilizer, growth-regulating chemicals can usually be avoided.

The relatively new concept of DIF can be used successfully on perennial plugs. DIF refers to the difference in day and night temperatures. It involves keeping the night temperature relatively consistent with the day temperature, then dropping it about 5°F for a couple hours starting at about 5:00 A.M. This checks growth, which results in shorter and stockier plants.

With rare exceptions, fungicides should be avoided in stages 1 and 2. Preventative sprays for *Botrytis* control are often used in stages 3 and 4. Strict sanitary culture, coupled with good water management, should help prevent diseases and the need for fungicides. Drenches for the primary diseases — damping-off and *Botrytis* blight — should be used on a preventative basis as needed.

Insecticides, as with fungicides, should be avoided in stages 1 and 2. Integrated pest management (IPM) should be used to monitor insect populations and plan treatments. The most common insect pests to look for on plugs are fungus gnats, shore flies, aphids, thrips, and whiteflies. See chapter 10 for more information on pest control.

Light

In stage 1, only low amounts of light are needed (5–10 foot-candles), if any at all (see appendix B on page 145). In stage 2, light should be greatly increased. For most crops, it is ideal to maintain adequate temperature and moisture without shade, because the high light will produce a shorter, tougher plant. In stages 3 and 4, as much light as possible is recommended for most crops. Shade can be used to control temperature and drying as required.

Media

The primary roles of the medium are to support the plant and to act as a reservoir for water and nutrients (including oxygen). Oxygen content is primarily controlled by medium compaction during flat filling and watering practices in stages 1 and 2, regardless of the medium used.

There are many good media that work well for plugs. Ones with finer and smaller components — as in seedling media, not outdoor container media — are preferable. The key factor in using any medium is knowing how to manage it and understanding that if you change the medium, you should anticipate changes in growing practices. The second important factor is a consistent source. Do not assume that your medium, even if purchased, is the same from batch to batch or bag to bag — have it tested periodically. For large plugs (50s) and 4.5-inch pots, one large, top-quality grower uses a medium of 53% sphagnum peat, 25% hypnum peat, 15% Styrofoam beads, and 7% calcined clay, to which the recommended rate of granular Esmigran micronutrients is added (see "Growing Media" section in chapter 8 on page 48).

As mentioned previously, media should already have enough nutrients incorporated to carry crops to stage 3. A pH of 5.5–6.0 is ideal for most crops. Problems with pH tend to show up in stages 3 and 4.

Finishing

The time to finish or sale is influenced by plug size, finish container size, average greenhouse temperature, and day length. At a large plug producer in Iowa, large plugs may be ready for transplant or sale in six to eight weeks. Timing trials at a large Michigan producer with 57 and 128 plugs suggested that most perennials can be ready for sale in a quart container in four to seven weeks at greenhouse temperatures of 65–70°F. One plug per pot is sufficient for quart-size containers. In a gallon container, five to eight weeks is required to finish a single plug at the above temperatures. Many perennials will be ready one to two weeks earlier if two plugs are planted.

Many perennials are responsive to day length (see chapter 12). In some cases, the day length may be just as critical or more critical than the temperature for plant growth. Perennials finish quickly from a plug at 65–70°F average temperatures. As the temperature is reduced, the finish time lengthens; so at 60°F, it may take two weeks longer than at 65°F. Most perennials do not require high levels of nutrients to finish from plugs. As with plug production, the rate and concentration of fertilizer to finish should be determined by the speed of growth and the plant quality desired (see next chapter on seedling care). Pests to watch for include aphids, fungus gnats, shore flies, white flies, and thrips. Diseases to watch for include *Botrytis,* powdery mildew, and rusts (see chapter 10).

Table 6-2 outlines a time table for producing a few common perennials from plugs.

Table 6-2. Sample seeded perennial schedules for marketing April 14 (week 15 of the year)

Crop	Sow date (week of the year)	Transplant date (week of the year)
Aquilegia	September 1 (36)	November 7 (45)
Arabis	October 7 (41)	December 14 (50)
Myosotis	October 7 (41)	December 1 (49)
Platycodon	February 7 (5)	March 7 (9)
Salvia	October 1 (40)	December 1 (49)

Source: Adapted from a presentation by Armitage, University of Georgia

Note: Local conditions may cause slight deviations from these dates. If seeds are sown into open flats rather than plug trays, the transplant dates should be 2–4 weeks earlier – for example, *Aquilegia* would be transplanted October 21 instead of November 7.

CHAPTER 7

Transplant and Seedling Care

Transplanting

Seedlings from Flats

The ideal stage for transplanting most seedlings from seed flats is when the second or third true leaf is fully developed and seedlings are large enough to handle efficiently. At this stage, the plants suffer the least amount of shock and reestablish growth the quickest. Too frequently, seedlings are left to become overgrown and spindly or hard and stunted; such seedlings do not produce top-quality plants.

Plug Seedlings

Seedlings grown as separate plugs (figure 7-1) are much more quickly and easily transplanted than seedlings from other germination methods. For rapid seedling removal during transplanting, the seedlings should be well-rooted but not root bound. Plug seedlings can be planted in pre-punched holes in the medium using both hands. They grow more quickly than bare-root seedlings.

Other Transplants

Plants started from methods other than seedlings are often rooted directly in cell packs. When rooted, they are either sold or transplanted to final containers, depending on the marketing strategy. Divisions may be potted directly to final containers (see next chapter on nursery production).

Figure 7-1. A plug seedling

Growing Media

Peat-lite, soil mix, or other mixes used for propagation may also be used for transplanting perennials (see propagation chapter, page 26). Many growers transplant seedlings or young plants directly to final containers and media (see next chapter on nursery production).

Cell Packs

Flats containing celled packs provide consumers or final bedding plant growers transplants with undisturbed root systems and are commonly used for perennial bedding plant sales. The selection of cell size and cell number per pack is a marketing decision; 36 to 72 cells per 11-by-22-by-3/4-inch flat are common (figure 7-2). Small cells do not support the water demands of large plants during marketing. Packs with few cells can be sold at a low price. Growers must anticipate local market needs in making these decisions.

Mechanization

Mechanized Flat-Filling

Mechanized flat-filling offers cost savings to producers through greater filling speed and reduced labor needs. The equipment must be utilized sufficiently to justify the investment. Consult suppliers to become familiar with the equipment available.

Mechanized Transplanting

Further savings in labor costs can be achieved from efficient flow during transplanting. All the materials needed should be set up in the proper location before the job is started. Growers of large numbers of perennials have effectively used moving belts and assembly-line techniques to improve the efficiency of transplanting. Partially automated transplanters are being used by some. For more information, see *Greenhouse Engineering*, NRAES–33, which is listed in the recommended reading section at the back of this book.

Environmental Considerations and Seedling Care

Supplemental Lighting

To accelerate seedling and small plant growth, some producers use high intensity discharge (HID) lighting, such as that used in large mass market stores and sports arenas, or other lamps to apply 500–1,000 foot-candles of light in seedling greenhouses. Others use a lighted germination chamber or cart to put the production of seedlings on a controlled production-line basis. The facilities should be in an area where air temperature can be maintained between 60–80°F with bottom heat (see figure 5-1 on page 30).

HID lighting configurations vary considerably by type of fixture selected. Suppliers can usually recommend the optimum configuration for a specific location.

Fluorescent light sources are commonly arranged to provide approximately 27 watts of energy per square foot of production area. This light level can be obtained from eight 40-watt fluorescent tubes evenly spaced across a 3-foot-wide bed. Warm white, cool white, natural white, and daylight fluorescent lamps have all been used alone or in combination with equal success. Warm white alternated with cool white lamps, or natural white alternated with daylight fluorescent lamps, have been effective in promoting good plant growth at a lower cost than special plant-growing lights.

After sowing, flats should be placed under lights. As seeds germinate and seedlings grow, the lights will need to be adjusted to provide a 6–8-inch distance from the seedlings for best growth. Placement farther away results in undesirable stretching of the seedlings.

A fourteen-hour day is often recommended. A slight increase in growth does occur with an eighteen-hour day. An automatic time clock is used to control the day length. Recently, some producers have successfully produced plants with continuous twenty-four-hour lighting. After the seedlings reach the stage for transplanting, they are gradually acclimated to the higher intensity of natural light over a period of two or three days.

Solar Radiation and Shading

Some perennial species thrive in full sunlight, others are easily stressed in full sun and tolerate partial shade, and still others require partial shading and will burn and die in full sun. In far northern locations with lower light intensity coupled with lower growing-season temperatures, shade species often may be produced in partial to full sun, even in summer. Table 7-1 on page 44 lists genera suited to various sunlight exposures.

Temperature

Proper ventilation and heating are necessary to produce top-quality plants. Horizontal air flow (HAF) is an effective method of providing adequate air movement around and through the plants (figure 7-3). The result

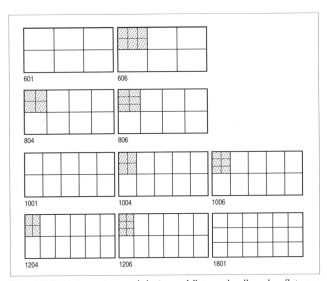

Figure 7-2. Various sizes and designs of flats and cell packs; flats are standard size 11 x 22 x ¾ inch

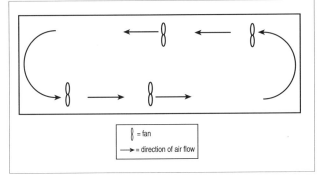

Figure 7-3. Horizontal air flow (HAF) in a single greenhouse

is more uniform temperatures and less disease problems such as from *Botrytis*. HAF is achieved by hanging low-velocity fans, such as window fans, just above plant height about every 50 feet along greenhouse sides and blowing in opposite directions on either side.

As a result of increased fuel costs, many growers are overzealous in their energy conservation efforts. If greenhouses are not heated sufficiently or vented, especially in the evening, the relative humidity increases. Condensation can develop on plants, which promotes the development of *Botrytis* blight, especially in the spring and fall.

In early spring when outside temperatures are low, many growers minimally heat the greenhouse. Temperatures below 55°F may severely slow growth, and the plants may not recover. This problem is especially serious for flats on greenhouse floors, and some growers place flats on risers to improve heating of the flat growing medium. During daylight hours, greenhouse air temperatures at crop level should not be allowed to go above 65°F on clear days and 60°F on cloudy days. Higher temperatures combined with low light results in soft, spindly growth. Keep the plants cool and slightly on the dry side to produce compact, stocky top growth and a good root system.

Watering

During warm spring days, plants may require two or three waterings daily if the plants are well-rooted. The amount of water supplied should wet the growing medium thoroughly. If the medium stays continually wet and soggy, you may need to check for root rots, raise the medium temperature, or change the medium.

Perennial producers have several irrigation methods to choose from: hand watering with a "rose" or water breaker (see figure 5-3 on page 31), using subirrigation, or using overhead sprinkler irrigation. An advantage to the hand watering method is accuracy. Hand watering can also be a liability if the person on the hose is not reliable. The major drawback to hand watering is the cost of labor. High-quality hand watering is expensive.

One alternative to hand watering is subirrigation with capillary mats (figure 7-4) or flood benches. Mats pose the challenge of holding plants to a marketable size. With water always available to plants, there is no check on growth. With hand watering, the frequency of watering can be controlled using water as a growth retardant. Mats can also often serve as a breeding ground for fungus gnats and shore flies. Highly organic media may increase this problem, and some perennials may be

Table 7-1. Light exposure requirements of genera

Require full sun	Grow well in sun or partial shade	Require partial shade
Achillea	Aconitum	Anemone
Adenophora	Alchemilla	Aquilegia
Alcea	Amsonia	Brunnera
Alyssum	Arenaria	Epimedium
Anaphalis	Aruncus	Helleborus
Anchusa	Astilbe	Hosta
Antennaria	Baptisia	Lamium
Anthemis	Belamcanda	Polygonatum
Arabis	Bergenia	Primula
Armeria	Campanula	
Artemisia	Ceratostigma	
Asclepias	Chelone	
Aster	Cimicifuga	
Boltonia	Clematis	
Cassia	Convallaria	
Catananche	Dicentra	
Centaurea	Digitalis	
Cerastium	Doronicum	
Chrysanthemum	Eupatorium	
Coreopsis	Filipendula	
Delphinium	Geranium	
Dianthus	Hemerocallis	
Dictamnus	Heuchera	
Echinacea	Iris (Siberian and Japanese)	
Echinops	Ligularia	
Erigeron	Lobelia	
Eryngium	Lysimachia	
Euphorbia	Macleaya	
Gaillardia	Mertensia	
Geum	Oenothera	
Gypsophila	Paeonia	
Helenium	Polemonium	
Heliopsis	Pulmonaria	
Hibiscus	Stachys	
Iberis	Thalictrum	
Iris (bearded)	Thermopsis	
Kniphofia	Tiarella	
Liatris	Tradescantia	
Limonium	Trollius	
Linum		
Lupinus		
Lychnis		
Lythrum		
Monarda		
Nepeta		
Papaver		
Phlox		
Physostegia		
Platycodon		
Rudbeckia		
Salvia		
Scabiosa		
Sedum		
Sidalcea		
Solidago		
Stokesia		
Verbascum		
Veronica		

Note: Requirements may vary slightly with location and species.

Herbaceous Perennials Production

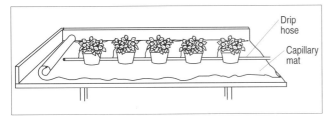

Figure 7-4. Subirrigation using capillary mats

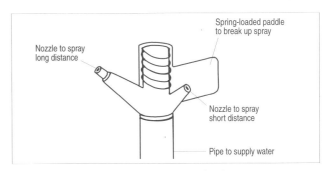

Figure 7-5. Rotating-impact nozzle for overhead irrigation

more susceptible than others to feeding from larvae of these insects.

Flood benches, another way to provide subirrigation, do not have these problems, as water is "flooded" onto the bench (which is really a large tray), allowed to remain until pots are wet, and then drained. For this reason, they are often called ebb-and-flow benches. A variation of the flooding irrigation system is to allow water to continually flow across the bench. If plants are in pots, the pots can be placed in troughs resembling rain gutters; water flows continually through the troughs or as needed. Although more costly to install, flood benches allow recycling of water and nutrients. Containing and recycling water and nutrients has already become an issue in Europe and may become a concern in North America, with increased pressure on water demand in some areas and groundwater pollution concerns.

Traditional overhead irrigation provides a circular spray pattern around a center pivot. This pattern results in overlap (overwatering) and gaps where hand touchup is required. Several overhead irrigation choices are available: plastic nozzles on stakes placed at 5- to 10-foot centers or brass spinner nozzles placed at 12-foot centers. Impact irrigation heads set on 20- to 25-foot centers are mainly used in nursery production. All of these are stationary systems that produce a circular pattern with its limitations. Proper design of an overhead sprinkler system will achieve a fairly uniform application of water. Making changes to a designed system can cause problems.

Another type of overhead system is a traveling boom fitted with either fan or cone nozzles. Boom sizes cover houses up to 40 feet wide with an almost indefinite length. Installation cost is significantly higher, and these systems are often found in high-turnover propagation and germination houses and plug operations. Controls for any of the overhead irrigation systems could be manual or solenoid valves controlled by a water sensor or time clock.

Rotating-impact sprinklers (figure 7-5) oscillate rapidly and provide what appears to be a continuous square

pattern. Seedlings transplanted to moist soil set under such a system can be watered in and brought to market without a hose going into the house to touch up or water. These systems tend to be less efficient at water utilization, with up to 50% of the water evaporating during hot, dry weather.

Using schedule 40 PVC pipe, a 96-by-32-foot house can be on-line with a sprinkler system in less than a day. Horticultural brokers sell nozzle sizes according to the pattern they deliver (for example, 6 feet by 6 feet to 18 feet by 18 feet; 18 feet by 18 feet to 25 feet by 25 feet; 5 feet by 40 feet; or 5 feet by 25 feet). Points to remember when installing a system include:

1. The orientation of the watering or spray pattern is essential. The pattern will vary with the type of nozzle used. Figure 7-6 on page 46 shows a bench-watering system that uses nozzles with different spray patterns to fully cover the bench.

2. The nozzle must be level to deliver a uniform pattern.

3. If the entire line of nozzles is not always needed, individual shut-off valves can be used. The shut off at the nozzle is not durable enough to withstand frequent on and off changes.

4. If the greenhouse is not heated during winter, the irrigation system must be drained.

5. Any thermostats or electrical outlets must be isolated from the water pattern.

6. Good water pressure and volume are essential. A minimum of 1¼-inch line is suggested.

7. A 30- to 36-inch clearance should be provided above the sprinklers. Do not hang baskets too low over the sprinklers, as they may block part or all of the spray.

Overhead sprinklers of whatever type will quickly reduce the stress of dry plants, because one can irrigate at the turn of a valve, thus reducing time and labor costs. An area will be thoroughly watered in about one-half

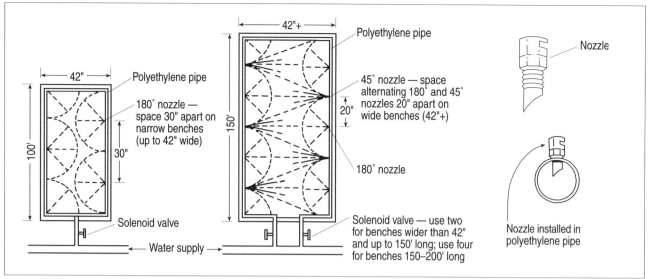

Figure 7-6. Bench-watering system for seedling flats

hour, depending on the level of dryness and media type. One precaution is that a grower may be prone to water later in the day since it is so easy to turn a valve. This will result in wet plants going into the night and increase the incidence of disease.

The following scenario gives an estimated cost comparison (in 1996 dollars) of hand watering versus mechanized irrigation. A good employee takes approximately three and a half hours to hand water a 148-by-32-foot house (this is the average-size house among three western New York producers). If this individual earns $9 per hour (including benefits), then the cost per watering would be about $32. A mechanized irrigation system can be installed in this same house for an estimated $400. The conclusion from these figures is that, in about a month, the mechanized system will have paid for itself. The price is right, too: about $0.07 per square foot. Assumptions in this scenario are that the person doing the watering is well-trained, the house is hand watered three times per week, and the house with mechanized irrigation contains plants with uniform water requirements.

Some producers in areas with poor water quality find that iron or lime residues accumulate on plant leaves. This problem is magnified by overhead irrigation systems. Water treatment, and sometimes water acidification, will reduce the severity of the problem. See *Water and Nutrient Management for Greenhouses*, NRAES–56, for more information (see recommended reading section on page 203).

Fertilization

With frequent applications of water, the fertility level in containers is quickly changed unless fertilizer control methods are applied. Control is best accomplished with some type of fertilizer proportioner. Two common types of fertilizer proportioners, a venturi type and a positive displacement pump, are shown in figures 7-7 and 7-8.

Generally, 100–150 ppm nitrogen, phosphorus, and potassium applied at every irrigation will produce high-quality plants. This nutrient level is obtained by applying 13⅓ ounces of 15-16-17 or similar analysis fertilizer in 100 gallons of water at each irrigation. Levels are maintained by implementing a carefully chosen fertilization program. Table 7-2 lists some common materials used to maintain nitrogen and potassium levels. In some programs, fertilization with soluble phosphorus also is required to keep phosphorus at 4–5 ppm.

Higher fertilization rates may be required for peat-lite mixes and some plants. For 200 ppm nitrogen, multiply the rates in table 7-2 by 1.33; for 250 ppm nitrogen, multiply by 1.67; and for 300 ppm nitrogen, multiply by 2.0. For perennials in flats or small pots, high fertilization rates often lead to excessively large leaves and plants.

The addition of soluble trace elements to the fertilizer stock solution is required for optimum plant nutrition in peat-lite mixes. "Peat-Lite Special" fertilizers contain a trace element supplement. Non-supplemented fertilizer preparations can be used by adding to the stock solution a soluble trace element mixture, such as 8 ounces of STEM (Soluble Trace Element Mix) per 100 pounds of fertilizer.

The optimum pH for organic mixes (such as peat-lite) is 5.5. For mixes containing at least 20% soil, it is 6.5. Irrigation water at a pH of 7.0–7.5 quickly raises mix pH to undesirably high levels if it contains significant levels of dissolved carbonates or bicarbonates. pH can be controlled by installing a double-headed injector resistant to acid corrosion (see figure 5-4 on page 31). Sulfuric, phosphoric, or (in rare cases) nitric or citric acid is injected into the water supply to acidify the water pH to the 5.5–6.0 range for peat-lite mixes and 6.5–7.0 range for soil mixes. Actual injection rates vary with the alkalinity of the water source as well as the type and rate of fertilizer used.

By developing an acid titration curve or evaluating water bicarbonates, commercial soil and fertility testing laboratories (such as those offered by some fertilizer companies) can accurately determine the amount of acid to apply. The greatest accuracy is obtained if samples already contain the type of soluble fertilizer to be used at the desired application rate.

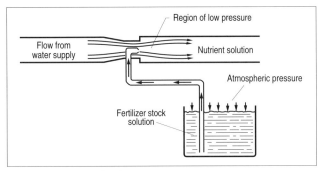

Figure 7-7. A venturi fertilizer proportioner

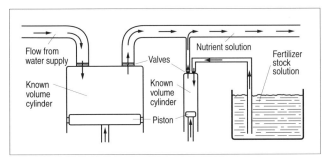

Figure 7-8. A positive displacement pump fertilizer proportioner

Table 7-2. Ounces of selected fertilizers per gallon of concentrate to make stock solutions to provide 150 ppm nitrogen

Nitrogen content of fertilizer (%)	Proportioner dilution ratio		
	1:15 (HOZON)	1:100	1:200
14 (potassium nitrate) (14-0-45)	2.2	14.5	29.0
15 (calcium nitrate) (15-0-0)	2.0	13.5	27.0
15 (15-16-17)	2.0	13.5	27.0
20 (20-10-20)	1.5	10.5	21.4
23 (23-0-23)[1]	1.3	8.8	17.6
Calcium nitrate *plus*	1.4	9.0	18.0
potassium nitrate	0.8	5.3	10.5

[1] Prepared by mixing equal parts by weight of ammonium nitrate and potassium nitrate.

Growth Retardants

Moderate fertilization, cool temperatures, cool water, and proper timing will reduce the need for chemical growth retardant applications. If growth retardants are used, they should be programmed just like applications of water and fertilizer.

No one growth retardant is used universally on all perennial plants. Follow label instructions for the chemicals chosen. Usually a growth retardant application is made when the plant leaf area covers the soil and before plant elongation begins. For listings of chemicals, consult the following books:

- Cornell University's *1995 Recommendations for the Integrated Management of Greenhouse Florist Crops: Management of Pests and Crop Growth*

- *The New England Greenhouse Floricultural Recommendations: A Management Guide for Insects, Diseases, Weeds, and Growth Regulators*

- *Floriculture Crops: Chemical Use Handbook — A Guide for Insecticide, Miticide, Fungicide, Growth Regulator, and Herbicide Application*

Complete citations for all of these books are included in the recommended reading section that begins on page 203. Chapter 12, which begins on page 87, contains some additional information about growth regulators.

CHAPTER 8

Nursery Production

Containers

Many growers are producing large plants in 1-, 2-, or 3-gallon containers, which are popular with retailers and landscapers. Seedlings, rooted cuttings, and bare-root divisions are potted into 1-quart to 1-gallon containers in the spring. The plant container selected depends on the plant size and anticipated plant vigor in the spring of the year. Plants are grown outdoors the summer after potting and are preferably sold the same year to avoid overwintering. The container size should allow for adequate root growth, enough moisture retention to prevent frequent drying, and enough mass to prevent the plants from blowing over in wind.

Some interest has been shown recently, and some research done, on the topic of container nursery production using copper compounds that are painted on the insides of pots to prevent root circling. In a study with perennials (Ruter, 1995), copper hydroxide–impregnated fiber pots did prevent root circling; however, there was no difference in plant growth between these and plastic pots for *Coreopsis* 'Moonbeam'. *Plumbago auriculata,* on the other hand, had increased growth in the copper-treated fiber pots, indicating that results may vary with species.

Growing Media

Various media, either purchased or formulated by the grower, are being used for nursery production of herbaceous perennials. Unless operating a large nursery, growers may be better off economically by purchasing me-

dia. When purchasing media, a grower's decision of what to buy will likely be based on cost and personal experience with a particular medium. Large nurseries and those with special plant needs or media concerns may formulate their own (see "Propagation Media" section in chapter 5, page 26). If making one's own mix, the recipe used will depend on the availability and cost of useful amendments. Whether media are purchased or not, soil tests are advisable to check for proper pH and nutrients, as there is variability occasionally—even among commercial bag mixes.

In addition to the components described in chapter 5 (see page 26), bark is often added at a rate of 25–50% by volume to outdoor container media. It can be either composted hardwood (such as oak or maple) or, more commonly, softwood (such as fir, pine, or hemlock). Bark is organic and continues to decompose in media, and the bacteria responsible for this decomposition use up nitrogen. So extra nitrogen should be added at a rate one-third to one-half higher than normal. Less should be added if the bark is composted or in large particles (which break down slower). Bark may have 50% air and 10% water porosity, or about 60% total porosity.

Soil is not generally recommended as a container medium because of potential problems with weed seeds, disease, insects, drainage, and even availability. Some growers use soil because it adds microorganisms and weight, and they feel this helps plants in pots become established better in landscape soils. Pasteurizing soil at 140–160°F for thirty minutes, perhaps with an aerated steam unit, helps to prevent problems with weeds, diseases, and pests (see "Weed Control," page 78).

Important considerations with soil are the texture (particle size) and structure (arrangement of the particles). Clay has the smallest particles (0.0002–0.002 millimeter in diameter), and sand has the largest (0.05–1.0 millimeter in diameter); silt is somewhere in between. The smallest particles in a mix, generally clay in a soil mix, have the greatest influence on air content, water content, and nutrient-holding ability of the medium. Plants grown in clay often have the poorest growth, usually due to low air porosity and lack of oxygen.

Soils are grouped by their percentages of sand, silt, and clay into textural classes. For instance, a loam might consist of 20% clay, 40% silt, and 40% sand. This relationship is often shown as a triangle with 100% clay, 100% sand, and 100% silt at the three corners (figure 8-1). The porosity of a clay might be only 3% air and 47% water, that of a silt loam might be 20% air and 40% water, and that of a sandy loam might be 40% air and 10% water.

Field soils cannot be used alone in containers without some modification to improve drainage and aeration. A good basic mixture consists of equal parts by volume of soil, peat moss, and perlite or vermiculite. Depending on the soil type, such a mix may be about 10% air and 50% water, or have 60% total porosity. The amount of lime, superphosphate, gypsum, and other fertilizers to add is best determined by a laboratory analysis of the mixture. Check with your state university soil testing lab or media supplier for greenhouse soil test kits.

Other container media components may include coir (coconut husk fiber), rockwool (for example, Grodan), sawdust, clay pellets or calcined clay (for example, Turface), polystyrene beads, rice hulls, and cocoa shells. Rockwool has become a common amendment in European media and is often used as a substitute for peat moss. It is becoming more popular in the United States. Rockwool is composed of finely spun fibers of rock. It is formed when rock is heated to high temperatures, air-blown, and rolled.

A preliminary study at the University of Vermont showed that growth for each of five perennials in commercial rockwool or coir media was equal to plant growth in peat-lite commercial media. Many composts are being tried and used successfully by perennial growers. In an unpublished study at the University of Vermont, a northeastern U.S. compost product was compared with a standard peat-lite commercial medium; there were no significant differences in performance for the several species studied.

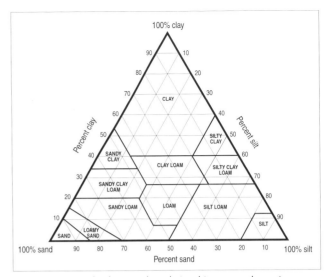

Figure 8-1. Triangle showing the relationship among the various components of soil

The most common media are:
- sand-peat (1:1 by volume)
- composted hardwood bark-peat-sand (1:1:1 by volume)
- pine bark-peat-sand (1:1:1 to 3:2:1 by volume)
- softwood bark (pine, fir)-peat (1:1 to 3:1 by volume)

The bark, peat, and sand medium may be about 20% air and 30% water, or have about 50% total porosity. Initial research at the University of Vermont showed no major differences in growth or flowering of daylilies between soil-based and bark-based media, or between two common peat-bark media for several perennials (Adam, 1988).

Many ratios of major media components and amendments can be used successfully as long as the appropriate fertilization and irrigation management is imposed by the grower to the plant/medium system. Growers should be wary of adding amendments and ingredients to purchased media without first testing for a change in physical characteristics such as porosity (see "Propagation Media" section in chapter 5 on page 26). As with most factors, the effect of a change in porosity will vary with species as well as with the type of amendment added (such as soil type). In initial research at the University of Vermont, adding 10% sand or 10% clay loam soil (by volume) to a commercial peat-lite medium did not affect final growth of *Campanula takesimana;* determining the effect of adding a larger amount of soil and using other soil types and other species needs more investigation (Herrick and Perry, unpublished).

Table 8-1 shows how porosity can change with the addition of various amendments. Adding sand to fir bark lowers air space from 32% to 15%, mainly by adding more solids since water porosity does not change. Adding sand to clay loam lowers water porosity from 55% to 42% (so the mix would dry out faster), again by adding more solids since air porosity in this combination does not change. With lower water capacity and low air capacity, this mix may have the consistency of concrete. Many growers like adding sand to increase weight so containers do not blow over as easily, but the implications of this on culture should be realized.

Measuring Media Porosities

When formulating a mix or amending an existing or purchased one, use the following simple procedure to measure porosities:

1. Tape the holes in a pot shut, then fill the pot with water. Measure how much water is added. Then dump out the water, remove the tape, and dry the pot. An alternative method is to use a plastic bag — completely line the pot with the plastic bag. This prevents the need to tape drain holes and possible leaks.

2. Place a plastic bag in the pot and fill the lined pot with mix. Water the mix and measure how much water is added. Warm water will help saturate hard-to-wet media such as peat-lite and organic-based media. Completely saturate the media — there will be a film of water right at the soil surface.

3. Calculate the percent total porosity of the mix by dividing the volume of water needed to saturate the mix (#2) by the total volume of the pot (#1).

$$\text{total porosity} = \frac{\text{volume of water added}}{\text{total volume of pot}}$$

4. After several minutes, remove the bag of mix from the pot, make a small hole in the bag, and allow it to drain. Collect and measure the drain water.

5. Calculate the air-filled pore space by dividing the volume of water drained from the bag by the total volume of the pot.

$$\text{air-filled pore space} = \frac{\text{volume of water drained}}{\text{total volume of pot}}$$

6. Calculate the water-holding capacity of the pot by subtracting the amount of air-filled pore space from the total porosity of the soil mix.

$$\text{water-holding capacity} = \text{total porosity} - \text{air-filled pore space}$$

Table 8-1. Effects on porosities (% by volume) of adding sand to fir bark and clay loam

Media component	% Water	% Air	% Solids
Fir bark (0–⅛ inch)	38	32	30
Fir bark: fine sand			
(1:1 by volume)	37	15	48
Fine sand	39	6	55
Clay loam	55	5	40
Clay loam: fine sand			
(1:1 by volume)	42	7	51
Fine sand	39	6	55

Hydrogels or hydrophilic polymers are amendments that have received much promotion and interest. These substances absorb hundreds of times their weight in water, supposedly decreasing watering frequency. This is especially useful in retail situations. A teaspoon of some of these amendments can absorb up to a quart of water in an hour.

Research on the effectiveness of these amendments for ornamentals has in general yielded mixed results. Initial research at the University of Vermont studied the effect of adding a cross-linked polymer compound to two media along with two different levels of controlled-release fertilizer. The results showed significant improvement in plant growth with only one of the three herbaceous perennials tested, and then in only one mix with one fertility level. Adding higher-than-recommended rates of polymer often led to a decrease in growth, even with both levels of fertility. This may be the result of excessive water, excessive fertility, or both held in the media. A lack of consistent beneficial results with polymers coupled with their high cost may render them unsuitable for commercial perennial production, at least without further trialing in a particular situation.

pH Adjustment of Mixes

It is especially important when formulating a growing medium to use soil tests to determine the pH before adding any amendments. This is crucial for having maximum nutrient availability to plant roots. Figure 8-2 shows the influence of pH on the availability of nutrients in organic soils. Most purchased peat-lite mixes already have the pH adjusted. Without this, they have an acid reaction, usually in the range of pH 4.0–5.5. When formulating your own mix, add lime to raise the pH to the range of 6.0–7.0 for a soil mix and 5.5–6.0 for a peat-lite mix. Dolomitic lime should be used, as it is slow-acting and thus reduces the chance of root in-

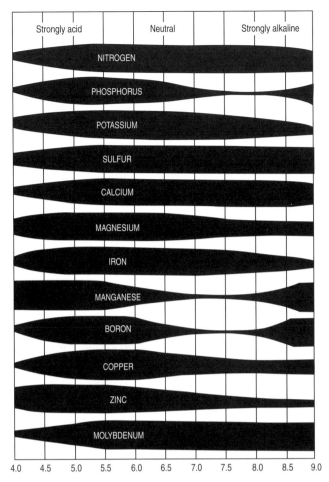

Strongly acid	Neutral	Strongly alkaline

NITROGEN

PHOSPHORUS

POTASSIUM

SULFUR

CALCIUM

MAGNESIUM

IRON

MANGANESE

BORON

COPPER

ZINC

MOLYBDENUM

4.0 4.5 5.0 5.5 6.0 6.5 7.0 7.5 8.0 8.5 9.0

Figure 8-2. Influence of pH on the availability of nutrients in organic soil – the widest part of the bar indicates maximum availability (Adapted from Lucas and Davis, 1961)

Table 8-2. Rates of dolomitic limestone necessary to raise pH to between 6.0 and 7.0

Initial pH	Rate of lime needed (lbs/yd³)
4.0–4.5	10–12
4.6–5.0	8–10
5.1–5.5	6–8
5.6–6.0	4–6

dium. Using a solution containing 100 ppm nitrogen from an N-P-K fertilizer (such as a 20-20-20) at every watering will be sufficient in most instances to ensure good growth with plants growing in 1-gallon containers. Rates may have to be increased to 150 ppm nitrogen or more to meet the nutritional demand of larger plants in 2- to 3-gallon containers. Research at the University of Vermont with daylilies showed that although nitrogen requirements varied with cultivars (as might be expected), 400 ppm generally resulted in optimum growth while 150 ppm resulted in salable plants (Adam, 1988). Although not seen in this study, lush optimum growth may encourage the development of sucking insects such as aphids. Microelements should be included in the solution if they are not already in the fertilizer. Check table 7-2 (page 47) for recommended mixing procedures to obtain the correct ppm in the fertilizer solution.

If considering "liquid feeding," be certain that the dissolved fertilizer is applied efficiently. Try to direct applications to the container medium. Applying soluble fertilizers through overhead irrigation — "fertigation" — may waste fertilizer and result in nutrients migrating to surface or subsurface water reservoirs. Liquid feeding is useful for intensive, quick cropping and for instant effects from nitrogen and other nutrients.

Controlled-release fertilizers offer another choice for fertilizing container-grown plants, and they are often applied by container nursery growers at planting or incorporated into media. Options include:

- soluble nutrient carriers encapsulated in a resinous coating (such as Osmocote) or elemental sulfur-coated products (sulfur-coated ureas plus phosphorus and potassium)

- organic nitrogen carriers (ureaformaldehydes plus phosphorus and potassium) that require microbial activity to release the nitrogen

- very slightly soluble nitrogen carriers (MagAmp plus potassium) that release nutrients by very slowly dissolving when moistened

jury. It also adds magnesium. Use table 8-2 as a guide for the incorporation of lime into a growing medium.

Soil tests should be taken three to six weeks after lime is incorporated to determine if the rate applied resulted in the desired pH. The suggested liming rates in table 8-2 should be reduced substantially if hardwood bark is a major component in a mix. Many hardwood bark products contain high levels of calcium (3–4% on a dry-weight basis). When calcium is released into the medium solution, a net increase in the pH results due to microbial activity. The amount of lime incorporated in hardwood mixes can be reduced by one-fourth to one-half (by volume), depending upon the amount of hardwood bark used and the amount of calcium contained in the bark.

Fertilization

Liquid fertilization is one option that growers (primarily greenhouse growers) use to ensure that appropriate levels of nutrients are maintained in the growing me-

Initial research at the University of Vermont has shown no differences in growth among four perennials using four types of controlled-release fertilizers in a common peat-lite medium at the study location. Results may vary in warmer climates. Initial research at the University of Maryland (Blessington, unpublished) with three common perennials (rudbeckia, coreopsis, and sedum) showed that, under their environmental and cultural conditions, good growth of all three perennials can be achieved with either 300 ppm nitrogen from 20-10-20 applied weekly or 9 grams of Osmocote 14-14-14 per 2-gallon pot. Good growth was also obtained with a combination of as little as 100 ppm nitrogen and 9 grams of Osmocote.

Some controlled-release fertilizers work best when preincorporated (Osmocote, MagAmp, ureaforms, and sulfur-coated ureas), although they can also be used as a topdress. More and more often, media can be purchased that have a controlled-release fertilizer already incorporated — check with your media supplier on this option. Other controlled-release fertilizers are best used as a topdress (some sulfur-coated ureas and ureaforms). Topdressing is particularly useful in situations where incorporation into the medium is not possible — for example, retail situations.

Initial research at the University of Vermont (Herrick and Perry, unpublished) showed that, out of four perennials tested, only daylily exhibited differences in growth between topdressing and incorporating four controlled-release fertilizers. With daylily, one fertilizer (14% nitrogen) was best incorporated, two fertilizers (17% and 18% nitrogen) were best topdressed. These results may vary with geographic location, so the trials should be redone in different climates prior to widespread use of the results.

If preincorporation is desired, select a controlled-release formulation that will release nutrients for a nine- or twelve-month period in warm areas or three- to four-month period in cool areas to minimize the need for supplemental fertilization. It may be necessary to apply additional nutrients in some instances.

When using controlled-release fertilizers for the first time, follow the manufacturer's suggested rates. Initial research at the University of Vermont indicates that halving suggested rates may result in salable plants in that climate (Perry and Herrick, unpublished). Common Osmocote amendment options are: 4 pounds of 14-14-14 per cubic yard or 2 pounds of 14-14-14 plus 2 pounds of 17-17-12 per cubic yard. In a study at the University of Connecticut with fountain grass

(*Pennisetum alopecuroides*), a topdressed rate of about 1.5 ounces of Sierra 17-6-10 per 2-gallon pot (Classic 600) was found to give the best growth and be the most cost-effective (Brand, 1996a). Although foliage height continued to increase with increasing rates of fertility, the greatest plant width and flower height occurred at this rate.

Winter release of three-month-release fertilizers or annual applications of twelve-month-release fertilizers in overwintering houses may damage plants if the application rate is normal to high and watering is infrequent and plants are dry. Apply such fertilizers in spring or early summer in order to get a full season's effect from them.

The effect of the timing of fertility on hardiness of perennials is currently being investigated at the University of Vermont. Initial studies in which plants were placed in a cold but not freezing greenhouse (35–40°F) in the fall showed no differences in hardiness for *Campanula* 'White Clips' or *Dianthus* 'Flashing Lights' with various fertility end dates. *Achillea* 'Summer Pastels' actually survived to lower temperatures with late-fall fertility (early October) and high rates of nitrogen (300 ppm applied weekly). Whether these same results would apply to plants subjected to fall frosts and freezing outdoors is under study. Initial results indicate that *Achillea* 'Summer Pastels' exhibits more and quicker regrowth at all freezing temperatures if fertilized with controlled-release fertilizer compared to weekly liquid feeding the season prior.

Be certain that micronutrients are also incorporated into the system. If the controlled-release fertilizer does not contain microelements, be certain to use one of the controlled-release microelement formulations in conjunction with the fertilizer supplying nitrogen, phosphorus, and potassium. FI No. 555 (previously known as Fritted Trace Elements) and Micromax are two examples of controlled-release microelement formulations. Use them at the manufacturer's suggested rates.

With some recent interest in sustainability and organic production practices, a study was done at the University of Vermont in which an organic granular fertilizer (Pro Gro 5-3-4 from North Country Organics in Bradford, Vermont) was compared with a controlled-release one (Nutricoat Type 140). Generally, similar results were achieved for most of the eight species, which were tested in both a commercial peat-lite medium (Pro Mix BX) and a commercial perennial compost product (from Vermont Natural Agricultural Products in Middlebury, Vermont).

There are pros and cons to consider when using either a synthetic or organic fertilizer product:

- Composition: Both can be balanced among several nutrients or provide a single nutrient such as phosphorus (for example, bone meal is an organic source of phosphorus, superphosphate a synthetic source).

- Analysis: Organic usually has a lower analysis but is usually sufficient for perennials, especially in field soils.

- Release: Synthetic (unless they are controlled-release) are usually faster compared to organic, which means they need to be reapplied at intervals (usually every three weeks) and may leach more readily into groundwater.

- Microorganisms: Organic fertilizers aid microorganisms, which in turn aid roots and growth.

- Problems: Organic products, such as fish-based products, may smell, making them unattractive to use on products that are for sale. Also, they may attract rodents and small wildlife (for example, bone meal attracts skunks). The wildlife in turn can injure plants, either by eating, root pruning, or merely uprooting the plants.

- Cost: Per unit element (such as nitrogen), organic often costs more, but consider the above factors. Not as much organic fertilizer is needed, so cost may not be a major issue, and the difference in cost obviously depends on the product. And organic fertilizers may result in a higher return for the end product if organically grown plants are highly desired by customers and so can command a higher price as a "niche" product (see the marketing section in chapter 11 on page 83).

Whatever the fertility method and material, the levels in the medium should allow for adequate to good growth, and nutrient levels should be monitored periodically even if there are no apparent problems. There are several methods you or a commercial lab can use. Contact your state cooperative extension soil-testing lab, a floriculture specialist, or a supplier for lab addresses and sources.

The most common and easily done method is perhaps the Spurway method (see table 5-2 on page 28). The saturated media extract (SME) method is applicable to field soils or container media (table 8-3). The pour-through (PT) method was developed in the 1980s at Virginia Polytechnic Institute for container media (table 8-4). While the guidelines for each of these tests are often based on research with a general range of crops

Table 8-3. Nutrient levels for media – saturated media extract (SME) method

Analysis	Low	Medium	High
Soluble salts (dS/m)[1]	0–1.0	1.0–2.0	3.0+
pH	3–4	5–6	7+
Nitrate-N (ppm)	0–50	50–200	200+
Phosphorus (ppm)	0–3	5–10	10+
Potassium (ppm)	0–100	100–200	250+

[1] Electrical conductivity (EC) units can be expressed in mhos or Siemens (S), which are equivalent, and may appear as dS/m = mS/cm = mmhos/cm.

Table 8-4. Nutrient levels for media – pour-through (PT) method

Analysis	Optimal level[1]
Soluble salts (dS/m)	0.6–2.0
pH	6–7
Nitrogen (N)	75–100
Phosphorus (P)	10–15
Potassium (K)	30–50
Calcium (Ca)	10–15
Magnesium (Mg)	10–15

[1] Elemental levels are given in ppm; levels determined in a pine bark medium with nursery species.

and may not apply to all perennials, they can serve to define a useful comparative baseline (Cabrera, 1996).

One of the more crucial analyses and levels to watch in container production is the level of soluble salts. These result from fertilizer applications and water itself. They are highest just before watering, because the water "flushes" the salts through the medium. For this reason, one of the best ways to control salts is to flush or "leach" the medium by watering until 10–30% of the water applied runs out of the pot.

Because of increasing environmental concerns about groundwater, drained water may need to be collected in the future and recycled (this may even be required in some areas now). This should be a consideration if establishing a new operation or renovating an existing one. Recycling will also conserve water, which is a concern in some areas with high water rates or low water supplies.

Leaching ability will vary with the type of medium and its components. Fertilizer elements have negative and positive charges (see the nutrients section in chapter 5 on page 28). The first word of a fertilizer is the component with the positive charge (for example, ammonium or calcium), and the second word is the component with the negative charge (for example, phosphate or nitrate).

Clay and organic particles have negative charges and attract the positively charged elements like a magnet. The negatives elements therefore are easily washed away with water, or leached. This is the reason nitrates readily appear in surface water and groundwater. Since nutrients move slowly in clay, they leach less readily than they do in sand, which has no charged particles and therefore holds no nutrients. Other measures used to control soluble salt buildup (which often appears as a white crust around the junction of the pot and medium or on the medium surface) are:

1. Keeping media from drying out frequently
2. Avoiding high concentrations of fertility at any one time — applying rather small amounts more frequently
3. Avoiding nutrients that cause high salt stress — nutrients with a high "salt index"
4. Balancing changes in the environment such as temperature and the need for water with the fertility program

Irrigation

Using irrigation to supplement rainfall is not as crucial for field production as for container perennials but is advisable in either case. Table 8-5 compares irrigation systems for container production. Overhead systems are the least expensive but most wasteful of water; up to half of the water applied is lost to evaporation. Such systems may also promote foliar and flower diseases such as *Botrytis* and mildews. Since they are inexpensive and easy to install, overhead systems are commonly used by growers. Spray stakes, however, are the most common (figure 8-3). Impact irrigation heads set on 20- to 25-

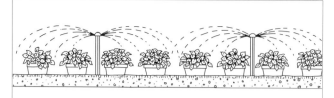

- 3/4" water line aboveground for spray stakes or 3/4"–1 1/4" line belowground for overhead
- If belowground: 6" deep if drained in winter, 3'–5' deep if not

Figure 8-3. Overhead spray stakes

foot centers are effective at water pressures of 30–60 pounds per square inch (psi). Drip systems (figure 8-4) are more expensive and less flexible, yet less wasteful of water.

Any of these systems can be a problem for small growers with many types and sizes of perennials, as different plants dry at varying rates. A solution might be to group plants according to their water needs into zones that can be irrigated separately. If the ground under containers is level and fairly solid, such as from ground cloth, a traveling overhead sprinkler can be used (figure 8-5). This saves the expense of a fixed overhead system or the expense of labor to water. However, a traveling sprinkler waters everything in addition to the container and so is wasteful of water.

An increasing concern in this country is the leaching into water supplies of fertilizers and chemicals from watering agricultural crops, including greenhouse and nursery crops. Laws regarding this are already in place in many European countries. Arid regions are concerned with saving water.

Recent research at North Carolina State University with container crops has shown that cyclic irrigation is more

Table 8-5. Comparison of container irrigation systems

System	Advantages	Disadvantages
Overhead–fixed or traveling	Inexpensive, good for various container sizes and layouts	Most wasteful of water, may promote foliar and flower diseases, water lines may need to be buried
Spray stakes	Inexpensive, easy to set up, usually no burying of lines needed, adaptable to various layouts	Also wasteful of water although less so than overhead
Drip or trickle	Less wasteful of water	Expensive, less adaptable to changing layouts, small capillary tubes may plug if water has any sediment (as with pond water)
Hand/manual	Most adaptable to various pot sizes, perennials, and layouts if waterer is highly skilled	Expensive use of labor, results may be variable depending on who waters
Subirrigation	Avoids polluting groundwater, most conservative of water, relatively inexpensive	May keep pots too wet leading to diseases and too lush growth, not adaptable to garden situations

efficient with less leaching of nutrients than a single application (Bilderback, 1996). Cyclic irrigation involves applying the same amount of water as with a traditional single application, only dividing the amount into portions that are applied over intervals. For example, rather than applying an inch of water at once, apply water maybe four times with ¼ inch at each application — the total applied is still 1 inch. The best cycle, with a 38% savings in water used, was to split the irrigation into two applications with a one-hour rest in between. Such cyclic irrigation is geared toward and most economical with a drip system, preferably one on a timer.

Subirrigation, which has been used sometimes in the production of evergreen seedlings but used little so far with perennials, possesses some potential (figure 8-6). This system is similar to the ebb-and-flood system used in greenhouses only it is in the ground partially or totally. Similar to the cyclic system, this system can be used where water is expensive or scarce, or when draining irrigation water may pollute groundwater.

Hand watering is still practiced by many, especially in retail situations. This allows precise watering, especially if many perennials drying at varying rates are involved. Hand watering can be an expensive use of labor, and its success is determined by the skill of the person on the end of the hose.

Water-absorbing agents such as hydrogels may be added to media to decrease watering frequency. However, consumers can mistake the appearance of these agents on soil surfaces as insects or exotic disease. See page 50 for more information on hydrogels.

Overwintering Containerized Perennials

One of the needs of container perennials, if they are held over winter, is increased protection from cold. When root and crown systems are underground, as is the case with field production, substantial protection against cold temperatures is provided by soil. Even in Ithaca, New York and Burlington, Vermont in the Northeast, soil temperatures at a 6-inch depth rarely go below 23°F, which, for hardy species, is well above the critical threshold below which cold temperature injury occurs to roots. But when roots and crowns are totally aboveground, as with container-grown plants, ambient air temperatures result in much lower winter temperature extremes in the container medium.

Temperatures parallel and are often comparable to air temperatures if the pots are not covered due to the lack of substantial temperature buffering capacity in the relatively small volume of medium. These colder root-zone temperatures increase the probability of cold temperature injury to roots of plants that are normally considered hardy when grown in-ground. Consequently, winter protection should be provided to containerized plants to minimize the risk of winter injury. Much informa-

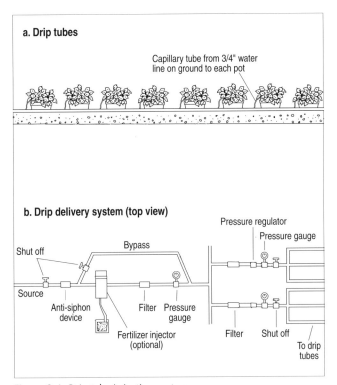

Figure 8-4. Drip tube irrigation system

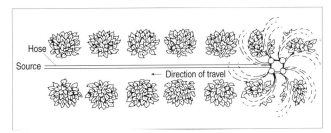

Figure 8-5. Travelling overhead sprinkler

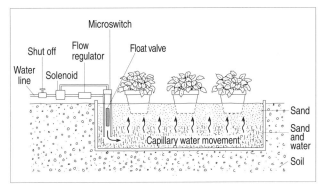

Figure 8-6. Container subirrigation system

tion on the basics of overwintering can be found in *Overwintering Woody and Herbaceous Ornamental Plants*, a proceedings from a 1995 Quebec meeting held by IQDHO (see recommended reading section at the end of this book).

The degree of protection should be a function of the expected minimum temperatures at the site, the usual length of time temperatures remain low, temperature fluctuation (which can be the most damaging factor to perennials in winter), the amount of natural snow cover (which is the best insulation against winter), the container size (the smaller the container, the more protection is needed), and the root hardiness (the lowest tem-

perature at which roots survive) of species being grown. Root and crown hardiness levels have only begun to be identified for herbaceous perennials by horticultural researchers (table 8-6).

According to preliminary research at the University of Vermont, the way plants are handled — the method of overwintering and type of exposure to cold — seems to be most crucial for intermediately hardy perennials. An initial study in Vermont examined the freezing of three species that were acclimated in a cool but not freezing fall greenhouse on two dates (November 15 and January 1) and for two durations (30 or 120 minutes). Results varied widely with species, which means that in a

Table 8-6. Root hardiness of several containerized perennials

Genus	Growing medium temperature causing significant injury[1]	Genus	Growing medium temperature causing significant injury[1]
TENDER		**INTERMEDIATELY HARDY** (continued)	
Aster lateriflorus var. *horizontalis*	28°F	*Tricyrtis hirta* 'Miyazaki'	21°F
Digitalis x *mertonensis*	24°F	*Verbena* 'Homestead Purple'	18°F
Geum Quellyon 'Mrs. Bradshaw'	24°F	*Veronica* 'Sunny Border Blue'	21°F
Hibiscus moschentos 'Disco' series	above 38°F	**HARDY**	
Houttuynia cordata 'Chameleon'	28°F	*Achillea* 'Coronation Gold'	8°F
		Achillea filipendulina 'Parker's Variety'	12°F
Kniphofia uvaria 'Pfitzer's hybrids'	27°F	*Campanula takesimana*	12°F
Polystichum tsussimense	above 38°F	*Dendranthema grandiflora* 'Baby Tears'	below 10°F
Thelypteris kunthii	28°F	*Dendranthema grandiflora* 'Debonair'	below 10°F
Tricyrtis formosana 'Amethystina'	28°F		
		Gaillardia x *grandiflora* 'Monarch Group'	12°F
INTERMEDIATELY HARDY		*Heuchera americana* 'Dale's Strain'	12°F
Astilbe x *arendsii* 'White Gloria'	15°F	*Hylotelephium* (*Sedum*) *spectabile*	
Campanula glomerata var. *acaulis*	15°F	'Brilliant'	−6°F
Caryopteris x *clandonensis*		*Lythrum salicaria* 'Robert'	12°F
'Longwood Blue'	21°F		
Chrysanthemum coccineum	21°F	*Monarda* 'Marshall's Delight'	8°F
		Penstemon fruticosus 'Purple Haze'	12°F
Coreopsis grandiflora 'Sunray'	18°F	*Phlox divaricata* subsp. *laphamii*	
Dendranthema grandiflora 'Emily'	above 10°F	'Chattahoochee'	7°F
Dendranthema grandiflora 'Megan'	above 10°F	*Phlox glaberrima* 'Morris Berd'	7°F
Dendranthema grandiflora 'Ruby Mound'	above 10°F		
Dendranthema grandiflora 'Triumph'	above 10°F	*Phlox paniculata* 'White Admiral'	8°F
		Physostegia virginiana 'Summer Snow'	7°F
Erodium x *variabile* 'Roseum'	18°F	*Rosmarinus officinalis* 'Arp'	12°F
Erysimum hieraciifolium	21°F	*Salvia* x *superba* 'Stratford Blue'	10°F
Gaillardia x *grandiflora* 'Goblin'	14°F	*Sedum* 'Autumn Joy'	−11°F
Hebe macrocarpa 'Margaret'	18°F		
Hemerocallis 'Joan Senior'	15°F	*Tanacetum coccineum* 'Robinson's Mix'	10°F
		Tiarella cordifolia var. *collina* 'Slick Rock'	12°F
Heuchera sanguinea 'Chatterbox'	14°F	*Tiarella cordifolia* var. *collina*	
Leucanthemum x *superbum* 'Alaska'	15°F	'Laird of Skye'	8°F
Phlox paniculata 'David'	21°F	*Tiarella cordifolia* 'Running Tapestry'	12°F
Tiarella cordifolia var. *collina* 'Dunvegan'	15°F	*Veronica repens*	7°F
Tiarella cordifolia var. *collina* 'Oakleaf'	21°F		

Source: Perry, DiSabato-Aust, Iles

[1] Unsalable, unacceptable regrowth

commercial situation, plants would have to be segregated according to their freezing response, or all plants would have to be treated according to the most tender.

In the study, *Achillea* 'Summer Pastels' was not susceptible to the date or duration of freezing; *Dianthus* 'Vampire' was injured at the longer duration but not affected by the date of freezing; and *Aquilegia* 'McKana's Giant Mix' was injured at both the earlier date and longer duration.

Coverless Pot-to-Pot Technique

Hardy species (such as some peonies and iris) can be overwintered by placing containers in contact with one another or as close together as possible. This is the case particularly in milder regions of the Northeast, such as Long Island or the Mid-Atlantic, or in areas that are guaranteed very heavy snowfall, such as the Lake Erie or Ontario snow belt areas in western New York and northern New England. For less hardy species, this approach is not advised because of the risks involved. Table 8-7 lists a few perennials researched with and without overwintering covering.

Table 8-7. Rating of herbaceous perennials after overwintering

Species	No cover	Cover[1]
Achillea filipendula (Yarrow)	2	4
Aquilegia hybrida 'McKana' (Columbine)	2	3
Artemisia schmidtiana 'Silver Mound'	4	4
Aster hybrida 'Hardy Blue'	3	1
Astilbe 'Bonn'	1	5
Dicentra hybrida 'Luxuriant' (Bleeding Heart)	1	3
Gaillardia 'Goblin', 'Kobold' (Blanket Flower)	2	4
Gypsophila paniculata 'Double Snowflake' (Baby's Breath)	4	4
Hemerocallis hybrida (Daylily, mixed)	1	4
Heuchera sanguinea 'Bressingham Hybrids' (Coral Bells)	3	4
Hosta undulata (Wavy-Leaf Plantain Lily)	3	5
Kniphofia uvaria (Tritoma, Torch Lily)	1	3
Leucanthemum (*Chrysanthemum*) x *superbum* (Shasta Daisy)	1	3
Limonium latifolium (German Statice)	4	4
Lupinus 'Russell Hybrids'	1	3
Monarda didyma (Beebalm, mixed)	2	4
Paeonia 'Felix Crousse' (Peony)	1	4
Rudbeckia hirta var. *pulcherrima* 'Rustic Colors'	3	1
Sedum spectabile 'Dragon's Blood'	5	5

Note: 1 = dead, 5 = excellent, 3–5 are salable; the number represents a mean of five replicates.

[1] Covered with two layers of poly with 12 inches of straw between the layers; trials took place in Swanton, Vermont in 1985 (USDA hardiness zone 4).

Thermoblanket Technique

This simple technique involves placing a sheet of insulating material over containerized plants during the coldest months of winter (figure 8-7). Coverings are usually secured by tucking the edges underneath the containers or by weighting down the edges with heavy objects such as stones, used tires, or lumber. Common thermoblanket materials include Microfoam, Polyfoam, Guilbond (available from Minnesota Distributing and Manufacturing, 1500 Jackson Street NE, Minneapolis, Minnesota 55413), Mirafy (thick felt used in road/pipe beds), The Winter Blanket (available from Laughton Nursery, 31 Lowell Road, Westford, Massachusetts 01886), or some of the new geotextiles such as Arbotex from Canada (available from Texel, 485 des Erables, St.-Elzear-de-Beauce, Quebec, Canada G052JO). It is essential that white reflective nursery polyfilm be placed over the materials, if it is not already adhered to them, to moderate temperatures and extend the life of the more expensive materials.

Because the covers trap latent heat from the soil surface, container, and container media, they provide substantial buffering from cold ambient temperatures during winter, particularly if snow cover is substantial. Before covering, conventional nursery stock must be laid down so that the coverings do not damage the aboveground plant parts. With most herbaceous perennials, the tops are killed by rigorous winter conditions prior to winter storage, and the tops are cut back before covering. Plant debris is removed prior to covering to prevent *Botrytis* blight and rots. Consequently, most containerized herbaceous perennials that are ready for storage can be left in an upright position and simply covered with the sheet of insulation. This also applies to most evergreen perennials.

Thermoblanket systems are relatively inexpensive as compared to other methods of winter protection. They also trap and contain moisture sufficiently to eliminate the need for supplemental irrigation during winter. Plants should be well-watered prior to covering.

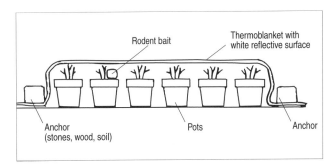

Figure 8-7. Thermoblanket technique of protecting plants from cold

Problems are difficult to detect within such systems, since the plants are visible only when the covering is opened up. Containers stored under polyblanket systems tend to warm prematurely during winter thaws or towards the end of the storage period. This can force shoot growth that could be injured upon the return of subfreezing conditions. Therefore, venting the covers may be advisable during unexpected periods of warm winter weather. Thermoblankets are usually so tight with respect to air exchange that ventilation is practically nonexistent. During short winters in warmer regions, this does not pose any problems; but in colder regions, where three to four months of cover are required, one must be concerned with the possible development of molds, decay, or rodent damage (see chapter 10).

In another approach, a framing system of inexpensive lumber, heavy-gauge wire rods, conduit, or pipe is built over the container beds and then covered with plastic. Although it allows air space between the plants and the cover, this system is seldom used because it is more labor-intensive and costly than merely laying covers directly over plants.

Plastic/Straw/Plastic (Sandwich) Technique

In this system, a layer of hay or straw is sandwiched between two layers of plastic (figure 8-8). Some growers have used this modification of the thermoblanket technique in cold locations or for plants that have root systems unusually sensitive to cold temperatures.

One layer of inexpensive clear or white plastic is placed directly over the plants to completely cover them. Then, a 6- to 12-inch layer of fluffed straw or hay is placed over the sheet of plastic. The straw is then covered by a second sheet of *white* plastic. White plastic is needed to reflect incoming light, which helps moderate temperatures. The first layer of plastic facilitates removal of the straw in spring.

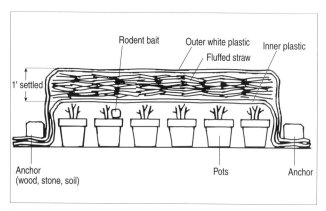

Figure 8-8. Sandwich technique of protecting plants from cold

The primary advantages of this system are that it provides the greatest degree of thermal protection of any of the unheated systems currently being employed by commercial growers, and it is one of the least expensive systems. In fact, plants are so well-insulated with this system that warming of the pots underneath at the end of winter is substantially delayed. As with the thermoblanket technique, the fact that one cannot see potential problems developing among the plants is a disadvantage.

Although it is more labor-intensive, another system researched in Iowa showed temperature moderating effects and protection similar to that provided with the sandwich system. In that system, pots were sunk 6 inches in ground troughs, then covered with a layer of polyfilm and 6 inches of bark mulch.

Quonset Structure Technique (Polyhouses)

Probably the most common system used to protect containerized plants, including herbaceous perennials, is the Quonset-style, polyethylene-covered structure (figure 8-9). Such structures are usually constructed of wooden frames to which uniformly bent galvanized pipe or metal conduit is attached. The bent pipe or conduit is usually referred to as a bow, and it provides the basic rib structure that supports either one layer or two air-inflated layers of polyethylene. The polyethylene and bows are secured to the wooden baseboards.

The plastic cover allows certain wavelengths of light to pass through. Subsequently, objects within the structure absorb this light and convert it to heat energy. The plastic cover traps a portion of this heat during the day. Stored heat radiates from the structure at night, thus cooling the structure as well as the objects within it. Under average conditions in milder climates, temperatures within these structures do not reach levels injurious to plants stored inside. However, conditions may prevail that can lower temperatures inside overwintering structures to levels that result in injury to plants — for example, extended periods of extreme cold (more than two consecutive nights when ambient temperatures go below 0°F). Thus, polyhouses do have thermal limits in terms of protection for many plants.

Fortunately, additional steps can be taken to protect plants stored inside polyethylene overwintering structures during periods of extreme cold. An additional layer of plastic or a sheet of one of the thermoblanket materials mentioned earlier (such as Microfoam or Polyfoam) can be placed immediately over the plants inside a

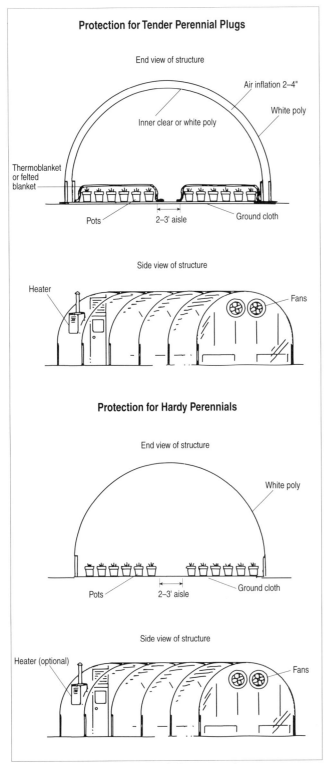

Protection for Tender Perennial Plugs

End view of structure

Air inflation 2–4"

Inner clear or white poly

White poly

Thermoblanket or felted blanket

Pots

2–3' aisle

Ground cloth

Side view of structure

Heater

Fans

Protection for Hardy Perennials

End view of structure

White poly

Pots

2–3' aisle

Ground cloth

Side view of structure

Heater (optional)

Fans

Figure 8-9. A Quonset-style polyethylene-covered structure

Currently, it is recommended that the extra blanket be placed over the plants only for the duration of the extremely low temperatures so as to avoid excessive moisture buildup in the container environment. A porous material such as Mirafy may be left on the plants, as it allows air exchange, and water will soak through to plants if they are dry. Placing a layer of bagged leaves, hay bales, or similar insulation around the outside of the overwintering house will add an extra amount of protection to the root area.

The process of taking the cover off the structure in spring is critical if plant injury is to be avoided. Gradual removal of the cover, in February for mild areas (such as USDA plant hardiness zones 6–8; see figure 2-1 on page 11) and March for cold areas (such as zones 3–5), is suggested. First, doors and windows should be opened at night, and then small vents should be cut into the ridge of the cover. Later, the vents should be enlarged. Finally, the cover is removed in late March to April.

Plants, especially those with foliage on them, must be checked frequently for outbreaks of *Botrytis* rot and sprayed as needed. *Phlox subulata* is especially vulnerable to fungal infections. It is essential that structures be large enough so that plants can be easily checked and treated.

Quonset-style polyethylene structures are rather expensive if one considers only the initial construction costs (materials and labor included). However, well-constructed frames and bows will last ten or more years before any major renovations are needed, so the initial cost is easier to bear if the entire life of the structure is considered. Furthermore, the thousands of plants in these frames can be covered with plastic in a matter of hours for large operations, so these structures are considerably more efficient than other methods of overwintering. They also afford the grower an opportunity to inspect the plants and to remedy any problems that may be noted. And if supplemental heating is also used, plants may be brought into bloom earlier.

Unfortunately, winter protection in polyhouses is limited, as previously mentioned. Plants that are considered marginally hardy when grown in containers should get additional protection in the form of a supplementary poly or thermal blanket laid inside the polyhouse. Or an entirely different technique can be employed, such as the plastic/straw/plastic technique previously described.

Also, polyhouses tend to heat during winter thaws or in late winter or early spring, when the amount of incom-

polyhouse. This technique (sometimes referred to as the supplementary polyblanket or thermoblanket technique) can create a microclimate in the immediate vicinity of the plants that is 8–10°F warmer than air above the blanket inside the structure. Thus, substantial protection can be afforded plants with one of the blanket techniques during periods of extreme cold.

ing solar radiation increases. This can force premature shoot growth if the houses are not properly ventilated. The use of pigmented (white) plastic as a cover for polyhouses helps to alleviate overheating to some extent, since approximately 50% of the incoming sunlight (depending on the type of plastic and the degree of pigmentation) is transmitted through the plastic. Even so, plants in houses covered with pigmented plastic can be forced too early during periods of unusually warm weather. For structures with an inner (bottom) and outer (top) plastic covering with air in between, the outer layer is usually pigmented polyethylene, while the inner layer may be pigmented or clear. This allows further control of the amount of light (and heat) penetrating the structure. Construction details and costs for several types of structures can be obtained from *Principles, Practices, and Comparative Costs of Overwintering Container-Grown Landscape Plants* (see recommended reading section at the end of this book).

Other Methods

The overwintering techniques discussed above are summarized in table 8-8. A variety of other techniques have been used to protect containerized herbaceous perennials during winter, including covered cold frames, earthen pits, sunken frames, root cellars, barns and sheds, a covering of evergreen boughs, and deep snow cover. Any measure that protects the plants adequately and is reasonable economically merits attention.

When to Cover Unprotected Plants or Uncover Protected Plants

Woody plants respond to both shortening days and dropping temperatures by going through as many as three levels of hardening. Most herbaceous perennials, however, have no woody portions. Tops of perennials may respond to shorter day lengths by sending hormone signals to the roots. Roots, especially the young terminals (root tips), do not acclimate to any great extent; they respond only to lower temperatures with what is termed "apparent" or "quiescent" dormancy. Being underground, where temperatures are warmer either from snow cover in the North or warmer soil in the South, roots have not had to adapt and so remain less hardy than the tops of evergreen and woody plants and more vulnerable to winter injury.

During the period of "false" dormancy that roots of herbaceous perennials undergo, short, warm periods of weather can start growth again, which results in even more chance of injury. For this reason, fluctuations in temperature can be harmful. As with most factors, the extent of injury varies with species.

Research by Maqbool (1986) at Michigan State University has shown that the more often temperatures cycle between 34° and 28°F, the poorer the survival of *Geum* and *Coreopsis*. However, cycling temperatures did not affect survival of stored plants of *Hemerocallis*, *Monarda*, *Hosta*, or *Lupine*. Results with *Campanula takesimana* at the University of Vermont indicate that some cycling may in fact induce a deeper dormancy and greater resistance to injury (Herrick and Perry, 1997). When 4-inch pots of this species were acclimated in a cool but not freezing greenhouse, they survived to lower temperatures after three cycles between 38° and 24°F. Whether this holds true with wider ranges of cycling, with other species, or with natural fall acclimation remains to be studied. Plants of this same species of *Campanula* that were held for longer periods at each freez-

Table 8-8. Comparison of containerized perennial overwintering methods

Method	Advantages	Disadvantages
Thermoblankets	Easy to install and remove, retains pot moisture, relatively inexpensive overall	Cannot see problems beneath the blanket; insufficient protection in cold climates, in areas that get little snow, or for tender perennials; rodents can be a problem
"Sandwich" technique (plastic/straw/plastic)	Inexpensive materials, excellent temperature moderation and protection, retains pot moisture	More expensive to install, rodents can be a problem, cannot see problems beneath the cover, need a recycle system for the straw
Polyhouses (Quonsets)	Best for temperature control especially if heated, can see problems inside the house, better control of moisture if ventable or equipped with fans, fewer rodent problems, better control of growth and flowering	Most expensive in materials and installation, temperatures may fluctuate widely if not controlled (through heating and venting)

Herbaceous Perennials Production

ing temperature (forty-eight hours versus thirty minutes) were less hardy.

Most containerized nursery stock is covered as late in the season as weather permits. It is not uncommon to see plants being covered as late as early December on Long Island or in the Mid-Atlantic area, or in mid to late November in New England. Waiting as long as is practically possible to cover plants (before the first major snowfall) will help plants achieve a level of hardiness that will minimize the risk of winter injury during winter storage. Research at the University of Vermont shows that the time of covering is not as crucial as the time of uncovering.

Most Long Island and Mid-Atlantic growers begin to uncover containerized plants during late February or early March, whereas those in upstate New York and New England usually begin the process in mid to late March. It is impossible to identify an exact date for uncovering containerized plants that have been stored for winter because of varying weather conditions each year. The challenge is to obtain a compromise between preventing premature shoot growth from overwintering plant parts and ensuring that unusually cold weather that can occur in late winter and early spring does not kill or injure plant parts. During this time frame, or as soon as snow has receded, growers normally remove covers and thermoblankets during a period of several days to a week when unusually cold temperatures are no longer expected.

Protected plants must be inspected frequently to ensure that shoot growth is not initiated. If any signs of such activity are evident, the storage environment should be vented if possible to introduce cool air into the system to slow plant development. Many growers will cut large holes in the sides of polyhouses to facilitate ventilation. The remaining poly is left in place to provide some protection if adverse conditions redevelop. Those using thermoblankets will roll coverings back but will keep them handy in case the weather shortly after uncovering becomes much colder.

Overwintering Disease and Rodent Control

Under some circumstances, microorganisms flourish because of the conditions that prevail in the overwintering environment. Spraying plants with a broad-spectrum fungicide or a combination of two or more fungicides just prior to storage can often prevent problems if a history of specific diseases is known. If there is no known problem, then such applications are a "shot gun" approach and may or may not help. Removing foliage before storage (when possible) helps prevent diseases. See Cornell University's *Pest Management Recommendations for Commercial Production and Maintenance of Trees and Shrubs* for chemicals and their rates of application (a complete citation for this book can be found in the recommended reading section, which begins on page 203). Table 8-9 lists genera most likely to require extra care in storage.

WARNING: Pesticide regulations and uses will vary from state to state. Growers should check with their state agency to see if chemicals are registered in their state.

Rodents such as field mice are often a problem with overwintered container perennials, especially with plants under covers. Most growers use some form of poison bait under the covers. The bait is placed in containers and is easily removed in the spring. Baits may or may not be effective, depending on rodent populations and food pressures (see page 77 for more information).

Table 8-9. Genera intolerant of wet overwintering conditions

Achillea	Clematis	Lychnis
Adenophora	Coreopsis	Oenothera
Alyssum	Delphinium	Paeonia
Anaphalis	Dianthus	Papaver
Anemone	Echinacea	Platycodon
Anthemis	Eryngium	Primula
Aquilegia	Euphorbia	Rudbeckia
Arabis	Gaillardia	Salvia
Armeria	Geum	Scabiosa
Artemisia	Gypsophila	Sedum
Asclepias	Helleborus	Sidalcea
Astilbe	Heuchera	Stachys
Aurinia	Iberis	Stokesia
Campanula	Iris (bearded)	Verbascum
Cassia	Kniphofia	Veronica
Centaurea	Liatris	
Ceratostigma	Linum	
Chrysanthemum (Dendranthema)	Lupinus	

CHAPTER 9

Field Production

For field production, choose a site with sandy or organic, fertile soil if possible. Perennials are easier to dig in sandy soil than in clay or rocky soil. The soil should have adequate organic matter content (at least 2–3%), or organic matter will need to be increased over time with mulches, composts, and other organic additions. Organic matter helps beneficial microorganisms, holds water, and provides nutrient balance through increased cation exchange capacity (CEC).

The site should also have good air drainage to prevent excessive frosts. In the North, a site with good snow cover is ideal. A less windy site will prevent excessive drying (and thus the need for constant irrigation) and result in less plant topple and damage. Windbreaks, or shelter belts, can help reduce wind damage (see figure 3-1 on page 18). Water quality should also be checked, as it may be a concern in some areas — particularly those with high salts (table 9-1).

Preparation

Preferably a year or two before planting, cover crops should be sown and managed to help lessen the weed population and improve soil tilth, fertility, and organic matter (table 9-2). When they are tilled in, cover crops are called "green manure." The two basic types of cover crops are legumes, such as clovers, hairy vetch, and alfalfa, and non-legumes, such as rye, oats, sudangrass, sorghum, and buckwheat. Non-legumes grow rapidly and are good for weed suppression. Legumes are slower to establish but add nitrogen to the soil when tilled in.

Table 9-1. Salinity levels for irrigation water

mS/cm[1]	Salinity level	Irrigation value
<0.25	Low	Excellent on most soils, normal leaching
0.25–0.75	Moderate	Satisfactory, moderate leaching suggested
0.75–2.25	High	Avoid use on soil with poor drainage, plant salt-tolerant crops, leaching necessary
>2.26	Very high	Not recommended for irrigation, a few salt-tolerant crops may be grown with special culture

Source: Adapted from Wilcox, 1955.

[1] mS/cm = millisiemens per centimeter. Millisiemen is replacing millimho (mmho) as the preferred unit for expressing conductivity (soluble salts) measurements. The value remains the same–only the name changes. To convert this value to ppm, multiply by 700.

Rye and oats are often sown in late summer through early fall, as are the legumes, which can also be sown in spring. Buckwheat, sudan, and sorghum are sown in spring or early summer as annuals for that season. Most legumes are perennials. Alfalfa is a long-lived one to use where needed for several years.

Soils should be tested, limed, and sometimes fertilized prior to planting. Since phosphorus is a crucial element, and it moves little in the soil compared to other elements, it is good to incorporate it prior to or at planting. Use a high-phosphorus fertilizer such as 0-46-0 (triple superphosphate) or 0-20-0 (superphosphate), which are synthetic, or 2-25-0 (bonemeal), which is organic.

Table 9-2. Cover and green manure crops

Crop	Advantages	Disadvantages	Sowing
NON-LEGUMES	Establish rapidly for short-term weed suppression	Contribute little nitrogen and nutrients	
Winter rye	Very hardy, widely adaptable, seed is inexpensive, much spring biomass produced	Rank spring growth can be hard to incorporate, may become a weed if not fully incorporated	Late summer to mid October, sow 2 bushels per acre
Oats	Protects soil in winter after frost-killed, residues may chemically suppress weeds	May need shallow spring incorporation	Sow in late summer, 100 pounds per acre
Ryegrass	Extensive root system captures residual nitrogen and reduces erosion, can be sown under crops	Perennial rye may winter kill in harsh climates	Sow mid summer to early fall, 30-40 pounds per acre
Sudangrass, sorghum- sudangrass	Fast-growing, tall and rank growth provides good weed suppression	Require warm season, good fertility, and moisture to perform well; may be hard to cut and incorporate	Sow late spring to late summer at 30-40 pounds per acre
Buckwheat	Fast-growing summer annual, decomposes rapidly so is easy to incorporate after flowering	Does not contribute much organic matter, can become weedy if sets seed prior to incorporation	Sow in late spring to mid summer at 60-70 pounds per acre
LEGUMES	Hold nitrogen in soils for future crops	Need good drainage and fertility, grow slowly so may need another "nurse" crop sown at same time (such as oats) to help compete with weeds	
Red clover	Tolerates some soil acidity and some poor drainage, can be under-sown in vigorous crops	Short-lived perennial	Sow in early spring or late summer at 10-15 pounds per acre
White clover	Low-growing, tolerates some shade and some soil acidity, useful in walkways	Expensive seed, poor competitor with weeds	Sow in spring or fall at 10-12 pounds per acre
Sweet clover	Biennial usually, deep taproot improves subsoils, widely adaptable to soil types	May deplete soil of moisture for subsequent crops	Sow in early spring or late summer at 15-20 pounds per acre, incorporate after flowering
Hairy vetch	Hardy overwintering cover crop, fixes much nitrogen if incorporated early summer, widely adaptable	May winter kill if sown late	Sow late summer to early fall at 30-40 pounds per acre, or at 25-30 pounds per acre with 1 bushel per acre of winter rye
Alfalfa	Long-lived perennial, fixes much nitrogen over several years	Requires deep, well-drained soil near neutral pH; not cost effective for short term; attracts some plant bugs	Sow in early spring or late summer at 15-25 pounds per acre

Adapted from a University of Vermont Cooperative Extension leaflet by Vern Grubinger.

As in container organic soils, the proper pH is essential in order for nutrients to be available to plant roots in mineral soils (figure 9-1 on page 64). Many soils are acidic, so the addition of lime is necessary to raise the pH (table 9-3). If a soil is alkaline, sulfur compounds must be used (table 9-4 on page 64). Optimum pH levels for mineral soils are 5–7, and a pH of 5–6 is best for organic soils.

Table 9-3. Lime requirements to raise pH to 7.0 for various soils

	Soil type		
Initial pH	Sandy loam	Silty loam	Clay loam
	tons lime/acre (lbs lime/1,000 ft²)		
4.5	6.0 (270)	9.5 (430)	13.0 (585)
5.0	5.0 (225)	7.5 (340)	10.5 (475)
5.5	3.0 (135)	4.0 (180)	6.0 (270)
6.0	1.5 (70)	2.0 (90)	3.0 (135)
6.5	0.7 (30)	1.0 (45)	1.5 (70)

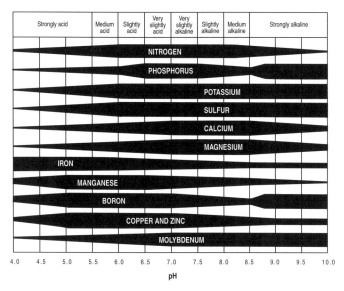

Figure 9-1. Availability of plant nutrients in mineral soil as influenced by pH; the wider the bar, the more available the nutrient (Adapted from Truog, 1947)

Table 9-4. Amounts of sulfur compounds needed to lower pH by ½ to 1 unit

Material	Soil type		
	Sandy loam	Silty loam	Clay loam
	lbs/100 sq ft (lbs/1,000 sq ft)		
Finely ground sulfur	⅜ (4)	½ (5)	¾ (8)
Iron sulfate[1]	2 (20)	3 (15)	4 (40)
Aluminum sulfate[1]	2 (20)	3 (15)	4 (40)

[1] Can soil drench: Add amount to 25+ gallons of water and apply to appropriate area.

Optimum levels of field soil nutrients will vary with soil type and crop, but general ranges can be given (table 9-5). Recommended levels will vary with the soil lab performing the soil test (different labs use different procedures), the CEC (cation exchange capacity) of the soil, and the Ca-Mg (calcium to magnesium) ratio. Consult a soil lab or specialist to help interpret individual results.

Cover crops should lessen or prevent the need for herbicides for weed control before planting. If cover crops are not desirable or possible, then preemergence herbicides may be used after soil preparation prior to planting. A postemergent herbicide may be used for general clearing before soil preparation. Care should be taken when using herbicides, as they do not distinguish between perennials and weeds, and any herbicide remaining in the soil may damage future desirable perennials. Damage may range from slow growth and an inability

Table 9-5. Optimum levels of field soil nutrients

Nutrient	Level (lbs/acre)
Available phosphorus (P)	30
Exchangeable potassium (K)	200–400
Exchangeable calcium (Ca)	800–16,000
Exchangeable magnesium (Mg)	150–2,000
Available manganese (Mn)	20–40
Available boron (B)	0.5
Available zinc (Zn)	3

to root cuttings to death (see weed control section in chapter 10, page 78). Prepare the seed or transplant area by plowing, discing, dragging, and rolling the ground with equipment, as is done for field cultivation of vegetables and agronomic crops.

Planting

Seeds are sown with a modified field seed planter as early in the season as feasible. (Field seed planters are modified to produce the fewer number of plants per row needed for perennials as compared to most agronomic and vegetable crops.) Transplanting of dormant or greenhouse-started materials is completed somewhat later after all chance of frost is past, often with equipment similar to that used in field vegetable production, such as two-row or three-row planters. A person seated on each row places plants in holes made by the planting machine. A plant's size affects its field survival.

Research at the University of Vermont has shown that plugs (273) need much more care than larger cells (36 per flat) when planted directly to a sandy field, especially if planted in mid summer. Fall planting of plug or cell plants directly to the field should be avoided, except for hardy species or in mild climates (USDA hardiness zones 6–8; see figure 2-1 on page 11). Otherwise, they have insufficient time to establish before winter. Transplanting time for bare-root plants and divisions is not as crucial and is often dictated by species and other factors.

At least four to six weeks should be allowed for root growth before soil temperatures drop below 40°F — about November 1 in USDA hardiness zone 4 (see figure 2-1 on page 11), and about two weeks later for each warmer hardiness zone. Starter fertilizer may be useful at planting, as shown by an unpublished study at the University of Vermont, especially if soil has low fertility or subsequent fertility is marginal.

After Planting

Many fertilizers may be sidedressed after planting around plants or along a row. If using an organic, balanced fertilizer, one application per season after planting may be sufficient. A balanced synthetic fertilizer is usually quicker to release and lose its nitrogen, so applications may be split over the season. Often 3 pounds of **actual** nitrogen are applied per 1,000 square feet per season; to split applications, apply 1 pound on May 1, 1 pound on June 1, and 1 pound on October 1. As an example, if a 5-3-4 organic fertilizer is used once per season and the desired rate is 3 pounds actual nitrogen per 1,000 square feet, then 60 pounds of fertilizer would be needed. This is because the fertilizer is only 5% nitrogen, so 20 pounds are needed for 1 pound of actual nitrogen, and 60 pounds are needed for 3 pounds of actual nitrogen.

Many field producers do not have irrigation systems, although irrigation is essential to ensure optimum growth, especially in times of drought. It is a form of insurance. Most growers estimate when to water by looking for signs of plant wilting and stress or feeling the soil (table 9-6). Overhead irrigation systems (fixed or traveling) are the cheapest and therefore the most common (figure 9-2). But they are also most wasteful of water; during hot, dry spells, up to 50% of the water applied may evaporate and never make it to the plants.

Soaker hoses are popular, especially for medium to small operations (figure 9-3). A few hoses may be moved along rows to save on the up-front costs. Only low water pressure is needed for these. Water is delivered only in the plant root zone, so these systems are conservative of water. Soaker hoses may be made of a permeable material such as recycled rubber, which emits water along its length. Or they may be made of an impermeable mate-

rial such as plastic, with holes or emitters spaced equally along the length. A combination of soaker and overhead systems is an impermeable hose with equally spaced spray emitters that spray water low and all over the ground (figure 9-4).

Flooded troughs are a cruder version of soaker hoses (figure 9-5 on page 66). They are easy to use and inexpensive, so they are common — especially in the West where there are large areas to water.

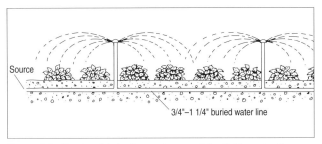

Figure 9-2. Overhead irrigation system used for field production

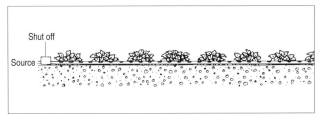

Figure 9-3. Soaker hose irrigation system used for field production

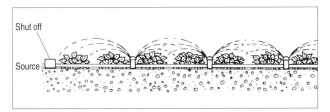

Figure 9-4. Spray emitters used for field irrigation

Table 9-6. Feel and appearance of field soil at various moisture levels

Percentage of remaining available water	Course texture soil	Medium texture soil	Fine texture soil
0% (dry)	Dry, loose, flows through fingers	Powder-dry, sometimes slightly crusted but easily breaks down	Hard, baked, cracked, sometimes has loose crumbs on surface
50% or less (low)	Still appears to be dry, will not form a ball with pressure	Somewhat crumbly, but will hold together with pressure	Somewhat pliable, will ball under pressure
50–100% (good to excellent)	Forms weak ball, breaks easily, will not stick	Forms a ball and is very pliable, sticks readily if relatively high in clay	Easily ribbons out between fingers, has a slick feeling
Above field capacity (over-irrigated)	Free water will be released with kneading	Can squeeze out free water	Puddles and free water form on the surface

Adapted from: *Irrigating Small Acreages,* Cooperative Extension Service, Michigan State University Extension Bulletin 320.

Hand watering fields is uncommon, as it requires so much labor. Only small areas, isolated blocks, or special needs plants are hand watered. Table 9-7 summarizes the various irrigation methods.

Herbicides may be used with the same precautions discussed earlier. Directed applications of a systemic herbicide may be used (see next chapter). Many who grow plants in the field prefer not to use herbicides and rely on cultivation instead. If using cultivation, it is crucial to allow enough space for mechanical cultivation between rows when planning field size and layout. Mechanical planting and cultivation often dictate the row width and spacing. Weeding around plants is done by hand.

Depending on the species and market, plants remain in the field for one or two growing seasons. Plants for filling early orders are dug in the fall and stored, while plants for filling April to June orders may either be fall dug and stored or dug in spring and processed directly. If plants are dug and stored over winter, controlled environments to provide low relative humidity and 32–38°F temperatures are needed to avoid plant loss.

Winter Protection of Field-Grown Plants

Field-grown plants may remain in the field to over-winter. For most species, no frost protection is required. Marginally hardy species must be protected by a layer of porous mulch, such as weed-free straw, evergreen boughs, or salt marsh hay. Plants subject to root rots must be grown in well-drained locations to survive wet spring conditions (table 8-9 on page 61) and may require periodic fungicide treatment. Raised beds may be necessary in heavy soils. Preliminary research at the University of Vermont has shown that a 2-inch layer of mulch may keep soil temperatures 5–10°F warmer than unmulched soil at a depth of 2 inches, especially during fall and spring.

Field growing-medium temperatures should be monitored, as they usually will be as much as 8–15°F warmer than surrounding air temperatures in fall and spring, and even more so in winter. In general, they should not drop below 28°F for the least hardy perennials. Grow-

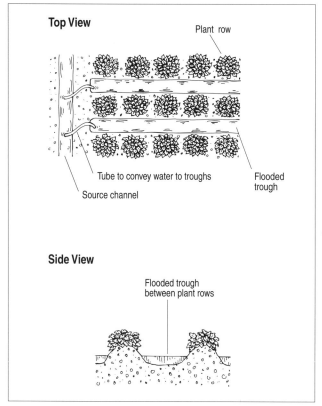

Top View

Plant row

Tube to convey water to troughs

Source channel

Flooded trough

Side View

Flooded trough between plant rows

Figure 9-5. Flooded-trough irrigation method

Table 9-7. Comparison of field irrigation systems

System	Advantages	Disadvantages
Overhead	Inexpensive, good for various layouts	Most wasteful of water, may promote foliar and flower diseases, may need to bury water lines
Soaker hoses	Inexpensive if a few are moved around a small nursery, conservative of water, uses less water pressure	Expensive and impractical for large nurseries
Spray emitters	Less wasteful of water than overhead systems, easy to install	More expensive, may need to be removed for field cultivation
Flooded troughs	Easy where water is plentiful, not as wasteful as overhead, least expensive system equipment	Uses much water
Hand or manual	Good for small blocks or beds, allows precise control, conservative of water	Expensive, not practical for most field nurseries

ers may be providing more protection than necessary by using mulches to avoid possible losses, but many consider this "cheap insurance" compared to the cost of overwintering structures. Many tender plants are often overwintered with hardier ones, and so the same maximum protection would be required for all plants. (For more information, see the section on "Overwintering Containerized Perennials" on page 55 of chapter 8.) In a University of Vermont study on garden phlox hardiness in the field in USDA hardiness zone 4 (see figure 2-1 on page 11), varieties proved to have quite different hardiness levels. Of the thirty-five cultivars tested, the most hardy were 'Fairy's Petticoat', 'New Bird', 'White Admiral', and 'Katherine.' The least hardy were 'Windsor', 'Starfire', 'Sandra', 'Dodo Hanbury Forbes', and 'Bright Eyes.'

CHAPTER 10

Pest Control

Managing pest populations requires precise knowledge of the following:

- what pest is present (which is determined through scouting)
- the level of the pest population and how many pests can be tolerated (this level is referred to as the *threshold)*
- the life stages of the pest that are susceptible to control
- chemical controls previously used
- the presence or absence of other pests or parasites
- the location of the pest population
- the host plants
- when workers will reenter the greenhouse or treated area
- legal constraints and environmental implications of chemical use

All of these factors are considerations in a comprehensive pest management program. In landscapes, many perennials tolerate diseases and moderate pest levels with no treatment. In production and retail situations, the plants may tolerate the same problems, but the threshold is very low since pest damage may render the plants unsalable. Pests that do not infest plants outdoors may do so indoors under greenhouse conditions. Some viruses, such as cucumber mosaic virus, may be only slightly damaging aesthetically to certain perennials (lobelia, for example); they may be of great economic concern, however, because they are easily vectored by insects and spread to economically important vegetable crops. Maintaining a diverse selection of plants, either in landscapes or a nursery, will help reduce the impact of any particular pest.

Single factors thought to be problems with crops are often found to be influenced by other production factors. An example is *Botrytis* disease, which is caused by a fungus but is often stimulated by poor environmental conditions (poor air circulation) and poor cultural practices (watering late in the day so foliage remains wet at night). Slugs also appear often under damp conditions. IPM (integrated pest management) practices help growers better understand the interactions of pests, the environment, and culture. IPM control techniques can be mechanical (such as screening), cultural (such as proper watering), and biological (such as releasing predators, parasites, and entomopathogenic organisms into the crop area). Chemicals are also an IPM option.

The following IPM suggestions relate specifically to herbaceous perennials.

- Inspect incoming plants for pest problems; quarantine them if necessary.
- Keep growing areas clean. (This includes removing weeds and dead plant materials.)
- When possible, cover all soil surfaces with concrete, black plastic, or weed barrier.
- Keep "pet" or favorite home garden plants out of crop areas.
- Grow resistant varieties whenever possible.
- When possible, keep unnecessary people out of the crop area, especially in greenhouses. Pests hitch rides.
- Sterilize growing media, if needed or applicable.

- Use physical barriers such as microscreening and doors in greenhouses.
- Use sticky traps to monitor for pests such as adult whiteflies, fungus gnats, shore flies, winged aphids, and thrips. Check and change strips weekly.

As many pests are quite small, a 10x hand lens like those available at stamp and coin shops is one of the most important IPM tools you can have. Some suppliers of other IPM scouting equipment are listed below. This partial listing is supplied with the understanding that no discrimination against excluded companies is intended, and no endorsement of companies listed is implied.

- Forestry Supplier, P.O. Box 8397, Jackson, Mississippi 39284; phone (800) 647-5368
- E. C. Geiger, Inc., Route 63, Box 285, Harleysville, Pennsylvania 19438; phone (800) 443-4437
- Gempler's Pest Management Supply, P.O. Box 270, Belleville, Wisconsin 53508; phone (800) 332-6744
- Great Lakes IPM, 10220 Church Road NE, Vestaburg, Michigan 48891
- Griffin Greenhouse and Nursery Supplies, 1619 Main Street, P.O. Box 36, Tewksbury, Massachusetts 01876; phone (978) 851-4346
- IPM Laboratories, Inc., P.O. Box 300, Locke, New York 13092-0300; phone (315) 497-2063; fax (315) 497-3129; e-mail IPMLABS@IPMLABS.COM
- W. H. Milikowski, Inc., 75 Chestnut Hill, Route 190, Stafford Springs, Connecticut 06076-4030; phone (800) 243-7170

A more complete discussion of IPM is beyond the scope of this text. For more information about IPM, consult *The Gardener's Guide to Common-Sense Pest Control*, which is listed under "Publications from Other Sources" in the recommended reading section beginning on page 203.

What follows is an abbreviated discussion of pests and diseases, focusing on the major ones found in both greenhouses and the field. This discussion is not meant to be exhaustive but to serve as a starting point for monitoring perennials. Specifics for individual genera are listed in appendix C beginning on page 159. New pests and diseases are always being observed, and plants not listed in the appendix may also have problems. Some pests and diseases may be a problem only outdoors, and others only indoors. Contact your state cooperative extension diagnostic clinic or department of agriculture for assistance in identifying unknown problems. The assistance of a professional is often useful, as problems are often common to several potential causes. Table 10-1 on page 70 provides some symptoms of problems and some of their possible causes. See the sidebar below for other references about pest control.

Many perennials are not listed on pesticide labels, so legal chemical treatments are not available for them and their insect, disease, or weed pests.

Diseases

Careful sanitation practices and good cultural techniques are critical for the production of disease-free perennials. Sanitation helps by keeping the disease organisms away from the plants, and good culture helps by keeping the plants vigorously growing so they will be less susceptible to infection.

Clean growing practices in a field production facility in the past included preplant soil fumigation with materials such as Vapam, Vorlex, or methyl bromide to reduce populations of soil fungi, insects, nematodes, and weeds. The soil in crop areas should be very well-drained to avoid root rot from fungi such as *Pythium* and *Phytophthora* species.

Container media must also allow for good air pore space to encourage healthy roots. Production in containers is best managed in areas covered with a weedproof fabric that allows water to drain through. Black plastic is commonly used under containers, but care must be taken to avoid puddling and consequent losses to root-rotting fungi.

> ### Useful References on Pest Control
> (See the recommended reading section beginning on page 203 for complete citations.)
>
> - *Herbaceous Perennials: Diseases and Insect Pests*
> - *The New England Greenhouse Floricultural Recommendations: A Management Guide for Insects, Diseases, Weeds, and Growth Regulators*
> - Cornell University's *1997 Pest Management Recommendations for the Production of Herbaceous Perennials*
> - Cornell University's *Weed Management Guide for Herbaceous Ornamentals*
> - *Herbaceous Perennial Insect, Disease, Weeds, and Fertility Guidelines* (from University of Maryland Cooperative Extension)

Table 10-1. Diagnosing problems

Symptoms	Some possible causes
LEAVES	
White powdery growth, mostly upper leaf surfaces	Powdery mildew
Fuzzy pale gray patches on lower leaf surfaces	Downy mildew
Yellowing of lower leaves	Nutrient deficiency, mites, root rot, water stress, low light from improper spacing
Round dead spots in leaves	Plant bugs, fungi, bacteria
Angular dead spots in leaves	Fungi, bacteria, foliar nematodes
Notches in leaves	Grasshoppers, some leaf beetles, black vine weevil
Holes in leaves	Loopers, caterpillars, flea beetles, slugs (slime trails), small animals (large holes)
Mosaic patterns, leaf cupping, distortion	Viruses, herbicide damage, potato leafhopper, spittlebug (usually meadow spittlebug), aster leafhopper
Grayish coloration	Root disease, poor drainage
Pustules of spores (often brown) on leaf undersides	Rust fungus
Discoloration of upper leaves, webbing	Mites
Discoloration, stippling	Thrips, lacebugs, aster leafhopper, potato leafhopper, spittlebug, mites, viruses
Sticky upper leaf surfaces, black residue, ants	Aphids, whiteflies, mealybugs, sooty mold
Lacework/skeletonized feeding	Oriental beetle, scarab beetles (including Japanese beetles) masked chafers, oriental beetles
SHOOTS	
Blight (rapid death)	*Botrytis*
Distorted young growth	Aphids, cyclamen mite, anthracnose, herbicide injury
Wilting	Root rot, vascular wilt, drought, stem base canker, damping-off (seedlings), European corn borer, stalk borer, fungus gnat larvae
Stunting	Water or fertilizer deficiency, root-feeding nematodes, vascular wilt, herbicide damage
Cankers (sunken dead areas) at base	Crown rot, damping-off (seedlings)
Swollen areas at base	Crown gall bacteria
FLOWERS	
Blight, gray mold	*Botrytis*
Spots	Thrips, standing water, pesticide spray damage
Generally discolored, webbing, stippling	Mites
Green, lack of color	Mycoplasma-like organisms
Deformed, stippled	Aster leafhopper, virus

Adapted in part from a presentation given by M. Daughtrey in March 1996 at Storrs, Connecticut.

Sanitation is most easily handled in greenhouses. Growers can control the cleanliness of the greenhouse environment by periodically disinfesting work surfaces and bench tops, using only new or surface-sterilized pots and flats, and using soilless mixes or steam-pasteurized soil mixes. Attention to details, such as keeping the end of the watering hose off the ground, providing soap for the workers to wash their hands after roguing out diseased plants, or regularly removing any plant debris, will make a real difference in the percentage of the crop lost to disease.

Bacteria

Diseases from bacteria and phytoplasma are less common on perennials than those from fungi. Often they may cause black spots with yellow halos, or black and wet lesions. Dramatic swollen areas on roots or stem bases are likely from crown gall. Many plants are susceptible to crown gall; discarding infected stock is the main control measure.

Similar to bacteria are the phytoplasma-like organisms that cause foliage to yellow and flowers to stay green. These are particularly seen on members of the Composite family and are controlled in part by controlling the aster leafhopper and the Composite weeds it feeds on (which may be infected).

Botrytis

A common disease problem to be faced by the perennial grower both indoors and outdoors is *Botrytis*. Flowers, leaves, and stems may all be attacked by this gray mold, and some types of perennials, such as peonies, are particularly vulnerable.

Botrytis spores are produced on plant debris and are airborne. Humidity control is all-important: if condensation on the plant surface can be prevented, the *Botrytis* spores will not have enough moisture to germinate and invade the plant. Water plants early in the day, and keep them well ventilated and well spaced. Registered fungicides are helpful in protecting plants against *Botrytis,* but environmental management is the first line of defense. Some concerns with fungicide use include potential injury to plants, residues, and the development of fungicide resistance.

Damping-Off

When perennials are grown from seed, they must be protected against the fungi that cause damping-off disease. Controlling damping-off in the seed flat also helps prevent later root rot problems. Damping-off is most frequently caused by *Rhizoctonia,* which causes seedlings to keel over after they have been girdled at the base. Many other fungi can cause similar symptoms, however, so it is best to use strict sanitation (which is effective against all disease organisms) and apply only broad-spectrum fungicide treatments that will control *Pythium* and other water molds, as well as *Rhizoctonia* and many other fungi.

An operation with scrupulous sanitation practices may find it possible to use fungicides on a case-by-case basis or spot-treat infected areas. Preventive fungicide application to the entire crop may result in phytotoxic responses in one or more sensitive plant species. Check the label for sensitive plants, or try the fungicide on only a few plants first.

Downy Mildew

This disease is less common on perennials than powdery mildew. It is different from powdery mildew in cause and symptoms. Downy mildew infection is promoted by water standing on the foliage, so applying irrigation only on sunny days, preferably in the morn-

ing when the foliage will dry, may help in its control. Symptoms are angular spots on the upper leaf surface or fuzzy patches of spores — either pale violet, gray, or white — directly opposite on the lower leaf surface.

This disease may be systemic, often overwintering within infected plants. Destroying infected plants may be the easiest option of control. Organic and synthetic sprays are available as well.

Leaf Spots

This group of many causal organisms (generally fungi) produce a common symptom — the spotting of leaves. Purple-rimmed leaf spots are characteristic of *Alternaria*. Brown, roughly circular leaf spots may be from *Ascochyta*. Purplish leaf spots may indicate *Colletotrichum;* in severe cases, leaf distortion occurs. Spots developing gray centers as they age is typical of *Septoria;* the tiny dots are spore cases. Oval tan spots on early spring foliage indicate *Didymellina*. Tiny, tan leaf spots in early spring may be from *Botrytis*. A round, pale leaf spotting known as "leaf smut" is from *Entyloma* (brown spores are produced inside the leaf).

Since these organisms need water to start new infections, they are commonly spread by rain or overhead irrigation. Proper watering is therefore a major means of control. Sprays are also available.

Nematodes

Nematodes can affect either the foliage or the roots and are an increasing problem with perennials. Foliar nematodes cause characteristic angular leaf spots, often on lower leaves. Remove infested leaves, and keep foliage dry. Root-knot nematodes cause swellings or galling on the roots, which may cause stunting, or in mild cases no aboveground symptoms. Until nematicides are available, severely infested plants should be destroyed. In field situations, marigolds have been interplanted with perennials to help ward off nematodes. Root nematode symptoms should not be confused with natural swellings on legume crops from nitrogen-fixing bacteria.

Powdery Mildew

Another major disease problem faced by perennial growers is powdery mildew. This will not be particularly troublesome on plants for spring sale, but the white mycelium and spores of the mildew fungus will coat the leaves of susceptible plants in mid to late summer and fall, discouraging late-season sales. A number of options are available for fungicidal control of powdery mildew. Highly susceptible plants such as phlox or *Monarda* may require sprays in early to mid summer prior to the onset of mildew and continuing through the season.

Powdery mildew is unique among most fungal diseases in that it does not require water to cause infections; rather, high humidity and temperature fluctuations are needed. So control of water and watering practices will not help much with this disease. Research at the University of Vermont (Perry, 1994) showed that under intense mildew pressure, spacing for improved air circulation had little effect in reducing mildew on garden phlox (*Phlox paniculata* 'White Admiral'). Some of the worst treatments were with mulches of bark or marble chips. Moderate control was achieved by the use of antidessicants, but best control was with weekly baking soda sprays (1½ tablespoons per gallon of water), biweekly applications of horticultural oil, or a combination of the two biweekly. Unfortunately, these chemicals are not yet registered for these purposes. Work by Dr. David Clement at the University of Maryland using biorational materials, such as horticultural oil, has given excellent control of powdery mildew on phlox and Gerbera daisy.

Some cultivars are more resistant to mildew than others. Garden phlox (*Phlox paniculata*) cultivars have been evaluated in Vermont and on Long Island (Daughtrey et al, 1993; Adam and Perry, 1987). 'David', a new white cultivar, has shown the best resistance, with little mildew seen in the trials. It will, however, show some infection in shady, damp locations conducive to powdery mildew. 'Orange Perfection', 'Starfire', and 'White Admiral' may have less mildew, although the latter may be quite susceptible depending on location. 'Adonis', 'Dresden China', and 'Mt. Fuji' are highly susceptible to powdery mildew.

Both at the Chicago Botanic Garden (Richard Hawke, personal correspondence) and at the University of Vermont, *Monarda* 'Marshall's Delight' was one of the cultivars most resistant to this disease. Others resistant in Vermont include 'Violet Queen' and 'Blue Stocking'. The *Monarda* most susceptible to powdery mildew in Vermont include 'Adam', 'Cambridge Scarlet', 'Croftway Pink', and 'Souris'. Some of the newer cultivars, including those from the Netherlands, are currently under study in Vermont for their supposed mildew resistance. Under intense mildew pressures, even 'Marshall's Delight' has been shown to have moderate to high susceptibility.

Root Rots

Root rots occur in media that remain too wet, especially with species that cannot tolerate such conditions (see table 8-9 on page 61). Symptoms are easily seen as discolored roots (brown instead of white) and mushy or rotten roots that often appear water-soaked. Fruiting structures (white mycelia or mustard-seed-shaped sclerotia) on killed stem tissue are another indication of such diseases. A brown canker (sunken, dead area) at the soil line of the stem may indicate the common *Rhizoctonia* crown rot. Keeping media well-drained and providing spacing for good air circulation can prevent such diseases and the need for chemical controls.

Rusts

These highly evolved fungi are specialized to attack only one host, or perhaps two in alternate stages of their life cycle. Symptoms common to rusts are pale spots on the upper leaf surface. Orange or brown spore pustules form directly opposite the spots on the lower leaf surface. Rusts that require an alternate host (often a tree or weed) can be controlled by keeping susceptible plants away from the hosts, often by several hundred yards, or, when the host is a weed, eliminating the weed. Chemical control is also an option. Cultivars vary in their resistance to rust diseases, so choosing appropriate cultivars of a susceptible species will help avoid the problem. Initial observations on New England asters at the University of Vermont show a wide range of susceptibility. The white cultivar 'Wedding Lace' was practically resistant to rust infections. A replicated cultivar comparison for rust resistance has begun in Vermont.

Viruses

Viruses may sometimes be a problem on perennials, more so indoors than outdoors (such as with impatiens necrotic spot virus — see below). Perennials are often asymptomatic (they show no signs of infection), but they may serve as carriers of the virus to other crucial plants, which is especially a problem in greenhouses. Outdoors virus diseases may weaken plants or affect their aesthetic qualities but often not significantly. One common virus, tomato spotted wilt virus (TSWV), may cause yellow ring spots or oak leaf–shaped line patterns.

Most viruses affect a wide range of plants and are often carried by insect vectors such as aphids, thrips, planthoppers, or leafhoppers. Control of such insects will therefore help prevent the spread of virus diseases. Viruses can also be spread via sap in vegetatively propagated plant material or in tissue culture. As there are no "viricides" to spray infected stock, the only control is to destroy infected plants.

Impatiens necrotic spot virus (INSV) is a common greenhouse virus that weakens plants and sometimes leads to death. Infected perennials may serve as a reservoir from which the virus can be spread by thrips to other landscape plants. Symptoms are highly variable depending on the host plant or cultivar. Use fava bean or petunia indicator plants to detect if thrips are carrying the virus. Monitor for thrips (as discussed below), and use test kits to determine if thrips or plants are infected. As there is no control, infected plants should be destroyed. In the greenhouse, begin a strict sanitation and thrips monitoring program.

Recent virus tests at Agdia, Inc. in Elkhart, Indiana with phlox, particularly *Phlox paniculata*, have shown tobacco ringspot virus (TRSV), cucumber mosaic virus (CMV), tobacco etch virus (TEV), tobacco streak virus (TSV), and INSV. *Physostegia* with bronze speckling on the leaves may be symptomatic of alfalfa mosaic virus (AMV), which is spread or vectored by aphids.

Insects and Related Pests

Control of insects, mites, and slugs that attack perennials is complicated by the wide array of cultivars of different kinds of plants grown in intermixed plantings or in close proximity to one another within the greenhouse or in the field.

Most of the injurious pests of bedding plant perennials are capable of very rapid development. Of major importance are the aphids, whiteflies, mealybugs, fungus gnats, and, depending on the temperature, thrips and spider mites (spider mites and thrips may not be a problem in cool spring greenhouses). "Worms" (caterpillars of moths and butterflies) generally have a longer life cycle, but because of the nature of their feeding habits may be very destructive in a short time in the closely packed plantings of perennial bedding plants in the greenhouse. Caterpillar injury is more apt to occur in the field.

Slugs and snails may be troublesome as well. In field production, growers may also face the problem of damage from root-feeding grubs (for example, black vine weevils, Oriental beetles, Asiatic garden beetles, and Japanese beetles, among others). Many of these beetles will also feed on the flowers and foliage of a number of perennials.

Good sanitation is an essential component of a successful operation. The growing area within the greenhouse or nursery and the area immediately adjacent to the greenhouse or nursery should be kept free of weeds, which may serve as reservoirs for insect and mite populations as well as weed seeds. For thrips, a 10–20-foot weed-free barrier around the greenhouse is suggested. Plant debris may also harbor pests and should not be permitted to accumulate within and around the growing site. It is also essential that purchased small plants or rooted cuttings be thoroughly inspected for the presence of insects prior to their placement in the greenhouse. This is especially true of those plants initially grown in the field and then transplanted into containers in the greenhouse for further growth or for spring sale. Insects may come in on aerial or subterranean plant parts, or concealed in the soil.

When chemicals are used to control pests, the grower must know not only what chemicals are labeled for use on a particular crop but also how sensitive the various crops are to the chemical(s) selected for use. Cautionary statements regarding varietal sensitivity are provided on product labels if the information is known. However, given the fact that phytotoxic effects are not known for all chemicals on all crops and cultivars, insecticide should be tried on a small number of plants before subjecting an entire planting to treatment. Usually, evidence of an injurious response will be obvious in a few days if the plant/chemical interaction is incompatible. Potential effects on water and the environment are other considerations when choosing chemicals.

Avoid applying treatments during periods of plant stress, which are usually associated with high temperatures or water deficiency. Wilting is a clear example of the existence of stressful conditions. It is best to treat plants when the foliage is dry. In many instances, labels suggest an optimum range of temperatures at which insecticidal treatment may be made safely. Cool temperatures may be a concern when applying insecticides and fungicides to perennials overwintered in the greenhouse. Applications made outside of the suggested temperature range may cause plant injury or be ineffective. In some instances, it may be desirable to terminate chemical treatments before the flowering phase in both the field and greenhouse, because the blossoms of many varieties are prone to spotting, discoloration, or shattering when exposed to chemicals.

The pesticide label should be carefully read — not only for suggested recommendations and directions for specific uses but also to be certain that all precautions for personal safety and protection of the environment are understood. It must also be emphasized that growers are obligated to maintain accurate accounts of pesticide use for state regulatory agencies when restricted insecticides are involved.

Aphids

Both the green peach aphid *(Myzus persicae)* and melon or cotton aphid *(Aphis gossypii)* are common pests of many perennials. The green peach aphid overwinters as black shiny eggs on *Prunus* outdoors. In greenhouse-produced perennials, the green peach aphid can have continuous reproduction throughout the year without an overwintering stage. Place yellow sticky cards near doors and vents to detect winged adults of this species. Inspect incoming plants on undersides of leaves and buds for small (1/14 inch long) green peach aphids that are pale green or yellow to pink. Colonies tend to be on the tips of new growth. Melon aphids are smaller than green peach aphids (1/16 inch) and are greenish-yellow to dark green. They have "tailpipes" darker than the rest of their bodies. There are many other species of aphids that may occur in field production.

Both aphids distort and deform new growth. Sticky honeydew (aphid secretions) and sooty mold reduce the aesthetic appearance of plants, and ants may be attracted to the honeydew. Green peach aphids transmit more than 150 viruses. Monitor crops closely to detect aphids before the perennials are in bloom, at which time control becomes more difficult. If spraying, control aphids before the crop flowers in order to prevent possible pesticide phytotoxicity and injury to the flowers. Systemic chemicals (those that move throughout the plant) tend to be more effective than nonsystemic ones for green peach aphids.

Some newer pesticides contain insect-killing fungi that effectively attack and kill aphids. Other pesticides contain insect growth regulators that affect the functioning or reproduction of aphids. If treating many types of perennials and using insect growth regulator chemicals, monitor those perennials that are particularly susceptible to aphids for effectiveness.

Eliminate weed hosts of aphids to help provide control. Natural enemies of aphids (ladybird beetles, syrphid flies, and aphid parasitoids) may help to regulate aphid populations in field production. Pesticides used on aphids may also eliminate these natural predators.

Aster Leafhopper (*Macrosteles qualrilineatus*)

Feeding of this insect causes discolored (stippled) and chlorotic foliage and deformed flowers from aster yellows disease. Visually inspect leaves for stippling damage; look on the undersides of leaves for adults, nymphs, and shed skins. Adults have six black spots on the head. Yellow sticky cards can be used inside to detect populations. These have one or more generations per year and are controllable by many insecticides.

Black Vine Weevil (*Otiorhynchus sulcatus*)

Black vine weevil larvae feed on roots, which will weaken or kill the plant. Larvae overwinter in the soil. Adults are black beetles with small yellow spots on the back. They hide during the day at the base of the plant under plant debris. Look for C-shaped leaf notching as evidence of adult feeding. Notching should be evident by mid June. Adults can also be monitored by using burlap bands and pitfall traps, but timely visual inspection of plants for notching works best. They have one generation per year and are controllable by physical exclusion barriers and insecticides. Since adults cannot fly, aluminum, wooden, or plastic strips can be used to keep them out of specific areas.

Cyclamen Mite (*Phytonemus pallidus*)

Feeding by these mites causes leaves to curl and twist or causes wrinkling of leaves so that pockets or pitlike depressions are formed. Buds may be blasted and will dry up and die. The mites overwinter as adults on plant material, and they are invisible to the naked eye (1/100 inch), which makes it difficult to detect them prior to onset of injury. If these mites have been a problem in the past, monitor for them frequently using a strong hand lens or microscope. Cyclamen mites may be spread by air currents, by direct contact between plants, or by workers who handle infested plant material. Space plants so they do not touch and remove and destroy infested plants. Insecticides are another option. However, because of this mite's ability to feed in tightly enclosed spaces, multiple applications may be needed.

European Corn Borer (*Ostrinia nubilalis*)

Boring in stems by these insects can cause dieback and death. Corn borers overwinter as larvae in the plants; larvae are cream-colored with brown spots along the sides and a dark head. Observe new growth flushes for early signs of larvae. One or two generations can occur per year. Remove infected stems before larvae become adults. Do not grow corn or potatoes near perennial field production. Discard as much decaying plant material as possible at the end of the growing season. This will remove any overwintering larvae.

Four-Lined Plant Bug (*Poecilocapsus lineatus*)

Feeding by these insects causes spotting of leaves which may develop necrotic centers. Extensive feeding can cause leaf drop. Signs of this pest should not be confused with leaf spot disease. Eggs overwinter in tender shoots. Adults are yellow-green with four black, longitudinal stripes. There is only one generation per year. Detection can be difficult, because they will quickly move to a hiding place when they notice movement. Remove weeds that can serve as alternate food sources. Start pesticide treatments early when the first nymphs are seen.

Fungus Gnats (*Bradysia* or *Sciara* Species)

Primarily a problem in greenhouses, fungus gnat adults are attracted to decaying plant tissue (fungi are a food source) and potting mixes with immature composts (those less than six months old). The first two generations are the most damaging during crop production. Fungus gnat larvae may bore into stems of succulent cuttings and feed on tender young roots. Adults, which fly around when a pot is disturbed, are a nuisance especially in retail situations. Fungus gnats may play a role in the transmission of several diseases. Use yellow sticky cards to monitor for adults. Place cards just above the soil surface. Horizontal placement will attract more adults. Use potato slices (1½ inches long by 1 inch wide) to monitor for larvae, especially during cool, overcast weather. Examine sticky cards and potato slices daily. Monitor young cuttings and developing roots for signs of feeding injury. Do not let standing water, soil debris, and organic matter lay on the floor, as they encourage fungus gnat development. Fungus gnats may be confused with shoreflies, which are more robust, have shorter antennae, and have five light-colored spots on each wing.

Whiteflies

There are three species of whitefly commonly found on perennials — greenhouse whitefly (*Trileurodes vaporariorum*), silverleaf whitefly (*Bemisia argentifolii*), and bandedwinged whitefly (*Trialeurodes abutiloneus*). One sign of their presence is honeydew and sooty mold on the leaves, which reduces the aesthetic appearance of the plants. Honeydew and sooty mold usually develop when there are high populations. Sooty mold may lead to chlorotic yellowing of the foliage. The presence of whiteflies may reduce the plant vigor with defoliation and stunting. Use sticky cards to monitor for adult whiteflies. Look for powdery white adults (1/16 inch long) on the undersides of uppermost foliage. They hold their wings flat over their bodies. Older (third and fourth) instar immatures are found on the lowermost leaves. Their pupae are white with parallel sides. Remove weeds and "pet" plants. Thorough spray coverage is needed on the undersides of leaves. If using insect growth regulators, use indicator plants to assess treatment effectiveness. In addition to insecticides, natural fungal-based pesticides are available.

Japanese Beetle (*Popilliae japonica*)

Adult feeding causes a lacy pattern on leaves (skeletonization). Larval feeding prunes turfgrass roots, causing dieback. Larvae, which overwinter as grubs in the soil, have a V-shaped rastral pattern of bristles that can be seen with a hand lens. Look for adult damage on indicator plants such as wild grape and roses. There is only one generation per year. Placement of pheromone traps may cause more feeding damage to susceptible host plants. If possible, use protective netting to protect plants. Insecticides and insect parasitic nematodes may also be used.

Asiatic Garden Beetle (*Maladera castanea*)

Similar in life cycle to the Japanese beetle, Asiatic garden beetle adults devour foliage of woody and herbaceous plants. Among over one hundred species of perennials in Vermont, these beetles were particularly attracted to yarrow and perennial geranium. Asiatic garden beetle larvae differ from those of Japanese beetle by having a rastral ring, not a V-shaped pattern. Larvae feed mainly on grass roots, and adults emerge in mid summer. Adults feed at night, especially when air temperatures are high. There is only one generation per year. Control measures are similar to those for Japanese beetle.

Lacebugs (*Tingidae*)

Lacebug feeding will cause leaves to discolor and appear bleached, and in severe cases weaken the plant to near death. These overwinter as adults in protective areas such as plant debris. Adults have lacy, transparent wings. Nymphs (immatures) are black and spiny and found on the undersides of leaves. With several generations per year, lacebugs feed on the undersides of leaves, and dark fecal spots may be present. Remove weeds, which can serve as alternate food sources, and monitor highly susceptible plants such as asters. Pesticides are available.

Oriental Beetle (Anomala orientalis)

Adult feeding on foliage causes skeletonization. Larval feeding prunes roots. Larvae, which overwinter in the soil, have two parallel lines of bristles that can be seen with a hand lens as a rastral pattern. Look for the one generation per year of adults on susceptible plants such as roses and dahlias in mid to late summer or near lights at night. Pesticides are available for adults, insect parasitic nematodes for larvae (grubs).

Potato Leafhopper (Empoasca fabae)

This pest causes discoloration and wilting of foliage. Leaves may also be smaller than normal and deformed. Leafhoppers overwinter in the South and migrate north in late April or early May. Adults are green with six white spots on the thorax. Yellow sticky cards inside can be used to monitor for the several generations of adults per year. Monitor outside by looking for feeding damage or by gently tapping foliage with a white sheet of paper. Pesticides are available.

Slugs (Mollusca)

Evidence of slug damage includes leaves that are cut off at the petiole or large and ragged holes chewed in the leaves. Look under boards, vegetation, and daytime shelter for these night feeders. Look for silvery slime trails on or near vegetation. Commercial slug baits are available in liquid, granular, and powder forms. When using these chemicals, read precautions, particularly if domestic animals live nearby. Although many home remedies such as beer are said to attract slugs (they drown in shallow dishes of it), sanitation or keeping the area around susceptible plants (such as hosta) free from organic matter often helps in control. Copper strips placed flat on the ground around susceptible perennials keep slugs from crossing.

Spittlebugs (Philaenus spumarius)

The meadow spittlebug feeding causes wilted, stunted, distorted, and discolored foliage. Spittlebugs overwinter as eggs inserted into shoots. Look for conspicuous "spittle" masses surrounding the nymphs. The one generation of adults is active during the summer. Pick out nymphs if the infestation is light, otherwise pesticides are available.

Stalk Borer (Papaipema nebris)

Boring from this insect can weaken, stunt, or kill plants. Stalk borers overwinter as eggs on grasses and weeds. Immature caterpillars are brown with white stripes interrupted by a purple band. Mature larvae are gray. If wilting is noticed, slice open a plant stem and look for the larvae. Natural enemies such as lady beetles and ground beetles help reduce populations of the one generation per year, as does removal of weeds and debris that the eggs and larvae need.

Tarnished Plant Bug (Lygus lineolaris)

Feeding by this bug causes spotting of leaves, which may develop necrotic areas. Extensive feeding may cause leaf drop. Adults, which are a mottled brown color with distinct yellow and black triangles on their sides, overwinter in protected areas. Visual inspection for the three to five generations of adults per year is difficult, as they move quickly. Clean production areas to remove overwintering sites, and spray when flower buds start to form.

Two-Spotted Spider Mite (Tetranychus urticae)

Adult two-spotted spider mite (TSSM) feeding can cause discoloring (stippling) of leaves, bronzing of leaves, and, in severe cases, leaf drop. No fecal spots will be seen on leaf undersides. TSSM overwinters as adult females in protected areas. Adults have eight legs, are greenish-colored, and have two dark spots on the back. Look on the undersides of leaves where mites like to feed. With a hand lens, look for live mites as well as empty egg cases, shed skins, and (in severe cases) webs. Tap leaves onto white paper to dislodge mites and make them more visible with a hand lens; wait a few seconds and the mites, which are about the size of a period, will be noticeable moving across the paper. There are several generations per year. They can be reduced temporarily by applying heavy irrigation or controlled with miticides or predatory mites.

Western Flower Thrips (Frankliniella occidentalis)

One of the more common, recent, and prevalent greenhouse pests, western flower thrips have a wide host range. Tender young growth is distorted and cupped in affected plants. Expanded leaves have silvery areas with black fecal spots. Flowers are blasted or streaked, as thrips feed on pollen. Thrips are an efficient vector of impatiens necrotic spot virus (see previous disease section). Use yellow or blue sticky cards to monitor for adult thrips. Although blue is more attractive to thrips, yellow cards are more effective for general pest monitoring, and the insects are easier to find on them. Check cards weekly to track population levels and to evaluate treatment effectiveness. Workers should avoid wearing bright yellow or blue clothing in order to minimize attracting thrips and spreading them around a nursery or greenhouse.

Inspect and quarantine incoming plants for five to seven days for signs of thrips larvae or adults. Tap foliage over a white sheet of paper to look for the slender insects (adults are $\frac{1}{25}$ inch in length; larvae are smaller at $\frac{1}{40}$ inch). Remove weeds inside greenhouses and maintain a 10- to 20-foot weed-free barrier outside. Remove crop debris and cull piles. Other thrips reported to feed on perennials include onion thrips, iris thrips, flower thrips, gladiolus thrips, daylily thrips, and hollyhock thrips.

Small Animals

Moles, voles, mice, chipmunks, squirrels, rabbits, and groundhogs sometimes invade overwintering structures and can be especially damaging to fleshy-rooted plants such as *Papaver*, *Adenophora*, or *Symphytum*. They will eat most perennials and burrow into pots over winter if alternate food (such as apple drops) and homes (such as tall grass) are not available.

Ultrasonic emitters, which are often fairly expensive, have yielded mixed results for controlling ground-dwelling animals. Many growers use poison baits with varying rates of success. If using poisons, heed all precautions — especially if domestic and desirable animals live nearby. To avoid poisons, many growers use spring traps for small rodents. Traps are usually effective if they are baited with peanut butter and placed at the entrance to a tunnel with a pot inverted over the tunnel opening and trap to simulate being underground.

Perhaps the most effective deterrent to mice and rats is a good cat or two. A few growers even use nonpoisonous snakes, as they can fit better between containers than cats. Recommended snakes include milk snakes, corn snakes, or black snakes. Obvious disadvantages of this method of rodent control are that snakes are inactive or not hardy during winter, and they may have a negative effect on employee relations.

Poisons are not recommended for larger animals such as groundhogs and rabbits. The animals may avoid the poison bait, and desirable animals may be killed by it

instead. If pests do get poisoned, their larger predators (such as some raptors) may in turn be poisoned. Hungry cats often are effective against smaller animals, as are cage traps. If using the latter to catch live animals, make sure local ordinances do not prohibit the relocation of animals.

When relocating animals, make sure they are taken far enough away outside their traveling distances to keep them from returning (at least a mile for chipmunks, 3 miles for squirrels, and a quarter mile for groundhogs). Groundhogs generally do not travel more than about 50 yards from home, so although they are nearby, they may not be a threat. If they are a problem, they may be lured away by placing a desirable food for them (such as native asters) and some thick-stemmed weeds (such as pigweed) far away from the desired plants. If all the openings for groundhog tunnels can be found, they can be sealed after poison fumigants are placed inside.

Spring traps are often used for mice, but many consider such traps inhumane for larger animals. Low electric wire fences — double strands at 6 and 15 inches high — have been used effectively by some growers for smaller animals. If guns or bow and arrows are used, be sure to follow all safety precautions, local ordinances, and state laws concerning hunting. Some communities may have ordinances concerning all forms of dealing with small animals.

Deer

Deer have been a problem for nurseries all along, but they have become more of a problem in recent years because of increased deer populations. Deer have become a major problem even in many urban areas, partly because of a lack of predators and laws in some communities that protect wildlife. Although no control system will work all the time, some are more effective than others. Much of the effectiveness depends on the size of the deer population, the availability of other preferred food sources, and the system itself. These and other factors explain why a repellent may work well at one site and not at another, or why a perennial is attractive to deer at one site and not another.

The least effective repellents are perhaps taste and smell repellents, which make plants smell or taste objectionable. If deer are hungry enough, or if they prefer a certain plant, they will easily overcome any objections. However, these repellents are the least expensive method of control and so are a good starting point. They can be purchased from many feed stores and suppliers.

Falling into the same category and having received study at various universities are soaps. It appears that the more odor from the soap, the more objectionable it is to deer. Odorous soaps (such as those found in fine hotels) may be purchased from hotel supply firms or wholesale grocers and food clubs. Large bars can be cut into quarters. Soap should be hung in its original wrapper or a cloth bag to keep it from dissolving too fast. It should be hung about every 10 feet from plants, stakes, fences, or similar aboveground objects. Human hair from hair salons is also reputed to work as a repellent.

Noise deterrents are moderately effective if used properly. Deer quickly become used to stationery objects and sounds, so if ultrasonic or similar sound emitters or radios are used, they should be rotated frequently. Mixed results have been reported with the often expensive ultrasonic units. If radios are used, they should be tuned to all-night talk shows, as human voices are supposedly more effective deterrents than music. They do not have to be very loud to be effective. Radios may be placed on timers to go on and off periodically throughout the night. A small instrument shelter, doghouse, or equivalent structure can be used to protect radios in the field from the elements. Outdoor speakers might also be installed. They can double in the day as a music source for employees and for broadcasting announcements. Louder noises, such as the sound canons used in orchards, can also be useful if they do not disturb neighbors or violate local noise ordinances.

Most effective are physical deterrents such as fences. A high fence (8–10 feet) is perhaps best but also most expensive. Less expensive is a double or triple strand electric fence. For a double fence, place strands about 2 to 3 feet off the ground, side by side and about 4 feet apart. The deer often refuse to jump both. The triple system is best, though, with two strands placed as stated above and another strand in between but about 5 to 6 feet high. This forms a fairly impenetrable triangle. While it is not too high for deer to jump over, they cannot clear all strands once the width is also considered. Some growers have had good luck with only one strand of electric wire that is baited with peanut butter. This latter system is perhaps the cheapest (as low as $2 per linear foot) of the more effective physical deterrents. Also relatively inexpensive are monofilament fishing lines strung about 2 feet apart and up to 8–10 feet high. Since deer have poor eyesight, hang flags or ribbons from such lines, and also from electric fences, so deer do not automatically try to charge through them. If guns or bow and arrows are used, be sure to follow all safety precautions, local ordinances, and state laws concerning hunting. Poison baits are not recommended, as they are often considered inhumane, are often illegal, and easily work into the food chain, where they kill predator animals as well.

While generally more applicable to a landscape than a nursery, deer-resistant perennials — perennials that deer generally do not eat — may be used or placed in more sensitive areas such as along property boundaries. Perennials not favored by deer, as noted by several individuals in various parts of the United States with very high deer populations, have been compiled in table 10-2. Even the plants in the table may be eaten if deer are under severe pressure and stressed for food.

Weed Control

Many different perennials are grown as ornamentals. Some are closely related to the weeds that are competing with them, which makes weed control difficult. Because field or landscape perennials can remain in the same area for a great length of time, weed control options are limited. Methods available include preplant herbicide treatments, cultivation and hand pulling, mulches, preemergence chemical weed control, and, occasionally, postemergence chemical control. Use of herbicides is difficult, as none can be used on all perennials without causing some phytotoxicity, and many growers have a mix of many types of perennials.

Weeds that a perennial grower or landscaper might encounter generally fall into four categories.

- Summer annuals complete a life cycle from germination to flowering in a growing season, often in a matter of a few weeks.
- Winter annuals germinate at the end of summer and overwinter as rosettes before flowering early the following season.
- Biennials are similar to winter annuals, only they germinate earlier in the season.
- Perennial weeds are like perennial ornamentals, usually living more than two years and often not flowering until the second season.

Knowing which weeds you are controlling and which group they fall into is important for mechanical and especially for chemical control, as different chemicals are designed for different weed types. If using cultivation to control weeds, it is important to keep summer annuals from going to flower and dispersing seed. This would not be as timely an issue with perennials, especially in the first year. Cultivating perennial weeds, on the other hand, may result in root divisions and even more of a problem.

Table 10-2. "Deer-resistant" perennials

Acanthus mollis	Bear's Breeches	*Lavandula*	Lavender
Achillea	Yarrow	*Leucanthemum*	Painted, Shasta Daisy
Ajuga	Bugleweed	*Liatris*	Blazing Star
Allium	Ornamental Onion, Chives	*Lilium lancifolium*	Tiger Lily
Alyssum saxatile	Basket of Gold	*Limonium latifolium*	Statice
Amsonia tabernaemontana	Blue Stars	*Linaria*	Toadflax
Anemone	Windflower	*Linum perenne*	Perennial Blue Flax
Angelica	Angelica	*Lythrum*	Purple Loosestrife
Artemisia	Senecio	*Matteuccia struthiopteris*	Ostrich Fern
Aruncus dioicus	Wormwood	*Mentha*	Mint
Asclepias tuberosa	Butterfly Weed	*Miscanthus sinensis*	Maiden Grass
Astilbe	Plume Flower	*Mitchella repens*	Partridgeberry
Athyrium nipponicum 'Pictum'	Japanese Painted Fern	*Monarda didyma*	Bee Balm
Baptisia	False Indigo	*Myosotis scorpioides*	Forget-Me-Not
Begonia x *tuberhybrida*	Tuberous Begonia	*Myrrhis odorata*	Sweet Cicely
Bergenia	Heartleaf Saxifrage	*Narcissus*	Daffodil
Boltonia asteroides	False Aster	*Nepeta*	Catmint
Buddleia davidii	Butterflybush	*Oenothera*	Sundrops, Evening Primrose
Calamagrostis	Feather Reed Grass	*Onoclea sensibilis*	Sensitive Fern
Calluna	Heather	*Origanum*	Oregano
Campanula	Bellflower	*Osmunda cinnamomea*	Osmunda Fern
Canna	Canna	*Osmunda claytonia*	Interrupted Fern
Carex elata	Sedge	*Osmunda regalis*	Royal Fern
Centaurea	Cornflower	*Paeonia*	Peony
Ceratostigma plumbaginoides	Plumbago	*Panicum virgatum*	Switch Grass
Chelone	Turtlehead	*Papaver orientale*	Oriental Poppy
Cimicifuga racemosa	Bugbane	*Pennisetum*	Fountain Grass
Convallaria majalis	Lily-of-the Valley	*Phalaris arundinacea*	Ribbon Grass
Coreopsis	Tickseed	*Phlox divaricata*	Woodland Phlox
Cynara cardunculus	Thistle	*Phlox paniculata*	Garden Phlox
Dennstaedtia punctilobula	Hay-Scented Fern	*Physostegia virginiana*	Obedient Plant
Dianthus	Sweet William, Pinks	*Platycodon grandiflorus*	Balloon Flower
Dicentra exima	Bleeding Heart	*Polemonium caeruleum*	Jacob's Ladder
Dictamnus albus	Gas Plant	*Polystichum acrostichoides*	Christmas Fern
Digitalis purpurea	Foxglove	*Potentilla*	Cinquefoil
Dryopteris	Wood Fern	*Primula*	Primula
Echinacea	Coneflower	*Prunella vulgaris*	Heal All
Echinops ritro	Globe Thistle	*Pulmonaria*	Lungwort
Erica	Heather	*Ranunculus*	Buttercup
Eschscholzia californica	California Poppy	*Rheum*	Rhubarb
Eupatorium	Joe-Pye Weed	*Rosmarinus officinalis*	Rosemary
Euphorbia	Spurge	*Rudbeckia*	Black-Eyed Susan
Festuca glauca	Blue Fescue	*Salvia*	Sage
Filipendula	Meadowsweet	*Saponaria*	Soapwort
Fritillaria imperialis	Crown Imperial	*Scilla*	Squill
Gaillardia x *grandiflora*	Blanket Flower	*Solidago*	Goldenrod
Geum	Avens	*Stachys byzantina*	Lamb's Ear
Gypsophila paniculata	Baby's Breath	*Tanacetum*	Tansy
Helleborus	Lenten Rose	*Thelypteris noveboracensis*	New York Fern
Heuchera	Coral Bells	*Verbascum*	Mullein
Iberis sempervirens	Candytuft	*Verbena*	Vervain
Imperata cylindrica 'Red Baron'	Red Baron Grass	*Veronica*	Speedwell
Iris	Iris	*Vinca*	Periwinkle
Kirengeshoma palmata	Kirengeshoma	*Viola labradorica*	Labrador Violet
Knautia macedonica	Scabiosa	*Yucca*	Yucca

Note: This table lists perennials that were noted to be "deer-resistant" by several individuals in various parts of the United States with very high deer populations. However, the plants in the table may be eaten by deer that are under severe pressure and stressed for food.

Several written references are available to help with weed identification (see sidebar). Also, several keys and photo sites of weeds exist on the Internet. Some of the above information on weeds was adapted from the Cornell *Weed Management Guide for Herbaceous Ornamentals* (see recommended reading section beginning on page 203), which contains more details about weeds and lists herbicides registered for perennials. Be sure to check with your state regulatory agency to see what materials are registered for use in your state.

Preplant or Site Preparation

For containers, select an artificial medium or soil free of perennial weeds and seeds such as nutsedge, bindweed, quackgrass, or Canada thistle. Placing containers on black plastic, or preferably ground fabric through which water can drain, will keep weeds from growing around pots. Ground cloths should be swept or washed free of soil in between crops to maintain their effectiveness. Keeping the ground around perennial production areas — whether for pot or field culture — free of weeds by mowing will keep weed seeds from blowing in. If growing container perennials in a greenhouse, be sure to read the labels of herbicides, as only a few are registered for indoor use. Never apply preemergence herbicides in covered houses, as several can volatilize and cause injury.

In the field, preplant weed control is the most important key to weed management. Select a site free of perennial weeds, or try to eliminate as many as possible before planting. Using cover crops such as buckwheat, oats, clover, and rye for one or two years prior to field planting and tilling them in will not only improve soil fertility but will also help decrease weed populations (see table 9-2 on page 63). Some weeds can be effectively controlled by digging up the clumps, forking up the roots and underground stems, or frequently and deeply cultivating the soil the previous growing season.

Difficult weeds may have to be removed by spraying them with a registered systemic herbicide. If such herbicide treatment is necessary, do not disturb the soil before treatment to allow the herbicide to move into the leaves, down the stems, and through the roots — thus killing the whole plant. There must be adequate foliage on a well-developed plant for the spray to be effective. Check the herbicide label for details on the herbicide application rate, time of application, and susceptible weeds. For some crops, a registered preplanting herbicide can be applied to the dry soil surface and immediately incorporated; planting follows the next day.

Weed Competition

When weed competition in the field is a factor, plant at a time most suitable to the perennials so they can better compete with the weeds. The quicker a plant grows because of sufficient light, water, nutrients, and an absence of disease and insect pests, the less important weed competition will be. Plant transplants at the proper depth to encourage optimum growth. Subsoiling, plowing, and rototilling fields may not only destroy tilth and damage soil structure if overdone, but often may bring dormant weed seeds to the surface where light causes them to germinate. For this reason, some field growers plant directly in annual cover crops after the crops die down over winter, use mulches, or do both — all without tilling the soil.

Mechanical Control

After field planting, frequent shallow cultivation will keep weed seedlings from becoming established and cause the least possible injury to perennials. Remove weeds close to the plants by hand pulling them when they are large enough to easily grab but not so large that their removal will disturb the roots of the desirable plants. Manual cultivation must be frequent to control successive generations of weeds stimulated to germinate (exposed to light) by the previous cultivation. Some growers have a weekly rotation; it should be three weeks maximum. Cultivation may destroy contact between weed seedlings and residual herbicides (if herbicides were applied since the last cultivation) and render the chemical ineffective.

Mulches

Mulches may be useful to control weeds in some perennials. Bark or wood chips must be deep enough (3–6 inches or more) to prevent weed growth but not so deep as to prevent perennial growth. Research at the University of Vermont (Pellett and Heleba, 1995) showed that 4 inches of bark mulch gave better weed control than 2 inches. Some low-growing plants may send roots out into the mulch and thus become more susceptible to drying. If deep enough, the mulch will prevent smaller weed seedlings from growing but will not be effective against larger seedlings and many perennial weeds, which can grow easily through it. Mulches may also increase rodent damage to plants.

Black plastic mulch is more effective than wood chip mulches against a wide variety of weeds, but it is not useful for many perennials. Many perennials spread by nature, and the center of plant clumps dies. Plastic mulches prevent such plants from spreading, and so they die after a few years. The plastic should be applied tightly over well-prepared, moist soil. Bury the edges in the soil to hold it in place. Cut small holes to insert the plants through the plastic and into the soil. Holes must be enlarged, or the plastic removed, as the perennials grow and increase in width.

Many other organic materials have been tried. One material tried recently is chopped newspaper. To prevent it from blowing around and weathering, it should be wetted and rolled into a mat after application on a calm day. Further control can be provided by applying a tackifier (substance like glue) to hold the paper together in a mat. In research at the University of Vermont, this mulch suppressed weed germination for two seasons without affecting growth of *Physostegia virginiana* but sometimes decreasing growth of *Gaillardia grandiflora* (Pellett and Heleba, 1995). Weed suppression with 4 or 6 inches of newspaper mulch was similar to that obtained with 4 inches of bark mulch.

Another benefit of organic mulches is their ability to moderate soil temperature. University of Vermont research (Pellett and Heleba, 1995) showed that both bark and chopped newspaper mulches moderated soil temperatures (loamy sand 3 inches deep) by more than 18°F when nonmulched soil was 97°F. At either soil depth tested (1 or 3 inches), there was no difference in temperature resulting from the different mulches.

A common problem in containers in many areas is liverwort and pearlwort growth on the soil surface. In a study in 1995 at the Long Island Horticultural Research Laboratory (Senesac and Tsontakis-Bradley, 1996), several herbicides were studied on three perennials, with varying rates of control and phytotoxicity. Mulches ($\frac{1}{2}$ inch deep) on pot soil surfaces were also studied, and little to no damage resulted to plants. All weed control methods provided good to fair control, with the best control from cinder ash, cocoa hulls, and newsprint.

Chemical Control

Herbicides for perennials, as for most crops, are classified according to when they are applied and how they act. Preemergence herbicides are applied before weed seedlings emerge and provide some residual activity. Postemergence herbicides are applied after the weeds have germinated. Postemergence ones can be either contact, which kill the plant part they contact, or systemic, which are absorbed and thus kill the entire plant. Postemergence herbicides labeled for perennials generally are nonresidual and have little or no soil activity.

Because of the wide variety of plants and a lack of research, there is not much information on the use of herbicides on perennials. Research on postplant, preemergence herbicides indicates that there are many potentially safe uses but also some that are probably unsafe for plants. Some herbicides may not cause immediate and apparent phytotoxicity to nontarget perennials but may affect growth processes such as rate of growth or ability to root from cuttings. Since herbicides are nonselective between related weeds and perennials, and some damage certain perennials but not others, plants in the field should be grouped according to herbicide tolerance if chemical weed control is practiced.

Preemergence herbicides are applied to a weed-free surface as granulars or sprays. Follow the label directions for rates, time of application, and other directions and limitations. Apply irrigation soon after treatment to spread and activate the chemical and to stimulate weed seed germination so they can be more easily killed. Repeat treatments may be needed in six to eight weeks. Make sure that the herbicide is kept off neighboring plants and turfgrass, unless it is also safe for use on them.

Postemergence systemic herbicides do not have a place in perennial planting maintenance, except as directed sprays or wiper applications. The herbicide must be kept from contacting the desirable plant.

CHAPTER 11

The Final Product

Herbaceous perennials ready to market may be dormant or in various stages of growth, including full flower. Plants are flatted, wrapped, or boxed for transport.

Conditioning Plants for Sale

Methods most commonly used to harden plants for marketing include maintaining lower temperatures for a week or more before sales, reducing the amount of water applied, or a combination of both treatments. Overhardening should be avoided, as it may delay flowering and reduce customer satisfaction.

Transport and Storage

Many plants exposed to prolonged periods of dark, enclosed storage deteriorate from disease, ethylene damage, or respiratory loss of photosynthates. Photosynthates are sugars and compounds produced from photosynthesis. They are needed for plant growth and used up when plants respire. Ethylene is the gas produced by decaying flowers and ripening fruit. It can cause growing tips to become injured or deformed or flowers on sensitive ornamentals to drop off or close (see table 11-1). To prevent damage to sensitive plants, do not store or ship them in enclosed spaces with fruit or vegetables. Combustion of gasoline and propane and welding can also produce ethylene.

While transportation and storage tolerances are not known for many perennials, the following principles are suggested as ways to maintain plant vigor.

Table 11-1. Some perennial flowers sensitive to ethylene gas

Achillea (Yarrow)	*Lathyrus* (Perennial Pea)
Aconitum (Monkshood)	*Lavatera* (Mallow)
Agapanthus	*Lilium* (Lily)
Allium (Ornamental Onion)	*Limonium* (Statice)
Alstroemeria (Peruvian Lily)	*Lysimachia* (Loosestrife)
Anemone (Windflower)	Phlox
Aquilegia (Columbine)	*Penstemon* (Beard-Tongue)
Asclepias (Butterfly Weed)	*Physostegia* (Obedient Plant)
Astilbe (Plume Flower)	*Ranunculus* (Buttercup)
Campanula (Bellflower)	*Rosa* (Rose)
Centaurea (Bachelor's Buttons)	*Rudbeckia* (Black-Eyed Daisy)
Delphinium (Perennial Larkspur)	*Saponaria* (Soapwort)
Dianthus (Pinks)	*Scabiosa* (Pincushion Flower)
Dicentra (Bleeding Heart)	*Silene* (Catchfly)
Eremurus (Foxtail Lily)	*Solidago* (Goldenrod)
Gladiolus	*Veronica* (Speedwell)
Gypsophila (Baby's Breath)	*Veronicastrum* (Culver's Root)
Kniphofia (Torch Lily)	

1. Ship only vigorous, pest-free, and disease-free plants.

2. Pack plants securely to avoid shipping damage.

3. Minimize the length of dark, enclosed storage by keeping plants uncovered in bright, indirect light.

4. Maintain temperatures above freezing but as cool as possible until plants are unpacked and placed in bright light.

5. Minimize the total shipping and storage period.

6. Keep the growing mix well-watered throughout this period.

7. Educate the buyer on correct plant handling procedures.

8. Discourage too-early deliveries, since this often results in plants being damaged by freezing. Deliveries after late March on Long Island and in the Mid-Atlantic, later farther north, avoid this problem.

Marketing and Merchandising

The first question to answer in sales is, "Who is your customer?" Herbaceous perennial customers can basically be categorized as shown below. Many retailers cater to some or all of these groups.

1. **Bedding plant buyers/consumers** — These customers are ready to convert from annuals, are "replacing" at least some annuals, want to try something new, and often look for small plants and low prices. Many will end up at mass merchandisers.

2. **Landscapers, both amateur and professional** — They often look for larger-size plants.

3. **Collectors and specialists** — This group is always looking for something new or unusual. They may specialize in a plant genus (such as daylily, hosta, or iris).

A perennial nursery in Michigan surveyed its customers in 1996 and grouped them into gardeners and non-gardeners (roughly equivalent to groups 3 and 1 above). They found that the gardeners were passionate about their hobby, wanted much cultural detail on each plant, preferred to buy perennials not in flower so they could watch blooms develop, wanted a good selection of top-quality plants right through the summer, and were loyal to brand names. They found that non-gardeners wanted color and flowers when buying and were more interested in a quick purchase than details. Both groups did not like to see small plants in big pots. All customers felt that the following factors were important: a clean display, a good selection, staff with a good attitude, and, of course, good-quality plants.

In a 1997 survey of home gardeners in New England, healthy plants were important to almost all respondents, followed by (in equal importance) a wide selection, informative signs and labels, and knowledgeable and friendly staff (Brand, University of Connecticut, personal correspondence). Two-thirds of the respondents relied on garden centers and nurseries as their main source of information; about half said that friends and magazine articles were their second choice.

In addition to the basic marketing and merchandising techniques that apply to other plants, herbaceous perennials require two things for successful marketing — information and selection. Results of a 1997 survey in New England showed that consumers highly valued unusual flower color in perennials. Other equally important factors were a good chance of success with the plant, the plant having many flowers, and the plant being northern-grown. The least important factors were a big plant spread and low price.

Information

The tens of thousands of perennials available yield almost limitless new selections for marketing, but to consumers and many landscapers (and even to some retailers), the selection may be overwhelming. To help customers make proper selections, educate them by providing the following:

- knowledgeable employees who stay current by attending training sessions, seminars, and meetings
- POP (Point of Purchase) materials — brochures, leaflets, labels, and signs used to provide information and help sell plants
- color photos on preprinted labels or laminated signs — these are crucial since perennials usually are sold because of their flowers and they are often not in flower
- displays (especially suggested groupings) and display beds/gardens

Most consumers and many retail garden store salespeople are still not very familiar with the many herbaceous perennials available and their garden culture. They may not even know what perennial means or other industry terms such as stoloniferous, bracts, or deciduous. This means that POP materials such as descriptive signs, posters, and leaflets are crucial. Check your local cooperative extension office, supplier, or trade associations for sources of materials. (See the list of recommended reading beginning on page 203 for books.) Most consumers continue to buy plants with flowers on them. This can be an advantage, as the range of perennial bloom times allows sales to be extended throughout the summer. But it can more often be a disadvantage, since few perennials are in bloom during the main spring buying period.

The main means to provide information on plants is with labels. Assuming that many customers are unfamiliar with perennials, more information may be required for perennials than for well-known annuals. And if the perennials are not in bloom (which is usually the case), color photos are crucial as well.

An increasing number of color pot tags are available for perennials, but if you are producing a large number of cultivars, many may not have preprinted tags. Avoid the temptation to use a generic label, such as "red peony," as is done in many mass market outlets. Also avoid using a label for a similar but not correct cultivar just because it has the same color flowers or other habit.

Unless you buy plants from a reputable supplier or have grown the plants yourself from seed or stock, it is helpful to either have plants in bloom when selling or force one or two into bloom to guarantee the cultivar. When there are many cultivars of perennials, labels are often switched or lost, resulting in mislabeled perennials and unhappy customers. Some retailers staple labels to pots.

If color pot tags are not available, you may have to simply produce a pot label with a name for each pot, then rely on a larger sign with descriptions and color photos for the group. Descriptions can be printed from the computer or handwritten (legibly) on cards that can be laminated together with a color print. If doing laminations, make sure it is a good process that will last a full season.

Some label manufacturers make special printers for their flexible labels. If using a standard computer printer for labels, make sure the labels do not jam or heat and melt in the printer. There are currently few, if any, outdoor labels guaranteed for use in thermal printers, and of course indoor labels will not stand up to outdoor weather or indoor watering. Some perennial retailers merely put a label containing the plant name in each pot and rely on a printed list or catalog for consumers to get more information.

Forcing perennials into bloom early, at least for display, is another way to have color on perennials for sale (see next chapter). In addition to having references for sale and using color, a key point in merchandising perennials is showing how they can be combined. This can be done through leaflets, store displays, or outdoor display beds that can also double as stock beds for cuttings.

If using display beds, make sure the plants are either planted in the ground or their pots are sunk in the ground or mulch so they are not showing. By sinking pots, displays can be changed frequently to keep something in flower, although in pots the plants will require more frequent care and watering. One Mid-Atlantic grower uses a pot-in-pot system, placing potted perennials in bloom into pots already sunk in the ground. Drip-tube irrigation keeps the pots watered. The pots can changed easily for a continual display of blooms.

Plants in display beds should be clearly labeled, and if you are selling plants in containers, then the same plants in the beds should be for sale nearby. Display beds need not be large — 10 feet by 8 feet is sufficient. In addition to or instead of display beds, tubs and barrels can be used to showcase plant combinations.

Direct mail cards or newsletters are used by many businesses to provide information, maintain an awareness with loyal customers, and advertise sales or special events. Customer addresses can be obtained from customers' checks, coupons, giveaways, or other means. Mailings can be done during the busy season to attract customers to your operation and away from a competitor's or during the slow season to (hopefully) stimulate business. Large mailings can be cheaper, as they are usually done with a bulk mailing permit; check at your local post office for details. The mailing itself can be a 5-by-7-inch postcard (which is large enough to be noticed and not lost in the mail), a colorful newsletter, or some other noticeable item.

You may be able to pay a horticultural marketing firm to do mailings for you on colorful postcards. All you have to do is supply them with the information. This allows you to concentrate on your business and not have to spend time to learn the complex postal business. Savings they can offer in postage costs through presorting and barcoding often justify the cost of the service.

Often a business will use a mailing to provide directions or a map or to point out top-quality service (although this is getting a bit overused in marketing), friendly and knowledgeable staff, a good or wide selection, and convenient or easy parking. Studies have found that these are some of the items consumers look for. Price is more of an issue with mass market customers. You cannot compete with mass marketers, so do not mention price except for special sales. Studies have also found that it is a lot cheaper and easier to keep an existing customer than attract a new one, hence the use of direct mailings.

Direct mailings and ads can be used to announce workshops. Many businesses find workshops an effective means to provide information and something extra for customers. Workshops may be given by employees with a specialty; sales representatives; local hobbyists, such as a rose specialist; or extension service personnel. Workshops can be a single event or a series of events over several weeks. They may or may not require preregistration and can be held on weekends or evenings.

When scheduling a workshop, keep in mind (as in all marketing) who your customers are and what their needs and schedules are. Retired persons can come to meetings on weekdays, a family may have weekend plans, and working couples might be free only on weekends. Tours of your operation are a kind of workshop and are often offered to garden clubs and local schools. Workshops can even be held off the premises, such as at a school (to talk to a class), a garden club, or a rotary meeting or similar meetings.

Direct mailings can also be done for special events, such as to announce a perennial plant of the week or month. Nonhorticultural persons and firms such as artists, handcrafters, or musicians can be employed for special events. Special events can include almost anything, and they can add some fun (and hopefully customers) to slow times. Other ideas for special events include: art or craft shows; food festivals; garden teas; animal displays and petting zoos; and presentations by hobby groups, such as garden railway societies.

Free advertising and opportunities to provide information should not be overlooked. Alert the local press of special events such as open houses or activities to benefit local charities. Write a "how-to" column or article for the local press, or provide similar information to the local radio and television media.

Regardless of which forms of advertising or events you use to market and merchandise, you should always keep your customers in mind. To gauge how customers feel, nursery owners will often walk around their facilities and listen to what people are saying or do a more formal survey of their customers periodically. Some even invite a group of customers each year to serve on a focus group or advisory board and to provide comments anonymously in return for a gift certificate.

Growers and retail firms are slowly gaining an increased presence on the Internet with web sites. Web sites can make a business known in an area. Crucial information such as directions and hours can be included. More elaborate sites include cultural information about the plants they sell, photos, listings of gifts or other nonplant items, and sometimes even a catalog with an order form. A recent survey found that although only about 10% of home gardeners use the Internet for gardening information, about 50% felt they would be using the Internet within the next two years (Mark Brand, University of Connecticut, 1997, personal correspondence). Much can be learned about what makes a good web site by simply visiting sites that already exist for garden businesses. Start with a garden gate to find sites, or at the web site "Perry's Perennial Pages" (see "Perennial Information on the Internet" on page 208).

Selection

If perennials are not a focus of sales, then a basic selection of popular ones (50–250 different varieties) may suffice (see tables 11-2 and 11-3 below and table 11-4 on page 86). If perennials are not a focus, a specialty "niche" may be useful, especially to compete with other businesses or mass merchandisers. A niche is needed if perennials are a main focus or *the* focus of the business (in which case, a total of 250–1,000 different varieties should be provided). For any focus, it is useful to have two groups of plants: a stable inventory of perennials common to most outlets (perhaps 60% of the inventory) and a specialty inventory of new or specialized plants (perhaps 40% of the inventory). Keep track of which perennials sell, and keep records so you can remember from year to year. Often demand will fluctuate unexpectedly; it may increase in response to an article in a local paper or national magazine.

Various plant sizes should be available, from quarts to gallons and larger depending on the plants, your customers' desires, and your market niche. Quarts are per-

Table 11-2. Top-selling perennials for 1993

1. *Hosta* (17% of firms listed as #1)
2. *Hemerocallis*
3. *Coreopsis*
4. *Astilbe*
5. Grasses (#8 in 1992)
6. *Phlox* (#5 in 1992)

Plants increasing in popularity:

Astilbe	*Geum*	*Salvia*
Coreopsis	Grasses	*Veronica*
Echinacea	*Hemerocallis*	
Ferns	*Heuchera*	

Plants decreasing in popularity:

Bergenia	*Dianthus*	*Lupinus*
Cerastium	*Gaillardia*	*Oenothera*
Chrysanthemum	*Geranium*	*Polemonium*

Source: Perennial Plant Association survey

Table 11-3. Top-selling perennials in Maine and Vermont (1982–1990)

Maine 1990	Vermont 1990	Vermont 1982
1. *Delphinium*	1. *Delphinium*	1. *Delphinium*
2. *Hemerocallis*	2. Daisies	1. *Phlox*
3. *Phlox*	3. *Phlox*	2. *Heuchera*
4. Bleeding Heart	4. *Digitalis*	2. *Papaver*
5. *Astilbe*	5. *Papaver*	2. *Coreopsis*
6. *Sedum*	6. Peony	3. *Lupinus*
7. *Hosta*	7. *Hemerocallis*	3. *Iberis*
8. Silver Mound	8. *Astilbe*	3. *Aquilegia*
9. *Coreopsis*	9. *Coreopsis*	4. *Campanula*
10. *Aquilegia*	10. *Hosta*	5. *Digitalis*

Table 11-4. Top-selling perennials, Bluebird Nursery, 1993–1994

1. *Coreopsis* v. 'Moonbeam'
2. *Hemerocallis* 'Stella d'Oro'
3. *Ajuga* r. 'Bronze Beauty'
4. *Scabiosa* c. 'Pink Mist'
5. *Hosta* f. 'Albomarginata'

6. *Sedum* s. 'Dragon's Blood'
7. *Rudbeckia* f. 'Goldsturm'
8. *Scabiosa* c. 'Butterfly Blue'
9. *Thymus serpyllum*
10. *Vinca minor*

11. *Campanula* c. 'Blue Clips'
12. *Coreopsis rosea*
13. *Lamium* m. 'Beacon Silver'
14. *Potentilla* n. 'Miss Wilmott'
15. *Veronica* 'Sunny Border Blue'

16. *Athyrium goeringianum* 'Pictum'
17. *Heuchera* a. 'Palace Purple'
18. *Aegopodium* p. 'Variegatum'
19. *Campsis radicans*
20. *Heuchera* s. 'Snow Angel'

21. *Arenaria verna*
22. *Ajuga* r. 'Burgundy Glow'
23. *Hosta* f. 'Francee'
24. *Dictamnus* a. 'Purpureus'
25. *Imperata cylindrica rubra* 'Red Baron'

Note: Scented geraniums, if grouped, would be #9. Bluebird Nursery is a wholesale operation and located in Clarkson, Nebraska.

haps the most common in primarily perennial operations; smaller sizes are provided for bedding plants and larger sizes for landscape plants. Some markets enable sales of large tubs or patio planters with several perennials combined inside.

No matter what the size, containers should not be sold off the ground but rather from waist-level, raised benches where plants can be easily handled and seen without customers having to bend over. As one grower observed, "Merchandise well displayed is already half sold." Carts or wagons can be provided to help customers handle several plants at once (and therefore increase sales), but make sure that the ground surface is flat and easily rolled upon or the carts have big wheels.

If your customers are not knowledgeable about perennials, then group plants according to their cultural requirements (such as sun or shade) or their type or use (such as in rock gardens). A recent trend is grouping them by themes, such as fragrant perennials, those that attract butterflies or other wildlife, native perennials, or cottage garden perennials. Plants are often grouped alphabetically by scientific name, which is best if your customers are perennial enthusiasts. Latin names may turn off customers not familiar with perennials.

Trends

Several trends have emerged recently. The degree of interest in them varies by region. Recent consumer trends are tender exotic perennials, upscale perennials, old-fashioned perennials, ornamental grasses, hardy ferns, shade plants, plants with lots of color, anything low-maintenance, companion planting of annuals and perennials, and perennials for height. Recent grower trends are greater variety; new cultivars; easy-to-grow plants; plants that show first-year color; and spring 1-gallon, summer 1- and 2-gallon, and fall 1–3-gallon sizes. Customer surveys are a good way to gauge trends in your area. Garden magazines or even fashion magazines are useful for realizing broader trends such as with colors.

In a recent study of Georgia landscapers, some perennial trends identified, from highest to lowest priority, were: plants requiring little water, low-maintenance plants, native or natural landscape material, color, plants requiring less pesticide use, and plants for small areas (Garber, 1996). The same study found that about 75% of the respondents bought directly from growers, the rest from rewholesalers — an emerging market segment. The small- and medium-sized firms purchased twice as many plants from rewholesalers as did the large firms.

A decade ago, most perennials were dug and sold from field beds. Now most are sold in containers. Studies on customer preference indicate that container type is not as crucial as the plant type and quality. Customers in some southern and urban areas feel plastic pots are less messy, more durable, and a sign of quality, while customers in many rural and other areas prefer non-plastic, biodegradable, or "environmentally safe" pots.

Many growers and retailers who use plastic pots encourage customers to recycle or return them, sometimes for a small refund. This creates good will as well as a market niche. Many types of plastic pots are recyclable in many parts of the country if they are clean. Check with your local recycler. Encourage customers to clean pots before returning them so you will not have to.

Pot color is an important consideration in this country, mainly as it relates to effects on soil temperature. Black pots tend to be warmer than white ones. Many color pots are available in Europe, and colors are related to flower and plant color for marketing purposes. Some larger wholesalers in North America are beginning to use pot colors to differentiate their plants and to signify higher-quality or more choice plant lines. In a customer survey, one West-Coast retailer found that, when given a choice, customers preferred plants in green pots.

CHAPTER 12

Forcing Out-of-Season Bloom

Nursery growers and greenhouse operators often want to force herbaceous perennials to bloom in late winter or spring, either for flower and garden shows or for merchandising. One point must be kept in mind: These plants are temperate species, so they will naturally respond to seasonal changes in temperature and day length. In the past, plants had to be sufficiently large and established to be able to flower. Much current research involves treating perennials in the small plant or plug stage to induce flowering later when plants are potted and grown larger (see chapter 6 on plug production, page 38).

Bare-Root Crowns

Much of the current research is being done with young plants or plugs. Different requirements may be needed for larger bare-root plants. Perennials from bare-root crowns may be grown into different types of plants by varying the storage and cultural environments.

In work at the University of Minnesota with bare-root crowns of *Dicentra* (Hanchek, 1991), at least four weeks at 41°F or less were needed for bud break. With less time or higher temperatures, plants would not grow subsequently or store as well. At 50°F or higher temperatures following the first four weeks, mature plant height was less, but this should be balanced against slower bud break. And although there are more and larger flowers produced for a longer time at 41°F, they develop slower.

So by altering temperature at different stages, growers can produce plants differently for different market needs.

If storing bare-root crowns of any perennials, keep them in loosely closed poly bags to prevent moisture loss and drying out. Storage just below freezing can meet the cold requirement many species need to flower when forced.

Temperature

Perennials that naturally bloom in spring are generally the easiest to force for spring sales. Many spring- and early-summer-flowering plants (*Dianthus, Digitalis,* and *Lupinus)*, including biennials, require cold treatment (vernalization) to induce flowering (obligate). This usually consists of a 35°F minimum, 45°F maximum temperature for a minimum of ten to twelve weeks. If colder temperatures are provided, roots may go dormant.

If plants still have foliage, ambient seasonal light or a minimum of 25–50 foot-candles in storage rooms is usually used, except if treating plugs under controlled conditions or if plants have a specific requirement. If plants have no foliage, the roots must be at least partially active and not totally dormant in order to respond to the temperature.

The cool period is usually followed by a warm 60–65°F period, two to eight weeks prior to sale. Some perennials, such as *Coreopsis verticillata* 'Moonbeam', may not require cold (they are nonobligate) but flower better and one to two weeks sooner with it (Hamaker et al, 1996a). Gibberellic acid (GA) can be used as a substitute for cold if giving plants a cold treatment is not possible; however, it is not commonly used.

Cooler temperatures, which are used by some growers to save energy, may result in much longer times to bloom and end up using and costing more in energy. Research has shown that *Coreopsis* flowers in seventy-five days at 60°F versus forty-seven days at 68°F (Yuan et al, 1995). Generally, there is a greater effect on flowering in going from 60–70°F than going from 70–80°F. *Campanula carpatica* 'Blue Clips' flowered in ten to eleven weeks at 61°F, eight to nine weeks at 66°F, and seven to eight weeks at 70°F in studies at Michigan State University (Whitman et al, 1996a). Several other perennials responded similarly, including *Platycodon grandiflorus* 'Sentimental Blue', *Veronica* 'Sunny Border Blue', *Coreopsis verticillata* 'Moonbeam', and *Coreopsis grandiflora*.

Fertility during cool periods should be 50–100 ppm nitrogen from nitrates, and in any warm period it should be 100–200 ppm nitrogen from any source. Prior to flowering and sales, switching to potassium nitrate at 100 ppm nitrogen will help harden off plants.

Growth Regulators

Since cool temperatures may result in taller plants and larger flowers, growth regulators may be needed to produce forced perennials as a greenhouse potted crop. Initial research at Michigan State University (Hamaker et al, 1996b) found that no growth regulator was effective on all several dozen perennials tested, although B-Nine and Sumagic worked on many. Only seven species responded to all growth regulators, and four of the taller species responded to none, at least at the rates tested.

Effectiveness of a particular growth regulator will therefore vary with species, maybe with cultivar, and with application rate. Growers should test growth regulators on a small scale before applying them to an entire crop.

To test regulators, the Michigan researchers suggest beginning with levels of 50 ppm for A-Rest; 2,500 ppm for B-Nine; 15 ppm for Bonzi; 1,500 ppm for Cycocel; or 10 ppm for Sumagic. Adjust rates, frequency, or both as needed to control height. Armitage (1996) recommends B-Nine sprayed at 3,000–5,000 ppm for columbine, candytuft, forget-me-not, and salvia. For balloon flower, pinks, and English daisy, he recommends Cycocel drenched or sprayed at 750–1,500 ppm. Some growth regulators may cause temporary chlorosis or may delay flowering by a week or more. Follow label directions as you would with any pesticide.

Light

Species that flower in summer may require long day lengths (LD) to bloom (obligate). These include *Asclepias*, *Artemisia* 'Silver Mound,' *Aruncus*, *Coreopsis* 'Moonbeam,' *Echinacea*, *Hibiscus*, *Rudbeckia* 'Goldsturm,' and some *Sedum* cultivars. Other perennials may not require LD but will bloom better with it, and most bloom a bit earlier (in six to ten weeks) with it. These include some *Achillea*, some *Campanula*, *Cerastium*, *Digitalis*, *Gaillardia*, *Lythrum*, *Monarda*, *Limonium*, and *Lobelia* 'Queen Victoria,' among others. If *Cerastium* is grown for foliage and not flowers, short days (SD) should be given. Some species, such as *Achillea millefolium* 'Summer Pastels,' require LD and bloom better as day lengths are increased from twelve to sixteen hours (Zhang et al, 1996).

Long day lengths may be created with night-interruption lighting from 10:00 P.M. to 2:00 A.M. nightly with incandescent lamps to provide 10–20 foot-candles of light to all plants; begin prior to March 30. Although only 5 foot-candles are needed to flower most perennials that require light, the extra light allows a margin of safety for uneven light levels. Some species, such as *Campanula carpatica*, *Coreopsis grandiflora*, and *Coreopsis verticillata*, may respond with blooming to light as low as 0.25 foot-candle (Whitman et al, 1996b).

Night lighting can be achieved by placing an incandescent light bulb every 150–200 square feet, 4–6 feet above plants. Some perennials may respond better with seven hours of light at night instead of four. There is some indication that extending the day by providing seven hours of light prior to dawn instead of providing a night interruption may decrease flowering (Hamaker et al, 1995). The ideal method is to provide a four-hour night interruption, or if not that a day extension in the evening to create a sixteen-hour day (Hamaker et al, 1996c). LD are provided ten weeks prior to sale.

Many fall-flowering species require SD to bloom. These are created by covering plants with blackout fabric from 5:00 P.M. to 6:00 P.M. each night until 7:00 A.M. to 8:00 A.M. the next morning. "Limited induction" is the concept of combining LD and SD. Except for a few perennials that specifically require both, the combination generally results in reduced height and longer time to flower, no matter which is first.

There are, of course, combinations of and exceptions to the above simple temperature and light regimes.

- Cold and day length requirements often vary with species and cultivar (for example, *Campanula persicifolia* requires cold and no LD while *C. carpatica* requires LD and no cold; *Lavandula* 'Hidcote' requires LD and cold, while LD are beneficial but not required for 'Munstead Dwarf').

- Perennials flowering with LD may require cold (for example, *Gypsophila, Lysimachia,* and *Achillea filipendulina).*

- Many LD perennials may flower without cold, although they are more vigorous or bloom better with cold (for example, *Achillea millefolium, Coreopsis, Delphinium* 'Blue Mirror,' *Dianthus* 'Zing Rose,' *Helenium, Phlox, Platycodon, Rudbeckia* 'Goldsturm,' *Scabiosa* 'Butterfly Blue,' and *Sedum* 'Brilliant').

- LD requirements can be replaced by cold for some species (for example, *Echinops).*

- Cold requirements may be replaced partially or totally by SD for some species (for example, *Coreopsis grandiflora).*

- Some perennials may bloom with SD but also with cold and LD (*Aquilegia, Lupinus).*

- Some perennials, especially late summer/early fall bloomers (for example, Aster hybrids) may require SD *after* LD, while some early-season bloomers (for example, Saxifrages, *Coreopsis* 'Early Sunrise') may require SD *before* LD.

Age and Genetics

The age of plants or their stage of life (juvenile or mature) has an effect on forcing. For example, young plants of some *Heuchera* appear to need little or no cold to flower, while mature plants require cold. Even for those requiring cold, the plant age at which cold is applied matters.

In studies at Michigan State University (Cameron et al, 1996a), perennials generally needed more than fifteen leaves before beginning a cold treatment. Extremes were *Salvia* 'Blue Queen,' which needed more than ten leaves, and *Iberis* 'Snowflake' or *Lavandula* 'Munstead Dwarf,' which needed more than forty or fifty leaves, respectively. In a study with *Aquilegia* 'McKana's Giant Mix' (Weiler, 1995), plants needed to have at least twelve leaves when cold began in order to fully flower after being given ten weeks of cold and then forced. Or if a plant such as bleeding heart *(Dicentra spectabilis)* is progressing toward flowering with LD that are interrupted by SD, it will flower only if given twelve weeks of cold before LD are resumed. *Asclepias tuberosa* and *Hibiscus* x *hybrida* are two other species that do not require cold *if* seedlings begun under LD are not interrupted by SD.

Genetic composition within a species affects forcing requirements. In one study (Weiler, 1995), shasta daisies from several seedling sources required between ten and eighteen hours of day length to bloom, depending on the source. Cuttings from three clones of baby's breath required fourteen to twenty-four hours of day length to fully flower, depending on the source plant. Much of this "ecotypic" variation results from the geographic location of the seed and stock source.

Perennial forcing/flowering requirements (table 12-1 on page 90) are one of the latest and most active areas of perennials research, with much new information coming from Michigan State University and the University of Georgia (Han and Rogers, 1984; Iverson, 1989; Hanchek, 1991; Runkle et al, 1995; Cameron et al, 1996b; Armitage, 1996). Studies often vary in their location, cultural practices employed, and other factors as mentioned above, so results may vary. But values in the table can serve as a useful baseline.

Table 12-1. Forcing requirements of several perennials

Name	Cold treatment (weeks at 40°F)[1]	Light conditions during forcing[2]	Approximate number of weeks of forcing required at a 60°F night temperature[3]
Achillea filipendulina	12	LD	—
Achillea millefolium 'Red Beauty'	12	—	4
f. *rosea*	12	LD	8–10
	6	LD	13–15
'Summer Pastels'	0	LD	5–6
Alcea rosea (some cultivars)	6–12	—	—
Allium sp.	12	—	4
Anchusa capensis 'Blue Bedder'	(8)	(LD)	—
Anemone hupehensis var. *japonica*	0–6	LD	11–15
Anemone sylvestris	(8)	(LD)	—
Anthemis marschalliana	12	—	4
Aquilegia, some cultivars	12	LD	7–9
Most cultivars	12	—	—
Songbird series, others	0	(LD)	6–8
Arabis cultivars	(4)	—	—
Arabis sturii	7–12	—	4
Arisaema triphyllum (atrorubens)	12	—	4–5
Armeria hybrids	0 (4)	—	8
Armeria pseudoarmeria (latifolia)	(15)	—	—
Asclepias tuberosa	15	SD + LD	—
	0 (4–8)	LD	—
Aster alpinus 'Goliath'	8–12	—	—
	10–12	LD	—
Aster cultivars	0	LD + SD	—
Astilbe cultivars	6–12	(LD), LD	4
Aubrietia cultivars	(4)	—	—
Aurinia saxatilis	12	—	2–3
Brunnera sp.	12	—	4
Campanula carpatica	0–12	LD	—
Clips series	0 (4–8)	LD	10–11
Campanula glomerata 'Joan Elliott'	12	—	4
Campanula persicifolia	12	—	7–9
Catananche caerulea	12 (4–8)	LD	4
Cerastium tomentosum (for flowers)	8–12	(LD)	—
Chrysogonum virginianum	4–6	—	4
Convallaria sp.	8–12	—	3
Coreopsis grandiflora	15	(LD)	—
'Early Sunrise' (Michigan State Univ. study)	0	SD + LD	6–8
'Early Sunrise'	12	(LD)	4–6
'Early Sunrise' (Univ. of Georgia study)	(8)	(LD)	—
'Sunray'	8–12	LD	10–11
Coreopsis lanceolata	0–12	LD	—
Coreopsis verticillata 'Golden Showers'	6	LD	11–13
'Moonbeam'	0 (4–15)	LD	8–10
Cynoglossum nervosum	12	—	4
Cypripedium species	12	—	2–7
Delphinium 'Blauspiegel' (Blue Mirror)	(12)	—	—
Delphinium sp.	—	—	12
Dianthus barbatus	12	LD	—
Dianthus 'Essex Witch'	12	—	4
Dianthus 'Zing Rose'	(12)	—	—

See page 93 for footnotes

continued on next page

Herbaceous Perennials Production

Table 12-1. Forcing requirements of several perennials *(continued)*

Name	Cold treatment (weeks at 40°F)[1]	Light conditions during forcing[2]	Approximate number of weeks of forcing required at a 60°F night temperature[3]
Dicentra spectabilis	4–12	–	4–5
Dodocatheon jeffreyi	12	–	4–5
Doronicum sp.	12	–	–
Echinacea purpurea	(15)	(LD)	–
	0	LD	–
'Bravado'	(4–8)	LD	–
'White Swan'	(4–8)	LD	–
Echinops bannaticus 'Taplow Blue'	6	LD	11–13
Erodium x *variabile* 'Roseum'	(4)	–	–
Eryngium planum	6–12	–	–
Euphorbia polychroma (epithymoides)	12	–	4
Fibigia clypeata	6–12	–	–
Gaillardia x *grandiflora*	0	LD	–
'Kobold' ('Goblin')	15	LD	–
	(8)	(LD)	–
Geum 'Borisii'	12	–	4
Gypsophila paniculata	(15)	LD	–
Gypsophila 'Pierre's Pink'	8–12	(LD)	–
Gypsophila repens	8–12	(LD)	–
Habernaria sp.	12	–	3–4
Helenium 'Butterpat'	0	LD	12–16
Hemerocallis sp.	6–12	–	–
Hesperis matronalis	6–12	LD	–
Heuchera 'Chatterbox'	12	–	8–10
Heuchera sanguinea	12 *or*	SD	–
Bressingham hybrids	12	–	–
Hibiscus cultivars	0	LD	–
Iberis sempervirens	12–15	–	–
Incarvillea delavayi	12	–	4
Iris cristata	12	–	4
Iris versicolor	12	–	4–5
Kniphofia cultivars	12 *or*	LD	–
Lavandula angustifolia	15	–	–
'Hidcote'	0–12	LD	–
'Munstead Dwarf'	12	(LD)	–
Leucanthemum x *superbum*	0–12	LD	4–7
	(8)	(LD)	–
'Snow Lady'	0	(LD)	–
Lewisia cotyledon	12	–	–
Liatris sp.	12	–	4
Lilium canadense	12	–	9–10
Lilium philadelphicum	12	–	6–7
Linum perenne	0	LD	–
'Sapphire'	12	–	–
Lobelia x *speciosa*	(15)	(LD)	–
	0	LD	–
Lupinus sp.	12	LD	2
	0	SD	5
Lychnis chalcedonica	0	LD	–
Lysimachia clethroides	12	LD	12–14
Lythrum salicaria	0	–	–
Mertensia sp.	12	–	4

See page 93 for footnotes

continued on next page

Table 12-1. Forcing requirements of several perennials *(continued)*

Name	Cold treatment (weeks at 40°F)[1]	Light conditions during forcing[2]	Approximate number of weeks of forcing required at a 60°F night temperature[3]
Morina longifolia	6-12	–	–
Myosotis sylvatica	0	–	–
Myosotis, Victoria series	(4)	–	–
Nepeta sp.	12	–	4
Oenothera fruticosa ssp. *glauca (tetragona)*	(8)	(LD)	–
Oenothera lamarckiana	12	LD	–
Oenothera macrocarpa (missouriensis)	(15)	LD	–
Paeonia sp.	12	–	–
Papaver sp.	12	–	–
Penstemon sp.	6-12	–	–
Phlox divaricata ssp. *laphamii* 'Chattahoochee'	4	–	4
Phlox paniculata 'Fairy's Petticoat'	6	LD	11-13
Phlox subulata	(8)	(LD)	–
Physostegia virginiana 'Alba'	12-15	LD	–
'Summer Snow'	6	LD	10-13
Platycodon grandiflorus mariesii	6	LD	12-14
'Sentimental Blue'	0 (4-12)	(LD)	11-13
'Astra'	(4)	–	–
Podophyllum peltatum	12	–	4-5
Polygonatum canaliculatum	12	–	4
Potentilla 'Versicolor Plena'	12	–	4
Primula sp.	6-12	–	–
Primula veris 'Pacific Giants'	0	–	–
Pulsatilla (Anemone) patens	12	–	2-3
Ranunculus sp.	12	–	–
Ratibida columnifera	0	LD	–
Rudbeckia fulgida var. *sullivantii* 'Goldsturm'	0 (12)	LD	12-14
Rudbeckia hirta	–	LD	–
Salvia superba	0	LD	–
Salvia x *sylvestris* 'Blaukönigin'			
'Blue Queen'	(8)	(LD)	–
'Blue Queen'	6	LD	6-8
'Blue Queen'	12	SD	11-13
'Blue Queen'	15	(LD)	–
Sanguinaria canadensis	12	–	4-7
Saponaria ocymoides 'Splendens'	12	–	4
Saxifraga x *arendsii* 'Purple Robe'	12	SD + LD	–
Scabiosa caucasica	(8-15)	(LD)	–
Sedum spectabile			
'Brilliant'	0	LD	16-20
'Brilliant'	12	LD	14-18
Silene 'Swan Lake'	(4)	–	–
Symphytum 'Rubrum'	12	–	4
Tanacetum coccineum	15	–	–
'James Kelway'	12-15	LD	–
Tradescantia x *andersoniana* 'Innocence'	12	–	4
Trillium grandiflorum	12	–	2-3
Veronica 'Blue Bouquet'	(8)	(LD)	–

See page 93 for footnotes

continued on next page

Table 12-1. Forcing requirements of several perennials *(continued)*

Name	Cold treatment (weeks at 40°F)[1]	Light conditions during forcing[2]	Approximate number of weeks of forcing required at a 60°F night temperature[3]
Veronica longifolia	15	(LD)	–
Veronica sp.	6–12	–	–
Veronica spicata	(12–15)	(LD)	–
Veronica 'Sunny Border Blue'	6 (12)	–	9–12
Viola cucullata	12	–	3–4
Viola cultivars	12	–	4

Note: Studies on forcing requirements often vary in their location, cultural practices employed, and other factors, so results may vary. But values in this table can serve as a useful baseline. sp. = species, ssp. = subspecies, var. = variety

[1] Parentheses indicate that conditions listed may help but are not required. A range of values or extra cultivar listings reflect differences reported from various sources.

[2] Parentheses indicate that conditions listed may help but are not required. Day length requirement: – = day neutral, no specific requirement; LD = continual long days of sixteen hours, either from a four-hour night interruption or day extension (the best growth often occurs if forcing conditions are preceded by four to six weeks of natural days); SD = less than twelve hours of light for six weeks

[3] – = unknown or unreported. For many species, long periods of nine to twelve or more weeks may be lessened by two weeks, or even by as much as a third, for every 5°F increase in temperature. For example, if twelve weeks of forcing are required at 60°F, then a temperature of 65°F may decrease forcing time by two weeks to ten weeks, and a temperature of 70°F may decrease forcing time by two more weeks to eight weeks.

APPENDIX A

Propagation Methods for Herbaceous Perennials

Table A-1. Propagation methods for herbaceous perennials

Scientific name	Common name[1]	Methods of propagation[2]	Period[3]	Comments/requirements[4]
Abronia sp.	Sand Verbena	S	Late spring	
		SC	Spring	Sand
Acaena sp.	New Zealand Bur	D	Spring, fall	Rooted stems
		S	Spring, fall	
Acantholimon sp.	Prickly Thrift	S		Slow, well-drained, transplants poorly
		SC	Late spring	
		SC	Late summer	Basal, non-flw
		L		Most sp., most reliable
Acanthus sp.	Bear's Breech	RC	Spring	
		D	Early spring, fall	Use care
		S		
Aceriphyllum: see Mukdenia				
Achillea sp.	Yarrow	S		
		SC	Mid summer	After flw, basal in spring
		D	Spring, fall	
Achlys triphylla	Vanilla Leaf	S		
		D		Rhizome
Achnatherum: see Stipa				
Acinos sp.	Calamintha	S		
		D		As Satureja
Aciphylla sp.	Colinso's Spaniard	S	Late summer	Fresh
Acomastylis: see Geum				
Aconitum sp.	Monkshood	S		
		D	Spring, fall	Roots poisonous
Acorus sp.	Sweet Flag	S		Fresh
		D		Every 3rd/4th year
Actaea sp.	Baneberry, Cohosh	S		Old seed germination ununiform
		D	Spring	
Actinella: see Hymenoxys				

See footnotes on page 144   *continued on next page*

Scientific name	Common name[1]	Methods of propagation[2]	Period[3]	Comments/requirements[4]
Actinidia sp.	Yang-Tao	SC L S Graft	Late summer Fall Spring, fall	Bottom heat
Actinomeris: see *Verbesina*				
Adamsia: see *Pushkinia*				
Adelocaryum: see *Lindelofia*				
Adenophora sp.	Ladybells	S SC	Early spring	Ripe, transplants poorly Basal
Adenostyles (Cacalia) alpina		S D		
Adiantum sp.	Maidenhair Fern	D S		Crowns, may be slow Spores, preferable
Adlumia fungosa	Climbing Fumitory	S	Early spring	
Adonis sp.	Pheasant's Eye	S D	Spring Spring, fall	Slow to flower, doubles sterile Difficult, use care, keep moist
Adoxa moschatellina	Muskroot	S, D		
Aegopodium sp.	Goutweed	D S	Fall, early spring	Invasive
Aethionema sp.	Stone Cress	S SC D	Spring, fall Summer Spring, fall	Off types usual Or basal Difficult
Aethiopappus: see *Centaurea*				
Agapanthus sp.	African Lily	D S	Spring	Clumps, offsets Ripe, 2–3 years to flw
Agastache sp.	Giant Hyssop	S D SC	Early spring Early spring Summer	Indoors Old clumps Semi-ripe or softwood
Agave sp.	Century Plant	S D		Slow Offsets, bulbils
Agrimonia sp.	Agrimony	RC S	Early fall Early spring	May self sow
Agropyron sp.	Wheat Grass	S, D		
Agrostemma: see *Lychnis, Silene*				
Agrostis: see *Stipa*				
Ajania sp.		S		
Ajuga sp.	Bugleweed	D, TC, S SC		When not flw, basal in spring
Albuca sp.	Hollyhock	S D		Offsets, bulbils
Alcea (Althaea) sp.		S SC	Spring, fall	Not common
Alchemilla sp.	Lady's Mantle	S D	Fall Spring, fall	Before flw, 2–3 years to flw
Alisma sp.	Water Plantain	D S	Spring	Ripe, keep wet
Alkanna sp.		S, RC		

See footnotes on page 144   *continued on next page*

Table A-1. Propagation methods for herbaceous perennials (continued)

Scientific name	Common name[1]	Methods of propagation[2]	Period[3]	Comments/requirements[4]
Allium sp.	Ornamental Onion	S	Spring	
		D	Spring	Dormant offsets, clumps
Allosorus: see *Cryptogramma*				
Alonsoa sp.	Mask Flower	S		
		SC	Late summer	Softwood tips, non-flw shoots
Alopecurus sp.	Foxtail Grass	D	Spring	
Alsine: see *Minuartia*				
Alstroemeria sp.	Peruvian Lily	S	Spring	Or sow ripe
		D	Spring	Old clumps
Althaea sp.	Hollyhock	S	Spring	
		D		Rootstock, difficult
Alyssoides urtriculata	Bladderpod	S	Spring, fall	As *Aurinia*
		SC	Early summer	
		D	Fall	Difficult
Alyssum murale, sp.	Madwort	S		Most common
		D	Spring	Difficult
		SC	Early summer	Or early spring before buds
Amaracus: see *Origanum*				
Amaryllis belladonna	Belladonna Lily	D		Dormant offsets
		D	Summer	Clumps, after leaves gone
		S		Ripe
Amberboa moschata	Sweet Sultan	S	Spring, fall	Sow direct
Ammophila sp.	Beach Grass	S		
		D	Late spring	Not fall–spring
Amsonia sp.	Blue Star	S	Spring	
		SC	Spring, summer	After flw easy, terminal
		D	Spring, fall	3 year+ clumps
Anacyclus pyrethrum	Mt. Atlas Daisy	S		Best
		SC	Spring	
Anagallis sp.	Pimpernel	S	Fall, spring	
		D	Spring	
		SC	Spring	
Anaphalis sp.	Pearly Everlasting	S	Late summer	Few off types
		D		
		SC	Spring	New shoots
Anchusa sp.	Alkanet, Bugloss	S		Not for cvs
		RC	Early spring	*A. azurea*
		D	Spring, fall	Difficult
		SC	Spring	Basal
Andropogon sp.	Bluestem	D	Spring	
		S		
Androsace sp.	Rock Jasmine	S		Slow, may take 2 years
		SC	Summer	Basal
		D	Spring	*A. villosa*
		D	Summer	Runners, rooted plantlets
Andryala sp.		S, D		
Anemone sp.	Windflower	S		Uncommon in U.S.
		RC	Winter, early spring	Autumn types, bottom heat
		D	Spring	Rhizomes, use care

See footnotes on page 144

continued on next page

Herbaceous Perennials Production

Scientific name	Common name[1]	Methods of propagation[2]	Period[3]	Comments/requirements[4]
Anemonella thalictroides	Rue Anemone	S	Summer	Fresh
		D	Fall	Well-established
		D	Early spring	Tubers from rootstocks
Anemonopsis macrophylla	False Anemone	S	Late summer	
		D	Spring	
Anemopsis californica	Yerba Mansa	D	Spring	
		S		Ripe, wet mix
Anethum graveolens	Dill	S		
Angelica sp.		S		Ripe
		D		Difficult
Anisodontea sp.		S	Spring	
		SC	Summer	Greenwood or semi-ripe
Anisotome sp.		D	Spring	
		S		As *Angelica*
Antennaria sp.	Everlasting, Pussy Toes	S	Spring	
		D	Spring	Stolons
Anthemis sp.	Dog Fennel	S		
		SC	Spring, summer	Basal before budding, or after flw
		D	Spring, fall	
Anthericum sp.	St. Bernard's Lily	S	Spring	
		D	Spring	Flowers 2 years after
Anthoxanthum sp.	Vernal Grass	S	Spring	Transplants poorly
Anthriscus sylvestris	Cow Parsley	S	Spring–summer	Outdoors, bolts from dryness
Anthyllis sp.		S		
		D	Spring, fall	
		SC		Shrubby sp.
Antirrhinum sp.	Snapdragon	S		Easy
		SC	Fall	Semi-ripe
Aphyllanthes monspeliensis		S	Spring	Sow ripe, sandy mix
		D		
Apios americana	Wild Bean	D		Roots, tubers
		S		
Apium graveolens	Wild Celery	S		
Apocynum sp.	Dogbane	D	Spring	Or remove suckers
		S		
Aponogeton sp.		D	Spring	Also offsets
		S		Keep moist, wet mix
Aposeris sp.		S		Self-sows
Aquilegia sp.	Columbine	S	Early fall	Alpine sp. slow – 2 years
		D	Spring, fall	Use care, difficult
Arabis sp.	Rockcress	S	Spring, fall	Not double cvs
		SC	Early summer	Basal or tip after flw
		D	Spring, fall	
Arachniodes sp.		S		Spores, as *Dryopteris*
Aralia sp.		S		Ripe or stratify
		RC		Shrub sp.
		D	Spring	*A. nudicaulis*–rhizomes
		Graft		Variegated forms

See footnotes on page 144

continued on next page

Table A-1. Propagation methods for herbaceous perennials *(continued)*

Scientific name	Common name[1]	Methods of propagation[2]	Period[3]	Comments/requirements[4]
Arctanthemum arcticum		S	Early summer	Often poor vigor
		SC	Summer	
		D	Spring, fall	
Arctotis sp.	African Daisy	S	Spring	
		SC	Fall	Bottom heat, sandy mix
Arenaria sp.	Sandwort	S	Spring	Cushion sp.
		D		Cushion sp., after flw
		SC	Summer	Larger sp., basal
Argyranthemum sp.		S	Spring	
		SC	Fall	
Arisaema sp.		S		Ripe
		D		Young offsets, tubers
Arisarum sp.	Mouse Plant	D		Dormant
		S	Spring, fall	
Aristolochia sp.	Birthwort	D	Fall	
		S	Fall	Ripe, or stratify
		RC		Herbaceous sp.
		SC	Summer	Climbing sp.
Armeria sp.	Thrift, Sea Pink	S		Variable seedlings
		D	Spring, fall	Or remove basal rosettes (offsets)
		SC	Summer	
Armoracia rusticana	Horseradish	S		Not variegated cv
		RC		Taproot
Arnebia sp.	Arabian Primrose	D		Use care, offsets
		S		Collect underripe
		RC	Late winter	Bottom heat
Arnica sp.	Mountain Tobacco	D	Spring	
		S	Early spring	Or ripe, *A. montana*, acidic mix
Arrhenatherum bulbosum (*elatius*)	Oat Grass	D		
Artemisia sp.	Wormwood	D	Fall, early spring	
		SC	Summer	Remove from mist as roots, woody sp.
Arthropodium sp.		S, D		
Arum sp.	Wild Ginger	D	Fall	After flw, also bulbils
		S		Slow, ripe, remove pulp (caustic)
Aruncus sp.	Goat's Beard	D	Spring, fall	2–4 years, difficult
		S	Fall	True from seed, dioecious
Arundinaria: see *Pleioblastus, Sasa* et al.				
Arundo donax	Giant Reed	D	Spring	
		RC	Winter	While dormant
Asarina sp.	Chickabiddy	S	Early spring	Self sows
		SC	Late summer	Tip, non-flw
Asarum sp.	Ginger	S		Self sows
		D	Spring, early fall	Slow to increase, usual method
Asclepias sp.	Milkweed	S		Transplant early, germ variable
		SC	Summer	
		RC	Early spring	
		D	Late spring	Difficult, use care, taproot

See footnotes on page 144

continued on next page

Herbaceous Perennials Production

Scientific name	Common name[1]	Methods of propagation[2]	Period[3]	Comments/requirements[4]
Asparagus sp.		S		Ripe, not direct sow
		D		
Asparella: see *Hystrix*				
Asperula sp.	Woodruff	D, S		
		SC	Early summer	
Asphodeline sp.	Jacob's Rod	S		Sandy mix
		D	Spring	Use care, several buds per, offsets
Asphodelus sp.	Asphodel	S		
		D		As *Asphodeline*
Aspidium: see *Polystichum,* et al.				
Asplenium sp.	Spleenwort	S	Fall	Spores, lime soil
		D		Sidecrowns if present
		SC		Frond stipe
Aster sp.	Aster	S		Fresh best
		SC	Spring, early summer	Soft growth best, easiest
		D	Early spring, fall	Ensure shoot on divisions
Asteriscus sp.		S		
		SC		Semi-ripe
Asteromoea (Kalimeris) mongolica		S		
		D	Spring, fall	As *Boltonia*
		SC	Late spring	Before budding, soft best
Astilbe sp.		S	Spring, fall	Often slow to flw, variable except for Spirea *A. chinensis pumila*
		D	Early spring, fall	2–3 eyes per division
Astilboides tabularis		D	Early spring	As *Rodgersia*
		S	Spring	
Astragalus sp.	Milk Vetch	S		Transplant early, may be slow
		SC		Non-flw basal with underground stem
		SC	Late summer	Softwood, often difficult
Astrantia sp.	Masterwort	D	Fall, early spring	Difficult
		S		Ripe, variable seedlings
Asyneuma sp.		D	Spring	As *Phyteuma*
		S	Fall	
Athamanta sp.		S		Transplant early
		D	Spring	Use care
Athyrium sp.	Lady Ferns	S		Spores
		D		Established crowns, bulbils if present
Atropa belladonna	Deadly Nightshade	S		Ripe, fresh, slow, erratic
		SC	Spring	Terminal shoots
		RC	Winter	Toxic sap
Aubrieta sp.	Aubretia	S	Early spring	Self sows, hybridizes
		SC	Early summer	Basal early spring/after flw
		D	Spring	Use care, difficult
Aurinia (Alyssum) saxatilis (saxatile)	Basket-of-Gold	S	Spring, fall	
		SC	Early summer	
		D	Fall	Difficult
Avena: see *Helictotrichon*				

continued on next page

Scientific name	Common name[1]	Methods of propagation[2]	Period[3]	Comments/requirements[4]
Avenastrum: see *Avenula*				
Avenella: see *Deschampsia*				
Avenula: see *Helictotrichon*				
Azolla sp.	Mosquito Fern	D		Budding-off in ponds, invasive
Azorella sp.		D		
		S		
		SC	Fall	Rosettes
Azorina (Campanula) vidalii		S		
Baldellia ranunculoides		S		Like *Alisma*
		D	Spring, summer	
Ballota sp.	Black Horehound	D		Herbaceous sp.
		SC	Spring, early summer	Softwood or semi-ripe, shrubby sp.
Balsamorhiza sp.	Balsam Root	S		Do not disturb taproot
Bambusa sp.	Bamboo	D	Spring	
Baptisia sp.	False Indigo	D	Late fall, early spring	Water divisions well, difficult
		S	Summer	
		SC	Summer	Soft, after bloom, hormone helps
Barbarea sp.	Winter Cress	D	Spring	
		S	Spring	Not cvs, 'Variegata'
		SC		
Batrachium: see *Ranunculus*				
Begonia grandis		S		Common in Europe
		SC	Summer	
		D	Winter	Bulbils
Belamcanda chinensis	Blackberry Lily	S	Spring	Flowers 2nd year
		D	Spring, fall	Like German iris
Bellevalia sp.		S		Use fresh
		D		Offsets
Bellidiastrum: see *Aster*				
Bellis sp.	Daisy	S		Common, flw 2nd year
		D	Spring, fall	For cvs
Bellium sp.		D		Preferred
		S		
Berardia subacaulis		S		
Bergenia sp.	Heartleaf Saxifrage	S		
		RC	Spring	Or basal
		D	Early spring, fall	Clumps of rhizomes
Berkheya sp.		S		
		D		Difficult
Berlandiera lyrata	Green Eyes	S		
Beschorneria sp.		D		2-year-old offsets
		S		Sow fresh, slow
Bessera sp.	Coral Drops	S		
		D		Corm offsets
Besseya sp.	Kitten Tails	S		As *Synthyris*
Beta vulgaris	Beet	S	Early spring	
Betonica: see *Stachys*				

continued on next page

Scientific name	Common name[1]	Methods of propagation[2]	Period[3]	Comments/requirements[4]
Biarum sp.		S		
		D		
Biebersteinia sp.		S	Spring	
		SC	Early summer	
		D		Difficult
Biscutella sp.		S		Difficult to transplant
Bistorta: see *Polygonum*				
Blandfordia sp.	Christmas Bells	S		
Blechnum sp.	Hard Fern	D		Rhizomes, also stolons some sp.
		S		Spores
Bletia sp.		D		
Bletilla sp.		D	Spring	
		S		Difficult, slow
Bocconia: see *Macleaya*				
Bolax: see *Azorella*				
Boltonia asteroides	False Chamomile	S		Some cvs ununiform
		D	Spring, fall	
		SC	Late spring	Before budding, easy, tips
Bongardia chrysogonum		S	Fall	As *Leontice*
Borago pygmaea (laxiflora)	Perennial Borage	D	Spring	
		S	Fall	
		SC	Summer	
Borderea pyrenaica		S		As *Dioscorea*
Bornmuellera sp.		S		As *Ptilotrichum*
		SC, D		
Bouteloua sp.	Gramma Grass	D	Spring	
		S		
Boykinia sp.		D, S		
Brachycome sp.	Swan River Daisy	S, D, SC		
Brachypodium sp.	False Brome	D	Spring	
		S		
Brasenia schreberi	Watershield	D	Spring	Rhizomes – whole or parts
		S		Sow in mud under water
Brauneria: see *Echinacea*				
Brevoortia (Brodiaea): see *Dichelostemma*				
Briggsia sp.		S, D		
		LC		New growth
Brimeura sp.		S		Ripe
		D	Fall	Bulbils
Briza sp.	Quaking Grass	D	Spring	
		S		
Bromus sp.	Brome	S		
Brunella: see *Prunella*				
Brunnera macrophylla	Siberian Bugloss	S	Late summer	Not variegated cvs, ripe
		RC	Early spring	
		D	Spring, late summer	Variegated cvs
Bryonia sp.	Bryony	S		Invasive, poisonous

continued on next page

Table A-1. Propagation methods for herbaceous perennials *(continued)*

Scientific name	Common name[1]	Methods of propagation[2]	Period[3]	Comments/requirements[4]
Buglossoides sp.		S		
		SC		Semisoft, preferred method
		D		
Bulbinella sp.		S, D		
Bulbocodium sp.	Spring Meadow Saffron	D	Summer	Older clumps, like *Colchicum*
		S	Summer	Sow fresh
Buphthalmum salicifolium	Ox Eye	D	Early spring	Or after flw, invasive
		S		
Bupleurum sp.	Thoroughwax	S		
		D		Alkaline soil
Butomus umbellatus	Flowering Rush	D	Spring	Keep wet, also root bulbils
		S		Sow fresh, keep wet
Cacalia: see *Adenostyles*				
Caccinia sp.		S		Like *Anchusa*, transplant early
Cachyrs sp.		S		Very slow
		D		Older plants
Calamagrostis sp.	Reed Grass	D	Spring	
Calamintha sp.	Calamint	S	Spring	
		D		
Calandrinia sp.	Rock Purslane	S		May self sow
Calanthe sp.		D		
Calceolaria sp.	Slipper Flower	S, D		
Calimeris: see *Kalimeris*				
Calla palustris	Water Arum	D	Spring	Of long rhizome, difficult
		S	Late summer	Difficult, keep wet
		SC	Summer	Root in wet mud
Callendrinia: see *Lewisia*				
Callianthemum sp.		S		Slow, even if fresh, difficult
		D		Larger plants, difficult
Callirhoe sp.	Poppy Mallow	S		Taproot, transplant early
		D		
		SC	Summer	Sandy mix
Callitriche sp.	Water Starwort	D		
		SC		Submerge in gravel
Calochortus sp.	Mariposa Lily	S		
		D		Bulbils from branch axils
Caltha sp.	Marsh Marigold	D	Spring	After flw
		S	Late summer	Fresh, self-sows, ununiform
Calystegia sp.	Bindweed	RC	Winter	Rhizome pieces, invasive
		S	Spring	
Camassia sp.	Quamash	S		Also by bulbils
		D	Fall	Clumps or offsets
Campanula sp.	Bellflower	S		Some sp.
		SC	Spring	Before flw, basal
		RC		
		D	Spring, early fall	Offshoots for alpine sp.

See footnotes on page 144

continued on next page

Herbaceous Perennials Production

Scientific name	Common name[1]	Methods of propagation[2]	Period[3]	Comments/requirements[4]
Canna x *generalis,* cultivars	Canna Lily	D S	Early spring	
Cardamine sp.	Bittercress	S D LC		Also bulbils some sp. *C. pratensis*
Cardiocrinum sp.		S D		7 years to flw Daughter bulbs, 3 years to flw
Carduncellus sp.		RC, S D		Lateral shoots
Carduus nutans	Plumless Thistle	S D		Self sows
Carex sp.	Sedge	D S	Spring	Cold to germinate
Carlina sp.	Carline Thistle	S RC	Fall	Ripe, not easily transplanted Difficult
Carpogymnia: see *Gymnocarpium*				
Carum carvi	Caraway	S	Early spring	Or ripe, transplant early
Caryopteris sp.	Bluebeard	S SC	Fall	Species Bottom heat, sandy mix
Cassia: see *Senna*				
Castilleja sp.	Indian Paintbrush	S		Parasitic early with *Raoulia*
Catananche caerulea	Cupid's Dart	S D RC	Early spring Fall Early winter	May be difficult
Cathcartia: see *Meconopsis*				
Caulophyllum thalictroides	Blue Cohosh	S D	Fall, spring	Ripe Or after flw
Cautleya sp.		D S	Spring	As *Hedychium* Sow fresh
Cedronella canariensis	Balm of Gilead	S SC D	Spring	Softwood
Celmisia sp.		S SC D	Early summer	Ripe, poor germ, slow, hybridizes
Celsia: see *Verbascum*				
Centaurea sp.	Knapweed	S D SC RC	Spring Spring, fall Spring	Woody cvs only *C. montana*
Centaurium sp.	Centaury	S D SC	Early spring Late summer	*C. scilloides*
Centranthus ruber	Red Valerian	S D SC	Spring Spring Spring	Usual Use care, difficult Basal, before budding
Cephalaria sp.		S D RC	Summer Spring Late fall	Fresh, easy Not for slow species

See footnotes on page 144

continued on next page

Scientific name	Common name[1]	Methods of propagation[2]	Period[3]	Comments/requirements[4]
Cerastium sp.	Mouse-Ear Chickweed	S	Spring	
		SC	Late spring, summer	After flw, bottom heat
		D	Spring, fall	
Ceratophyllum sp.	Hornwort	SC		Wet soil, invasive
		D		As *Myriophyllum*
Ceratostigma sp.	Leadwort	SC	Spring, summer	Non-flw shoots best
		D	Spring	Rooted suckers
		S, RC, L		
Cerinthe glabra	Honeywort	S		
Ceterach: see *Asplenium*				
Chaenorhinum sp.	Dwarf Snapdragon	S	Spring	
		D		
		SC	Spring, late summer	Basal or soft
Chaerophyllum sp.		S		Ripe or stratify
		D		
Chamaemelum nobile	Chamomile	S		
		D		Cultivars
Chamaenerion: see *Chamerion*				
Chamaepericlymenum: see *Cornus*				
Chamaepeuce: see *Ptilostemon*				
Chamerion sp.		S	Spring	
		D	Summer	Rooted runners
		SC	Spring, fall	Alpine sp.
Chartolepis: see *Centaurea*				
Chasmanthium (Uniola) latifolium	Northern Sea Oats	D	Spring	
		S		
Cheilanthes sp.	Lip Fern	D		Use care
		S		Spores, some sp. rare
Cheiranthus: see *Erysimum*				
Chelidonium majus	Swallowwort	S		Sow direct, self sows
Chelone sp.	Shellflower	D	Early spring, fall	
		SC	Spring	Soft tip before budding
		S	Spring	Easy if cold period
Cherleria: see *Minuartia*				
Chiastophyllum oppositifolium		D	Spring, late summer	
		S	Fall	
		SC	Early summer	Side shoots
Chimaphila sp.	Pipsissewa	D		Use care, use native soil
Chimonobambusa sp.	Square Bamboo	D		
Chionochloa sp.	Snow Grass	S, D		
Chionodoxa sp.	Glory of the Snow	S		Sow fresh
		D		Of offset bulblets
Chionohebe sp.		S		Rarely available
		SC		

See footnotes on page 144

continued on next page

Scientific name	Common name[1]	Methods of propagation[2]	Period[3]	Comments/requirements[4]
Chionophila jamesii	Snow-Lover	S		As *Penstemon*
x *Chionoscilla allenii*		S		Sow fresh
		D		Of offset bulblets
Chlidanthus fragrans	Perfumed Fairy Lily	S	Spring	5 years to flw
		D	Spring	Offsets, 3 years to flw
Chloris sp.	Finger Grass	S		
Chondrosum: see *Bouteloua*				
Chrysanthemum: see *Leucanthemum*				
Chrysanthemum x *morifolium*: see *Dendranthema grandiflorum*				
Chrysogonum virginianum	Golden Knee	D	Spring	Clump formers
		S		Ripe, collect as difficult to buy
		L	Summer	
		SC		Avoid summer heat
Chrysoplenium sp.	Golden Saxifrage	S	Fall	As *Parnassia*
		D	Spring	
Chrysopogon gryllis		S		
		D	Spring	
Chrysopsis: see *Heterotheca villosa*				
Chusquea sp.		S		Easy
		D	Spring	Difficult
		L	Summer	Young culms
Cicerbita sp.		S		As *Lactuca*
Cichorium sp.	Chicory	S	Spring, fall	
Cicuta virosa	Water Hemlock	D		Very toxic
Cimicifuga sp.	Bugbane	S		Fresh best, transplant early
		D	Spring, fall	
		RC		
Circaea sp.	Enchanter's Nightshade	S		
Cirsium sp.	Plume Thistle	S		Invasive
		D		Stoloniferous roots, invasive
Cladium sp.		D		As *Carex*
		S		
Claytonia sp.	Spring Beauty	S		
		D		Also offsets
Clematis sp.	Virgin's Bower	S		Sow ripe best, not cvs
		L	Early summer	Early spring – old wood
		SC	Late spring	Herbaceous sp. difficult
		Graft	Early spring	*C. viticella/vitalba*, cleft
		D		Herbaceous sp., may be difficult
		TC		Difficult sp.
Clinopodium (Satureja)	Wild Basil	S	Spring	
		D		
Clintonia sp.		D	Spring	
		S		Ripe, remove pulp, slow
Cnicus benedictus	Blessed Thistle	S		Self sows
		D		

See footnotes on page 144

continued on next page

Scientific name	Common name[1]	Methods of propagation[2]	Period[3]	Comments/requirements[4]
Cochlearia officinalis	Scurvy Grass	S	Spring	
		D		
Codonopsis sp.	Bonnet Bellflower	S	Spring	
		SC	Spring	Basal shoots
		D		Use care, older plants
Colchicum sp.	Autumn Crocus	D	Summer	Older clumps
		S		Of spores, sow fresh
Collinsonia canadensis	Horse Balm	D		Established dormant clumps
Colobanthus sp.		S		Self seeds
		D		Of offsets
Colocasia sp.	Taro, Dasheen	D		Suckers
		RC		Corm sections
Coluteocarpus vesicaria		S		As *Iberis*
		D	Spring, fall	
		SC	Summer	After flw
Comarum: see *Potentilla*				
Commelina sp.	Dayflower	S		
		SC		Bottom heat, easy
Conandron ramondioides		D	Spring	
		LC		
		S		Only from hand pollination
Conradina sp.		SC	Spring	New shoots
		S		
Convallaria sp.	Lily of the Valley	D		After flw, stoloniferous sp.
		S		Ripe best
		SC		Subshrub sp., difficult
Convolvulus sp.	Bindweed	S	Spring	
		SC	Summer	Semi-ripe heel
		D	Spring	
Coptis sp.	Goldenthread	S		Sow fresh, dioecious
		D	Spring	Difficult
Corallodiscus (Didissandra) sp.		S, SC		
Corbularia: see *Narcissus*				
Coreopsis sp.	Tickseed	S		Common, uniform
		SC	Spring–fall	Basal
		D	Spring, fall	
Coris sp.		S	Spring	
Cornus canadensis, suecica	Bunchberry	S		Sow fresh, slow
		D	Fall	Rooted stems
		SC	Summer	Mist
Coronaria: see *Lychnis*				
Coronilla sp.	Crown Vetch	S		
		D	Early spring	Some sp.
Cortaderia sp.	Pampas Grass	D	Late spring	
		S		Short-lived, variable
Cortusa sp.		S		Ripe
		D	Early spring, fall	
		RC	Late summer	Thick, mature roots

See footnotes on page 144

continued on next page

Herbaceous Perennials Production

Scientific name	Common name[1]	Methods of propagation[2]	Period[3]	Comments/requirements[4]
Corydalis sp.		S		Sow fresh, often difficult
		D	Spring	Or after flw
Corynephorus canescens		S		Self sows
Cosmos atrosanguineus	Black Cosmos	SC	Spring	Basal, as *Dahlia*
Cossonia: see *Morisia*				
Cotula sp.	Brass Buttons	D		Of roots
		S		
Cotyledon: see *Rosularia*				
Crambe sp.	Sea Kale	S	Spring, fall	Sow fresh
		RC	Spring	4–6-inch, pencil thick
		D	Spring	
Craspedia sp.	Billy Buttons	S	Spring	Sow fresh
		D	Spring	Use care
Crassula sp.		D		
		SC		Woody sp.
Cremanthodium sp.		S		Sow fresh
Crepis sp.	Hawk's Beard	S		Short-lived plant
		D		*C. aurea, C. jacquinii*
Crinum sp.	Spider Lily	D	Spring	Of bulbil offsets
		S		
Crocosmia sp.	Montbretia	D		Also corm offshoots
		S		Ripe best, loamy mix
Crocus sp.	Crocus	S		Wild sp.
		D		Of bulbils
Crucianella: see *Phuopsis*				
Cruciata (Galium) laevipes		S	Late summer	Fresh
		SC		
		D		Stoloniferous roots
Cryptogramma sp.	Rock Brake Fern	D		
		S		Spores, acid mix
Currania: see *Gymnocarpium*				
Curtonus: see *Crocosmia*				
Cyananthus sp.	Trailing Bellflower	S	Spring, fall	
		SC	Summer	
Cyclamen sp.	Persian Violet	S	Summer	Ripe best
		D		Cormels
		SC		From stem crowns
Cyclobothra: see *Calochortus*				
Cymbalaria sp.		S		Self sows, some sp. invasive
		D		Long-rooted stems
Cymbopogon sp.	Lemon Grass	D	Spring	
Cymophyllus fraseri	Fraser's Sedge	D	Spring	As *Carex*
		S		

See footnotes on page 144

continued on next page

Scientific name	Common name[1]	Methods of propagation[2]	Period[3]	Comments/requirements[4]
Cynara sp.	Cardoon, Artichoke	S	Spring	
		D	Summer	Basal sprouts after flw
		RC	Early spring	Sandy mix
Cynoglossum sp.	Hound's Tongue	S		
		SC	Spring	Basal
		D	Fall, spring	As *Anchusa*
Cyperus sp.	Umbrella Sedge	D		Tubers of *C. esculentus*
		S	Spring	
		SC		Of umbels, root in water
Cypripedium sp.	Lady's Slipper Orchid	D	Early spring	Not endangered sp., difficult
		S		Use native soil
Cyrtomium sp.	Holly Fern	S	Fall	Spores, early, fast
Cystopteris sp.	Bladder Fern	S	Summer, fall	Spores
		D		Also bulbils
Dactylis glomerata	Orchard Grass	D		
Dactylorchis: see *Dactylorhiza*				
Dactylorhiza (Orchis) sp.		D		
		S		Sow fresh
Dahlia hybrids	Dahlia	S	Early spring	
		RC		Basal or of tubers
Dalea sp.	Indigo Bush	S		
Darlingtonia californica	Cobra Lily	S		Sphagnum medium
Darmera (Peltiphyllum) peltata	Umbrella Plant	D	Early spring	
		S	Spring	Hybrids likely
Datisca cannabina		S		
		D		Established plants
Davallia sp.	Hare's Foot Fern	D		Rooted rhizome pieces
		S		Spores
Decodon verticillatus	Water Willow	S, D		
		SC		Roots easily in water
Dedronella: see *Meehania*				
Degenia velebitica		S		
Deinanathe sp.		D		
		S		Ripe, fresh
Delosperma sp.		SC	Late summer, fall	Sandy mix, bottom heat
		S		
Delphinium sp.	Larkspur	S		Fresh seed < one year, species
		SC	Spring	Basal, solid stems
		D	Early summer	Cvs, may be difficult
Dendranthema sp.	Chrysanthemum	SC		
		D	Spring	
Dendrocalamus sp.	Bamboo	D		
Dennstaedtia punctilobula	Hay-Scented Fern	D		
		S		Spores
Dentaria: see *Cardamine*				
Derwentia (Parahebe) perfoliata		D	Spring	

continued on next page

Scientific name	Common name[1]	Methods of propagation[2]	Period[3]	Comments/requirements[4]
Deschampsia sp.	Hair Grass	D		
		S		Variable
Desmodium canadense	Beggarweed	S		Transplant early
Dianthus sp.	Pinks	S		Usual method
		D	Spring–summer	Some sp. difficult
		SC	Spring–summer	Non-flw stems; avoid heat; hormone not needed for soft, early growth
		TC		
Diarrhena japonica		S, D		
Diascia sp.	Twinspur	D	Spring	
		SC	Summer	
		S	Early spring, fall	
Dicentra sp.	Bleeding Heart	S	Spring	
		SC	Spring	Thin, after flw; slow, difficult,
		D	Summer	Preferred method, 2–3 or 3–5 eyes per; corms fall, early spring *D. cucullaria*
		RC	Summer, fall	*D. spectabilis* taproot, use care
Dichelostemma (Brevoortia) sp.		D		Bulbils, offsets
		S		2–3 years to flw
Dicranostigma sp.		S		
Dictamnus sp.	Gas Plant	D	Spring, fall	Difficult, old clumps
		S	Spring	Usual method, also difficult
		RC		Clean cuts
Didissandra: see *Corallodiscus*				
Dielytria: see *Dicentra*				
Dierama sp.	Wand Flower	S	Spring, fall	
		D	Spring	
Digitalis sp.	Foxglove	S		Usual method
		D	Spring	
Dionysia sp.		SC	Summer	Tiny shoots, difficult
		S		Some sp.
Diopogon: see *Jovibarba*				
Dioscorea sp.	Yam	S	Spring	
		D		Dormant tubers
Diosphaera: see *Trachelium*				
Dipcadi sp.	Brown Bells	S		
Diphylleia cymosa	Umbrella Leaf	D	Spring	
		S		Sow fresh
Diplarrhena sp.		D		Also from aerial plantlets
		S		
Diplazium sp.		D		Bulbils of *D. proliferum*
		S		Spores
Dipsacus sp.	Teasel	S	Spring, fall	Sow direct, self sows
Disporum sp.	Fairy Bells	D	Spring	As *Tricyrtis*
		S		
Dodecatheon sp.	Shooting Star	S		Ripe
		D		
		SC	Fall	

See footnotes on page 144

continued on next page

Scientific name	Common name[1]	Methods of propagation[2]	Period[3]	Comments/requirements[4]
Doronicum sp.	Leopard's Bane	S		
		D	Spring, fall	After bloom
Dorycnium sp.		SC	Summer	Bottom heat
		S	Fall	Variable seedlings
		D		
Doryopteris sp.		S		Spores
		D		Crowns, occasional leaf bulbils
Douglasia sp.		S	Late spring	Ripe
		D		Use care
Draba sp.		S	Spring, fall	Sow fresh or stratify
		D	Spring	Base cuttings
		SC	Summer	Soft
Dracocephalum sp.	Dragonhead	S		
		D	Spring, fall	
		SC	Spring	Basal, young growth
Dracunculus sp.	Dragon Arum	S		Sow fresh, remove pulp
		D		After flw
		D	Fall	Bulbils (tubercles)
Drapetes sp.		S, D		
		SC	Spring	Softwood
Drepanostachyum sp.	Bamboo	D		
Drosera sp.	Sundew	S		
		LC		*D. gemmae,* some sp.
		RC		Fleshy-rooted sp.
Dryas sp.	Mountain Avens	S		Ripe
		SC		Heel, semi-ripe, stick flat
		D		Rooted stems
Dryopteris sp.	Wood, Shield Fern	S		Spores
		D		Sprouts, some sp.
Drypis spinosa		SC		
		S	Early spring	Sandy mix
Duchesnea sp.	Indian Strawberry	S	Early spring	
		L	Summer	Remove rooted runners
Eccremocarpus sp.	Glory Flower	S	Spring	Indoors
		S	Late summer	Overwinter 40–45°F
		SC	Early summer	Leaf bud, soft tip
Echinacea sp.	Cone Flower	S	Late summer	
		D	Spring, fall	
		RC	Summer, fall	
		SC	Spring	Basal
Echinodorus sp.	Burhead	D	Spring	As *Alisma*
		S		Ripe, keep wet
Echinops sp.	Globethistle	S		Species
		D	Spring, fall	May be difficult
		RC	Winter	
Echioides: see *Arnebia*				
Echium sp.	Viper's Bugloss	S		
		SC	Summer	Semi-ripe lateral shoots

See footnotes on page 144   *continued on next page*

Scientific name	Common name[1]	Methods of propagation[2]	Period[3]	Comments/requirements[4]
Edraianthus sp.	Grassy Bells	S SC D	Spring Early summer	From side shoots
Egeria (Elodea) sp.		SC	Spring	Submerge in gravel or sand
Eichhornia sp.	Water Hyacinth	D		Young plants on runners
Eleocharis sp.	Spike Rush	D		Washed sand in water
Elisma: see *Luronium*				
Elmera (Heuchera) racemosa		S LC SC D	Spring Fall Spring, early fall	
Elodea sp.	Pondweed	SC	Spring	Submerge in gravel or sand
Elymus sp.	Lyme Grass	D S	Spring	Invasive
Encelia sp.		S SC		Transplant early Do not overwater
Endymion: see *Hyacinthoides*				
Eomecon chionantha	Snow Poppy	S RC D	Spring Early fall Early fall	Sow fresh, plant in spring
Epigaea sp.	Trailing Arbutus	S SC TC L	 Summer, fall Summer	Semi-ripe or hardwood Deep pink forms
Epilobium sp.	Willow Herb	S D SC	Spring Summer Spring, fall	Rooted runners Alpine sp.
Epimedium sp.	Barrenwort	S D RC	Fall, spring Spring, fall Late winter	Not for hybrids Usual method, after flw Rhizomes
Epipactis sp.	Helleborine	D		Stolons, use care
Equisetum sp.	Horsetail	D S		Rooted offshoots, invasive Spores, difficult
Eragrostis sp.	Love Grass	D, S		
Eranthis sp.	Winter Aconite	S D	 Summer	Sow fresh Tubers
Eremurus sp.	Foxtail Lily	D S	Early fall Fall	Of crown, use care Ripe, years to flower
Erianthus: see *Saccharum*				
Erigenia bulbosa	Harbinger-of-Spring	S D		Sow fresh Of tuberous clump
Erigeron sp.	Fleabane	S SC D	 Spring Spring, fall	Species Basal Of clumps, cvs
Erinacea anthyllis		S SC	 Early fall	 Heel

See footnotes on page 144　　　　　　　　　　　　　　　　　　　　　　　　*continued on next page*

Table A-1. Propagation methods for herbaceous perennials *(continued)*

Scientific name	Common name[1]	Methods of propagation[2]	Period[3]	Comments/requirements[4]
Erinus alpinus	Alpine Balsam	S		Many cultivars also
		SC	Spring	Gritty mix
		D		
Eriogonum sp.	Wild Buckwheat	S	Fall, spring	Ripe, may self sow
		D	Early spring	
		SC	Summer	Heeled greenwood
Eriophorum sp.	Cotton Grass	D		As *Carex*
		S		Wet, peaty soil
Eriophyllum sp.	Woolly Sunflower	S	Fall	Sandy mix, fresh best
		D	Spring	
		SC		
Eritrichium sp.	Alpine Forget-Me-Not	S		Difficult
		SC	Summer	Softwood
Erodium sp.	Storksbill	S	Spring	Hybridizes, some sp. dioecious
		D	Spring	
		SC	Early summer	Basal
		RC	Spring	*E. reichardii*
Eryngium sp.	Sea Holly	S		Must be fresh
		RC	Early spring	
		D	Spring, fall	Also basal plantlets, use care, difficult
Erysimum sp.	Wallflower	S	Early summer	
		D	Spring, fall	
		SC	Summer, fall	After flw, heel
Erysium: see Barbarea				
Erythraea: see Centaurium				
Erythronium sp.	Trout Lily	S		Ripe
		D	Late summer	Offsets, some sp.
Eulalia: see Miscanthus				
Eunomia: see Aethionema				
Eupatorium sp.	Boneset	S		Uniformity varies with season
		D	Spring, fall	
		SC	Summer	Tip of non-flw shoots, usual method
Euphorbia sp.	Spurge	S		
		D	Spring, fall	Not of old/woody centers, difficult
		SC	Spring	Terminal before budding
		SC	Summer	Semi-mature after flw, warm water 15 minutes before sticking
Euryops sp.		S		Self sows
		SC	Early summer	Soft or semi-ripe with heel
Euthamia: see Solidago				
Fallopia (Polygonum) sp.	Knotweed, Smartweed	S, RC		
		SC	Late winter	Climbers, nodal (2 buds)
		D	Spring, fall	
		SC	Summer	Soft tip
Fallugia paradoxa	Apache Plume	SC, S		
Fargesia sp.	Bamboo	D		
Farsetia aegyptica		S		As *Fibigia*
Felicia rosulata: see Aster natalensis				

See footnotes on page 144

continued on next page

Scientific name	Common name[1]	Methods of propagation[2]	Period[3]	Comments/requirements[4]
Ferula sp.	Giant Fennel	S	Fall	Sow fresh, transplant early
		D		Use care
Festuca sp.	Fescue	D	Fall	Evergreen sp.
		D	Spring	Or after flw
		S		Variable seedlings
Fibigia sp.		S		
Ficaria: see *Ranunculus*				
Filipendula sp.	Meadowsweet	D	Spring, fall	Often easier than S
		S		Sow fresh
		SC	Spring	
		RC		Some sp.
Foeniculum vulgare	Fennel	S		
		D	Spring	
Fontinalis antipyretica	Water Moss	D	Spring	Large clumps, anchor to rough stone
Fragaria sp.	Strawberry	S	Early spring	
		D		Or rooted runners
Francoa sp.	Bridal Wreath	S	Early spring	
		D		
Frankenia sp.		S		
		D		
		SC		
Frasera sp.	Green Gentian	S	Spring	Cool
		D	Late winter	Clumps
Freesia cultivars		S		
		D	Fall	Offsets
Fritillaria sp.	Fritillary	S	Spring	Or ripe, slow
		D		Of bulbils
Fuchsia sp.	Lady's Eardrops	SC	Spring	Internodal, young shoots, cvs
		S		
Fumana sp.		S		Species
		SC	Summer, early fall	Heel, after flw
		D	Spring	May be difficult
Funkia: see *Hosta*				
Gagea sp.		S		
		D		Offset bulbs
Gaillardia sp.	Blanket Flower	S	Spring	Dwarf cvs may be variable
		SC	Spring	
		RC	Early spring	Or root sprouts, cvs
		D	Spring, fall	Use care
Galanthus sp.	Snowdrop	S		Ripe, 4 years to flw, protect from ants
		D	Fall	Offset bulblets, or after flw
Galax urceolata	Coltsfoot	D	Early spring	Use care, roots and stolons, slow
		RC		Rhizomes
		S	Spring, fall	Slow
		SC	Summer	Leaves with stem section
		TC		Slow

See footnotes on page 144   *continued on next page*

Scientific name	Common name[1]	Methods of propagation[2]	Period[3]	Comments/requirements[4]
Galega sp.	Goat's Rue	D		Of crowns
		S		
Galeobdolon: see *Lamium*				
Galium sp.	Bedstraw	S	Late summer	Not common in U.S., fresh
		SC		
		D		Stoloniferous roots
Galtonia sp.	Summer Hyacinth	S		Ripe
		D		Offsets
Gaura lindheimeri		S		Usually true to type
		D	Spring	Clumps
		SC	Summer	
Gazania sp.	Treasure Flower	S	Early spring	
		SC	Summer	Heel
Gentiana sp.	Gentian	S		Most sp., ripe
		D		Few sp. only
		SC		Sp. without rosettes or taproot
		L		
Geranium sp.	Cranesbill	S		Only 'Buxton's Blue,' species
		SC	Spring–fall	Firm shoots, basal, *sanguineum* fall, *soboliferum* spring, *cinerarium* spring
		RC	Spring, fall	Rhizomes, some sp.
		D	Spring, fall	Easy before fully leafed
Geum sp.	Avens	S		May not come true
		D	Spring, fall	Cultivars, easy
Gillenia (Porteranthus) sp.	Bowman's Root	S	Spring, fall	
		D	Spring	
		SC		Tip
Gladiolus sp.	Gladiolus	S		Species
		D		Offset cormlets
Glaucidium palmatum		S		
		D	Spring	Use care
Glaucium sp.	Horned Poppy	S		
		D		Short-lived, difficult to transplant
Glechoma hederacea	Ground Ivy	SC	Spring, summer	Stem tip or softwood
		S	Fall	
		D	Spring, fall	
Globularia sp.	Globe Daisy	S		Ripe
		D, SC		
Gloriosa superba	Glory Lily	S	Late winter	Sandy mix
		D	Spring	Use care, or offsets, toxic
Glyceria sp.	Sweet Grass	D	Spring	
		RC	Winter	Rhizomes
Glycyrrhiza sp.	Licorice	D	Early spring	Deep roots
		S	Spring, fall	
Gnaphalium (Anaphalis) sp.	Cudweed	D	Spring	As *Helichrysum*
		S	Spring	
Goniolimon (Limonium) sp.	Statice	S	Spring	Usual method
		RC		
		D		Slow to spread

See footnotes on page 144

continued on next page

Scientific name	Common name[1]	Methods of propagation[2]	Period[3]	Comments/requirements[4]
Gratiola officinalis	Hedge Hyssop	S		
		D	Spring	Poisonous
Grindelia sp.	Gum Plant	S		
		SC	Late summer	Shrubby sp.
Groenlandia densa	Frog's Lettuce	SC	Spring, summer	Scaly resting buds in spring
Gromania: see Sedum				
Gunnera sp.		S	Fall	Sow fresh, difficult, slow
		D	Spring	Lie flat on ground
		SC		Basal leafy buds
Gymnocarpium sp.	Oak Fern	D		
		S		Spores
Gymnospermium sp.		S		
Gymnothrix: see Pennisetum				
Gynerium: see Cortaderia				
Gypsophila sp.	Baby's Breath	S		Doubles
		SC		After flw, vegetative shoots best
		TC		
		Graft		Seldom used now
		D		*G. repens*, after flw; difficult others
Habenaria sp.	Fringed Orchis	D, S		
Haberlea sp.		S		As *Ramonda*
		D		
		LC		
Hacquetia epipactis		S		Fresh seed
		D	Early spring	Use care
		RC		
Hakonechloa macra		D		
Halacsya sendtneri		S		
		SC	Summer	Needs ophite stone
Haplocarpha sp.		S	Early spring	
		SC	Summer	Heel
Haplopappus sp.		S, D		
		SC		Semi-ripe, sandy mix
Haplophyllum patavinum		S		Self sows
		D		
Harpalium: see Helianthus				
Hebe sp.		SC	Late summer	Heel, semi-ripe
		S		Seedlings variable, 3-4 years to flw
Hedyotis: see Houstonia				
Hedysarum sp.	French Honeysuckle	S	Spring	Sow ripe seed
		L		
		D	Spring	Established plants, use care
Helenium sp.	Helen's Flower, Sneezeweed	S		
		SC	Spring, early summer	Basal, soft growth best
		D	Spring	
Heleocharis: see Eleocharis				

continued on next page

Scientific name	Common name[1]	Methods of propagation[2]	Period[3]	Comments/requirements[4]
Helianthella sp.		S		As *Heliopsis*
		D		
Helianthemum sp.	Rock Rose	S		Species
		SC	Summer, early fall	Heel, after flw
		D	Spring	May be difficult
Helianthus sp.	Sunflower	S		
		SC		Basal, soft growth best
		D		After flw
Helichrysum sp.	Everlasting	S		Prefers sandy soil
		D		Some sp.
		SC		Semi-ripe tips, woody sp.
Helictotrichon sp.	Oat Grass	D	Spring	
		S		Cold to germinate
Heliohebe hulkeana		SC	Late summer	Heel, semi-ripe
		S		Seedlings variable, 3–4 years to flw
Heliopsis helianthoides	Oxeye Daisy	S		Reliably true
		SC	Spring	Prior to budding
		D	Spring, fall	
Heliosperma: see *Silene*				
Helipterum sp.	Everlastings	S		As *Helichrysum*
Helleborus sp.	Hellebore	S		Sow fresh, flw 2–3 years
		D	Spring	Of roots, not *H. foetidus*, difficult
		SC		Young vegetative shoots
Helonias bullata	Swamp Pink	S		Sow fresh
		D		Tubercles, after flw, usual method
Heloniopsis orientalis		S	Spring	Or ripe
		D		After flw
Hemerocallis sp.	Daylily	D	Spring–fall	Mature plants, cut back leaves to 6"
		TC		
		S		Breeding
Hepatica sp.	Liverleaf	D	Spring, fall	Older clumps, doubles
		S	Early summer	Maybe 1 year to germ
Heracleum sp.	Hogweed	S		Ripe
		D		Rootstock, toxic sap
Herniaria sp.	Rupturewort	D	Spring	Short-lived
		SC		Bottom heat
		S		Short-lived
Hertia: see *Othonna*				
Hesperaloe sp.		S		As *Nolina*
		D	Spring	Offsets
Hesperis sp.	Rocket	S	Spring, fall	Usual method
		SC	Spring	Double forms, basal
		D	Fall	When dormant
Hesperochiron sp.		S		As *Romanzoffia*
Heterotheca sp.	Golden Aster	D		
		S		Self sows but not invasive

See footnotes on page 144

continued on next page

Herbaceous Perennials Production

Scientific name	Common name[1]	Methods of propagation[2]	Period[3]	Comments/requirements[4]
Heuchera sp.	Coral Bells	S	Spring	Not cvs
		LC		
		SC		Avoid heat
		D	Spring, early fall	Single divisions of clumps
		TC		
x *Heucherella* sp.		D, SC, LC		
Hexastylis: see *Asarum*				
Hibanobambusa tranquillans	Bamboo	D		
Hibiscus sp.	Mallow	D	Fall, spring	Fall easier
		L	Summer	
		SC	Spring, early summer	Shrubby sp., bottom heat
		S	Spring	
		TC		
Hieracium sp.	Hawkweed	S		Not *H.* x *rubrum*
		D		Also runners
Himalayacalamus hookerianus		D		
Hippocrepis comosa	Horseshoe Vetch	S	Spring, fall	Transplant early, may self sow
		D		
		SC		Non-flw stems
Hippolytia (Tanacetum) herderi		S		
		SC	Summer	Softwood, with heel, alpines
Hippuris vulgaris	Mare's Tail	SC		Submerge
Holcus sp.		D	Spring	
		S		Species
Homogyne sp.		S		Ripe, fresh
		D		
Hoorebekia: see *Grindelia*				
Hordeum sp.	Barley	S		
Horkelia sp.		S		
Horminum pyrenaicum	Dragon Mouth	S		Self sows, preferred method
		D	Spring, fall	
Hosta sp.	Plantain Lily, Funkia	D	Spring, early summer	Most common, single eye
		TC		
		S		Breeding, not true, species
Hottonia sp.	Water Violet	S		Keep wet
		D		
		SC		In water or mud
Houstonia (Hedyotis) sp.	Bluet	S	Spring	
		D	Spring, fall	
Houttuynia cordata		D	Spring	
		SC	Spring, summer	
		S		
Hugueninia tanacetifolia	Tansy-Leaved Rocket	S		
Hulsea sp.		S		
		D		As *Andryala*

See footnotes on page 144   *continued on next page*

Table A-1. Propagation methods for herbaceous perennials *(continued)*

Scientific name	Common name[1]	Methods of propagation[2]	Period[3]	Comments/requirements[4]
Humulus sp.	Hops	S	Fall	Not for cultivars
		RC		Sucker shoots
		SC	Spring	Semi-soft
Hutchinsia (Pritzelago, Thlaspi) alpina		S	Spring, fall	Sow fresh or stratify
		D	Spring	Base cuttings
		SC	Summer	Soft
Hyacinthella sp.		S		Sow fresh
		D		Offsets after flw
Hyacinthoides sp.	Wood Hyacinth	S	Spring	Or when ripe
		D		Bulblets
Hyacinthus orientalis	Hyacinth	S		
		D	Fall	Bulbils from "scoring" bulbs
Hydrastis canadensis	Golden Seal	D	Fall	Rhizome, after foliage dies
		S		Sow ripe, slow
Hydrocharis sp.	Frogbit	S		Keep wet
		D	Winter	Buds on pond bottom
Hydrocotyle sp.	Pennywort	D		Rooted stems
		S		
Hydrophyllum sp.	Waterleaf	S		
		D	Spring, fall	
Hylomecon japonica		D		As *Chelidonium*
		S		
Hylotelephium: see *Sedum*				
Hymenocallis sp.	Spider Lily	S		
		D		Offsets
Hymenoxys sp.	Alpine Sunflower	S		
		D		Some sp.
Hyoscyamus sp.	Henbane	S	Summer	Old seed erratic germ, self sows
Hypericum sp.	St. John's Wort	S	Spring	Sow fresh < one year
		SC	Summer, fall	Basal softwood, terminal fall
		D	Spring	Layers
Hypochaeris sp.	Cat's Ear	S		As *Arnica*
Hypolepis sp.		S		Spores self sow
		D		Defoliates before rooting
Hypoxis sp.	Star Grass	S		
		D	Summer	Just after flw
		D	Fall	Short runners
Hyppolytia: see *Hippolytia*				
Hypsela sp.		D	Spring	
Hyssopus officinalis	Hyssop	S		
		SC	Early summer	Softwood
Hystix patula	Bottle Brush Grass	D	Spring	
		S		

See footnotes on page 144

continued on next page

Table A-1. Propagation methods for herbaceous perennials *(continued)*

Scientific name	Common name[1]	Methods of propagation[2]	Period[3]	Comments/requirements[4]
Iberis sp.	Candytuft	SC	Summer	After flw, hormone helps
		D	Spring, fall	Difficult
		S		Nonuniform flw
Iliamna sp.	Wild Hollyhock	S		Slow, erratic
		D		
Imperata cylindrica	Japanese Blood Grass	D	Spring	
Incarvillea sp.	Hardy Gloxinia	S	Spring	
		D	Summer	After flw, difficult
Indigofera sp.	Indigo	SC		Semi-ripe laterals with heel
		RC, S		
		D		Remove suckers
Indocalamus sp.		D	Spring	2nd year or older shoots
Inula sp.		S		
		D	Fall, early spring	Tubers
Ipheion sp.	Spring Starflower	S	Spring	
		D	Late summer	Offsets, for varieties
Ipomopsis sp.		S	Late summer	
Iris cristata		D		
		SC	Late spring	Base of fans, mist
Iris sibirica	Siberian Iris	D	Spring, fall	
Iris sp. (Germanica type)	Bearded Iris	D	Summer	After flw, cut foliage back to 6"
Isatis sp.	Woad	S	Spring, fall	*I. boissieriana* spring
		D		*I. glauca*
Isophyrum sp.	False Rue Anemone	S	Summer	Fresh
		D	Fall	Well-established plants
Ivesia gordonii		S		
		D		As *Potentilla*
Ixia sp.	Corn Lily	S	Fall	Flw 3rd or 4th year
		D		Offsets, flw 2nd year
Ixiolirion sp.	Siberian Lily	D	Summer	Offsets, after flw
		S	Fall	
Jankaea heldreichii		D	Spring	Multistemmed, use care
		LC	Summer	Slow, variable
		S	Summer	
Jasione sp.	Sheep's Bit	S		Prefers sandy soil
		D, SC		
Jeffersonia sp.	Twin Leaf	S	Summer	Fresh, ripe
		D	Early spring	Woody central root
Jovibarba (Diopogon) sp.		D	Summer	Secondary rosettes
		S		Rare
Juncus sp.	Rush	D	Winter	Dormant clumps
		S		
Jurinea sp.		D		Usual method
		S		As *Carlina*

See footnotes on page 144

continued on next page

Scientific name	Common name[1]	Methods of propagation[2]	Period[3]	Comments/requirements[4]
Jurinella moschus		S		Not easily transplanted
		RC		As *Carlina*, difficult
Jussiaea: see *Ludwigia*				
Kalimeris (Asteromoea) sp.		S		
		D	Spring, fall	As *Boltonia*
		SC	Late spring	Before budding
Kelseya uniflora		D	Spring	
		SC		Porous, limed medium, soft tip
		S	Fall	
Kentranthus: see *Centranthus*				
Kernera sp.		S		As *Cochlearia*
Kirengeshoma sp.		D	Spring	
		S		May be slow (10 months)
		SC	Spring	
Kitaibelia vitifolia		S	Spring, fall	
		SC		
		D		
Knautia sp.		S		
		SC		Basal
Kniphofia (Tritoma) sp.	Torch Lily	S		Species only
		D	Early spring	Or after flw
Koeleria sp.	Crested Hair Grass	D	Spring	
		S		
Koellia: see *Pycnanthemum*				
Korolkowia: see *Fritillaria*				
Lactuca sp.	Lettuce	S		
Lagenophora sp.		S	Spring	Not invasive
		D		
Lagotis stolonifera		S, D		
		SC		Rooted runners
Lamiastrum: see *Lamium galeobdolon*				
Lamium (Lamiastrum) galeobdolon	Yellow Archangel	D		Of stolons
		SC		Terminal, easy
Lamium sp.	Dead Nettle	S		Non-variegated cvs
		SC		Rooted runners, easy
		D		*L. orvala*
Lamyra: see *Ptilostemon*				
Laserpitium sp.		S		Hard to transplant
Lasiagrostis: see *Stipa*				
Lastrea: see *Dryopteris, Thelypteris* et al.				
Lathyrus sp.	Sweet Pea	S, L		
		RC	Spring	
		SC	Spring, fall	Non-flw shoots
		D		Non-climbing sp.
Lavandula sp.	Lavender	S		Self sows where warm, slow
		SC	Summer	One year wood, hormone helps
		L		Older plants
		D	Fall	Of roots, difficult

See footnotes on page 144

continued on next page

Scientific name	Common name[1]	Methods of propagation[2]	Period[3]	Comments/requirements[4]
Lavatera sp.	Tree Mallow	S	Late summer	Biennial sp.
		SC	Spring, fall	Basal shoots
		SC	Early summer	
Leibnitzia sp.		S		
Lemna sp.	Duckweed	D		Small colonies onto water surface, may be invasive
Leontice leontopetalum		S		Slow, deep pots, dry
Leontodon (Microseris) sp.		S		
		D		As *Pilosella*
Leontopodium sp.	Edelweiss	S		Fresh, some sp. difficult
		D	Early spring, fall	Root
Leonurus sp.	Motherwort	S, D		
Lepachys: see *Ratibida*				
Lepidium sp.	Cress	S, SC		
Leptandra: see *Veronicastrum*				
Leptarrhena pyrolifolia		S		Acid, moist medium
		D		As *Heuchera*
Leptinella sp.		S		Fresh
		D		
Leptosyne: see *Coreopsis*				
Leucanthemella serotina		S		
		D	Spring, early fall	
		SC	Spring	Basal
		SC	Summer	Softwood, with heel, alpines
Leucanthemopsis sp.				As *Leucanthemum*
Leucanthemum sp.	Daisy	S	Early summer	Often poor vigor
		SC	Summer	
		D	Spring, fall	
Leucogenes sp.	No./So. Island Edelweiss	S		Ripe
		SC	Early summer	
Leucojum sp.	Snowflake	S	Summer	Sow ripe
		D	Spring, fall	Older clumps
Leucorinum montanum		S		Hard to transplant
Leuzea sp.		S		Related to *Centaurea*
		D		
Levisticum officinale	Lovage	D		
		S		Sow fresh, self sows
Lewisia sp.		S		Fresh, hybrids likely, best for rosettes
		D	Summer	Offsets, evergreen sp.
		LC	Summer	With stem portion
Leymus sp.		D	Spring	Invasive
		S		
Liatris sp.	Blazing Star	S	Fall	Ripe, true to type
		D	Spring, fall	Roots, also from corms

 continued on next page

Table A-1. Propagation methods for herbaceous perennials *(continued)*

Scientific name	Common name[1]	Methods of propagation[2]	Period[3]	Comments/requirements[4]
Libertia sp.		D	Spring	Use care
		S		
Ligularia sp.	Leopard Plant	D	Spring, fall	
		S		Species, some cvs
		RC		5–6" length, easy, better cvs
Ligusticum sp.	Alpine Lovage	S	Fall	
		D		
Lilium sp. and hybrids	Lily	D	Summer	Scales or stem bulbils on some sp.
		S, TC		
Limnanthemum: see *Nymphoides*				
Limnanthes douglasii	Poached Egg Flower	S	Spring, fall	Often grown as annual
Limonium sp.	Sea Lavender	S		Species
		D	Spring	Difficult
		RC	Spring	*L. latifolium*
Linaria sp.	Toadflax	S	Spring	*L. alpina* – sow direct
		S	Early spring	Includes some cvs
		D		
		SC	Spring, late summer	Basal or soft
Lindelofia sp.		S	Early spring	Flw 2nd year
		D		Use care
Linnaea borealis	Twin Flower	D, L		
		SC	Spring	Rooted stem sections
Linosyris vulgaris: see *Aster linosyris*				
Linum sp.	Flax	SC	Summer	Non-flw shoots, basal
		S		Most common and reliable
		D	Spring, fall	May be difficult, short-lived
Lippia (Phyla) sp.		SC	Early summer	Semi-ripe, bottom heat
		S		
Liriope sp.	Lily Turf	D	Spring, fall	Named cvs, acid soil, shade
		S		Species
		TC		
Lithodora sp.		SC		Semi-ripe, non-flw shoots
		S		
Lithophragma sp.	Woodland Star	S		Moist soil, shade
		D	Early spring	Or bulbils
Lithospermum sp.	Gromwell, Puccoon	S		
		SC	Summer	Hard to transplant
Littorella uniflora	Shoreweed	SC		Stolons, submerge
Llogdia serotina		S		
		D		Rhizome
Lloydia sp.	Snowdon Lily	S	Spring	
Lobelia sp.		S	Fall	Most common, hybridize
		D	Spring, fall	Fall–basal, spring–rosettes
		SC	Summer	*L. siphilitica*, leaf bud
		L		*L. cardinalis* under mist
Lomara: see *Blechnum*				
Lotus sp.	Trefoil	S	Spring	Species
		SC	Summer	Semi-ripe
		D		Cultivars, hard to transplant

See footnotes on page 144

continued on next page

Herbaceous Perennials Production

Scientific name	Common name[1]	Methods of propagation[2]	Period[3]	Comments/requirements[4]
Ludwigia (Jussiaea) sp.	False Loosestrife	S		Wet, submerge aquatic sp.
		SC	Early spring	
		D	Spring	Where possible
Luetkia pectinata		S	Spring	
		D		
		SC	Spring	Soft tip
Lunaria sp.	Honesty	S		
		D		L. rediviva
Lupinus sp.	Lupine	S		
		SC	Early spring	Basal
		D	Early spring	Difficult
Luronium natans		SC	Summer	Runners
Luzula sp.	Wood Rush	D	Spring, fall	
		S		Species
Lychnis sp.	Catchfly	S		Ripe
		SC	Summer	Basal in spring
		D	Spring, fall	Non-flw stems
Lycopus sp.	Bugleweed	D		Rhizomes
		S	Spring	
Lycoris sp.	Spider Lily	S		Ripe
		D		Offset bulbs
Lygodium palmatum	Climbing Fern	D		Moist, very acid soil
		S		Spores
Lymanthiemum: see Nymphoides				
Lysichiton sp.	Skunk Cabbage	D		Young basal plants
		S	Late summer	Ripe, wet mix
Lysimachia sp.	Loosestrife	SC	Spring	
		S		Not common in U.S.
		D		
		RC		Many sp., invasive
Lythrum sp.	Loosestrife	S		Not true, invasive
		SC	Spring	Tip, before budding, easy
		D	Spring, fall	Woody roots, difficult, slow
Macleaya (Bocconia) sp.	Plume Poppy	D	Early spring	Suckers, or while dormant
		S		
		SC	Spring	Basal
		RC		
Macrochloa: see Stipa				
Maianthemum sp.	Canada Mayflower	D		
		S		Humus soil
Majorana: see Origanum				
Malva sp.	Mallow	S		May self sow
		SC	Spring	Tip, before budding
		D	Spring, fall	Difficult
Malvastrum (Sphaeralcea) sp.		S		
		D		
		SC		Softwood, bottom heat
Mandragora sp.	Mandrake	S	Spring	Or when ripe
		RC	Winter	Taproot

See footnotes on page 144

continued on next page

Scientific name	Common name[1]	Methods of propagation[2]	Period[3]	Comments/requirements[4]
Manfreda sp.		S		Slow
		D		Offsets, bulbils
Marrubium sp.	Horehound	S	Late spring	Erratic
		SC	Spring	New growth
		L, D		
Marsilea sp.	Pepperwort	D		Wet soil
		S		Spores (abrade sporocarps)
Matricaria sp.	Matricary	S, SC, D		
Matteuccia sp.	Ostrich Fern	S		Spores
		D		Side crowns some sp.
		SC		Stolons
Matthiola fruticulosa	Stock	S, D		
Mazus sp.		S		
		D		Runners
Meconopsis sp.	Asiatic Poppy	S	Late summer	Ripe, slow in spring
		D	Spring, fall	After flw, some sp.
Meehania sp.	Japanese Dead Nettle	D		Rhizomes, rooted stolons
		S, SC		
Megasea: see *Bergenia*				
Melandrium: see *Silene*				
Melanthium sp.	Bunchflower	D		Difficult, as *Veratrum*
		S		Sow ripe
Melica sp.	Melic	D	Spring	
		S		
Melissa officinalis	Lemon Balm	S		Self sows, slow
		D	Spring, fall	Basal shoots
		SC		
Melittis melissophyllum	Bastard Balm	D	Spring	
		S, SC		
Mentha sp.	Mint	D, SC		
		RC		Invasive, rhizomes
		S		May self sow, hybridizes, some infertile, *M. pulegium* and *requienii*
Menyanthes trifoliata	Marsh Trefoil	D	Late spring	
		RC	Summer	Rhizomes, wet soil
Mercurialis perennis		D		
		SC		Stolons, invasive, shade
Merendera sp.		S	Summer	Spring flw sp., moist in spring, dry in summer
		S	Spring	Fall flw sp.
Mertensia sp.	Bluebells	S	Summer	Shade, *M. maritima*
		D	Spring, fall	Use care, fall after foliage best
		SC		
Mesembryanthemum: see *Delosperma*				
Meum athamanticum	Baldmoney	D		Difficult
		S		Sow fresh
Michauxia campanuloides		S	Spring	Sow direct

See footnotes on page 144

continued on next page

Scientific name	Common name[1]	Methods of propagation[2]	Period[3]	Comments/requirements[4]
Microderis: see *Leontodon*				
Microglossa: see *Aster albescens*				
Micromeria sp.	Savory	S		May self sow
		SC	Summer	Softwood and semi-ripe
Microseris: see *Leontodon*				
Milium effusum	Wood Millet	S		May hybridize, self sows
		D		
Milla biflora	Mexican Star	S	Spring	As *Ipheion*
		D	Late summer	Offsets, for varieties
Milla uniflora: see *Ipheion uniflorum*				
Mimulus sp.	Monkey Flower	S	Spring	Or sow direct
		D	Spring	
		SC	Spring, summer	Softwood
		SC	Late summer	Shrubby sp., semi-ripe
Mindium: see *Michauxia*				
Minuartia sp.	Sandwort	S	Spring	
		D		After flw
		SC	Summer	Cvs, greenwood
Miscanthus sp.	Eulalia	D	Spring	
		S		Indoors in cool climates
Mitchella sp.	Partridge Berry	D	Spring	Rooted stems, acid soil, shade
		S		Slow, remove from berry
Mitella sp.	Bishop's Cap, Mitrewort	D		Rhizomes or stolons
		S		May self sow
Moehringia muscosa	Sandwort	S	Early spring	
		D	Fall	Lime and humus soil
Molinia sp.	Moor Grass	D	Early spring	
		S		Cold to germinate
Molopospermum peloponnesiacum		S		Sow fresh
Moltkia sp.		S		
		L		
		SC		Lime soil
Monarda sp.	Bee Balm	S		Species only
		D	Spring, fall	
		SC	Spring, fall	Prior to budding, basal fall–winter
Moneses uniflora	Wood Nymph	D	Spring	Use care, as *Pyrola*
Montbretia: see *Crocosmia*				
Montia (Claytonia) sp.	Miner's Lettuce	S		Self sows
Moraea sp.	Butterfly Iris	S	Spring	Summer flw sp.
		D	Fall	Winter flw sp.
Moricandia arvensis	Violet Cabbage	S		
Morina sp.	Whorl Flower	S		Ripe, sow direct
		RC		Large and thick, well-drained mix
		D		Risky, taproot, slow
Morisia monanthos		S	Fall	
		RC	Winter	Sandy soil, keep dry

continued on next page

Scientific name	Common name[1]	Methods of propagation[2]	Period[3]	Comments/requirements[4]
Muehlenbeckia sp.	Wire Plant	D		*M. axillaris*
		S		
		SC	Summer	Move when well-rooted
Muhlenbergia sp.		S		
		RC		Rhizomes, invasive
Mukdenia (Aceriphyllum) rossii		D		As *Heuchera*
		S		Self-sterile
Muscari sp.	Grape Hyacinth	D	Late summer	Bulb clusters
		S	Late spring	Sow fresh, ripe
Myosotidium hortensia		S	Fall	
		D		Difficult, taproot, use care
Myosotis sp.	Forget-Me-Not	S		
		SC	Spring, summer	
		D	Spring, early fall	
Myriophyllum sp.	Milfoil	SC		Wet soil, invasive
		D		
Myrrhis odorata	Myrrh, Sweet Cicely	S		Ripe, self sows
		D		Use care
		RC	Spring, fall	
Narcissus sp.	Daffodil	D		Clumps
Nardus stricta		D		Acid soil
		S		
Narthecium sp.	Bog Asphodel	S		
		D		Peaty, moist soil
Nasturtium sp.	Watercress	SC	Spring	Roots easily in water
		S		
Naumbergia: see *Lysimachia*				
Nectaroscordum siculum	Sicilian Honey Garlic	S	Early spring	
		D		Offset bulblets
Nelumbo sp.	Lotus	S		Flw 3rd year, keep wet
		D		Submerged in gravel, difficult
Neopaxia: see *Claytonia*				
Nepeta sp.	Catmint	SC	Spring, summer	Stem tip or softwood, easy
		S	Fall	
		D	Spring, fall	
Nerine sp.		D		Offset bulblets
Nierembergia sp.	Cupflower	S	Spring	
		D	Spring	Rooted stems, creeping sp.
		SC	Summer	Heel, subshrub sp., sandy
Nipponanthemum nipponicum		S		
		D		
Nitella sp.	Stonewort	D		
		SC		Submerge
Nitholaena: see *Cheilanthes*				
Nomocharis sp.		S	Spring	Acid, moist, shade, epigeal
Nothoscordum sp.	False Garlic	D		Offset bulbs
		S		May be invasive

See footnotes on page 144

continued on next page

Scientific name	Common name[1]	Methods of propagation[2]	Period[3]	Comments/requirements[4]
Nuphar sp.	Cow Lily	D		Rhizomes, invasive
Nymphaea sp.	Water Lily	S		Sow submerged with pulp, usually sp.
		D		Rhizomes, submerge pot
		TC		
Nymphoides sp.	Floating Heart	D	Fall	Stems with rooted nodes
		D	Spring	
		S		Sow submerged, erratic
Oenanthe sp.		SC		Stem tip
		D		*O. crocata* toxic to livestock
		L		Often spontaneous
Oenothera sp.	Evening Primrose	S	Spring	
		RC	Summer	
		D	Fall, spring	After flw
		SC		Some sp. even root in flw
Olymposciadium: see *Seseli*				
Omphalodes sp.	Navelwort	S		
		D	Spring	Use care, difficult
Omphalogramma sp.		S		Related to *Primula*
		D	Spring	Acid soil, moist
		LC		
Onobrychis sp.	Holy Clover	S		Sow direct
Onoclea sensibilis	Sensitive Fern	S		Spores
		D		Rhizome
		RC		Rhizome
Ononis sp.	Rest Harrow	S	Spring	Sow direct or ripe in fall, taproot
		SC	Early summer	Shrub sp., bottom heat
		D	Early spring	Before growth
Onopordum sp.	Cotton Thistle	S	Spring, fall	Sow direct best
Onosma sp.		S		Well-drained mix, high pH
		SC	Summer	Some sp. irritate skin
Ophiopogon sp.	Mondo Grass	D		Acid soil, like *Liriope*
		S		Ripe, not for cvs
Ophrys sp.		S		Sow direct, difficult
		D		Tuber, during flw
Opithandra primuloides		SC		
		S		
Opuntia sp.	Prickly Pear	D		Joints, lay flat on soil
		S		
Orchis (Dactylorhiza) sp.		S		Some sp. self sow
		D		Tubers, humus and acid soil
Oreobroma: see *Lewisia*				
Oreopteris sp.	Mountain Fern	S	Summer	Spores, as *Thelypteris*
Origanum sp.	Marjoram, Oregano	S	Spring	
		D		Some sp.
		SC	Spring, summer	Softwood
Ornithogalum sp.		D	Fall	Offsets, bulbils
		S		Ripe

See footnotes on page 144

continued on next page

Table A-1. Propagation methods for herbaceous perennials (continued)

Scientific name	Common name[1]	Methods of propagation[2]	Period[3]	Comments/requirements[4]
Orobanche sp.	Broomrape	S		Parasitic, sow direct onto host roots
Orobus: see Lathyrus				
Orontium aquaticum	Golden Club	S	Summer	Submerge, often self sows, sow ripe
		D	Early summer	Rhizome
Orostachys sp.		S		
		D	Spring, summer	Secondary rosettes
Orthilia secunda		D		
		S		Use native soil, as Pyrola
Oryzopsis miliacea	Rice Grass	D	Spring	
		S	Spring	Sow direct
Osmunda sp.	Flowering Fern	S		Sow very fresh spores, cvs come true
		D		Massive rootstock
		TC		
Osteospermum sp.	Star of the Veldt	S	Spring	Most flower 1st year
		SC	Summer	Heel, sandy mix
Ostrowskia magnifica	Giant Bellflower	S		Slow, difficult, flw in 3 years
		RC		Thick, stick vertical
Othonna sp.		S		
		SC	Early summer	O. cheirifolia by softwood
Othonnopsis: see Othonna				
Ourisia sp.		S		Fresh, peat soil
		D	Spring	
Oxalis sp.	Shamrock	S		Sow ripe, acid soil
		D		Also offsets
Oxygria digyna	Mountain Sorrel	S		Self sows, acid soil
		D		
Oxypetalum: see Tweedia				
Oxyria digyna	Mountain Sorrel	S		
		D		
Oxytropis sp.	Locoweed	S	Early spring	Sow direct, hard to transplant
		D		May need appropriate Rhizobium
Ozothamnus sp.		SC	Summer	Semi-ripe
Pachistima: see Paxistima				
Pachysandra sp.	Spurge	D		
		SC	Summer	Branches or rhizomes
		S		P. procumbens
Paederota sp.		S		As Veronica
		D		Use care
		SC		
Paeonia hybrids	Peony	D	Early fall	Minimum 3 eyes/buds per
		S	Fall	Firm, ripe; 4–5 yrs. to flw
		G, L, RC		Tree types
Pancratium sp.		D		Offsets
		S		Ripe, as Hymenocallis
Panicum sp.	Panic Grass	D	Spring	
		S		Species

See footnotes on page 144

continued on next page

Herbaceous Perennials Production

Scientific name	Common name[1]	Methods of propagation[2]	Period[3]	Comments/requirements[4]
Papaver sp.	Poppy	S		Most sp.
		RC	Late summer, winter	After flw, *P. orientale*, horizontal
		D	Late summer	After plants dormant
Paradisea sp.	St. Bruno's Lily	D	Early spring	Or after flw
		S	Spring	
Parahebe sp.		D	Spring	
		S		Hybridizes
		SC	Late summer	
Parathelypteris: see *Thelypteris*				
x *Pardancanda* sp.		S		
Pardanthus: see *Belamcanda*				
Paris sp.		D		Rhizome, use care
		S	Fall	Ripe, use native soil, slow, dioecious
Parnassia sp.	Grass of Parnassus	S	Late fall	
		D	Spring	
Parochetus communis	Shamrock Pea	S		If fertile
		RC		Rooted runners
		D		
Paronychia sp.	Whitlowwort	D	Spring	
		SC		Bottom heat
Parrya (Phoenicaulis) sp.		S	Spring, fall	Sow fresh or stratify
		D	Spring	Base cuttings
		SC	Summer	Softwood, as *Draba*
Passiflora sp.	Passion Flower	SC		Heel or nodal
		G		Onto *P. caerulea* for more hardiness
		S		
Pastinaca sativa	Parsnip	S	Late spring	Fresh, slow, photodermititis from sap
Patrinia sp.		D	Spring	Easy
		S		As *Valeriana*
Paxistima canbyi	Mountain Lover	SC	Late summer	Semi-ripe, bottom heat
		D		
Pedicularis sp.	Lousewort	S		Use native soil
		D	Spring	
Pelargonium endlicherianum	Stork's Bill	SC		
		S		
Pellaea sp.	Cliff Brake Ferns	S		Spores, as *Adiantum*
Peltandra sp.	Arrow Arum	D	Spring	Rhizomes or secondary shoots
		S		Moist loam, as *Calla*
Peltiphyllum: see *Darmera*				
Peltoboykinia sp.		S	Spring	Not cvs
		LC	Fall	
		SC		
		D	Spring, early fall	As *Heuchera*
Pennisetum sp.	Foxtail, Fountain Grass	D	Spring	
		S		*P. orientale*
Penstemon sp.	Beardtongue	S		Species
		D	Spring	Basal tufts, some sp.
		SC	Late summer, fall	Semi-ripe
		SC	Spring, early summer	Non-flw stems, softwood

See footnotes on page 144   *continued on next page*

Scientific name	Common name[1]	Methods of propagation[2]	Period[3]	Comments/requirements[4]
Pentaglottis sempervirens		S		As *Brunnera*
Percidium: see *Leibnitzia*				
Perezia sp.		SC, S, D		
Perovskia sp.	Russian Sage	SC	Summer	Excessive moisture may rot, or laterals with heel, rooting hormone if woody
		S		Species
		D		Uncommon
Persicaria (Polygonum, Tovara) sp.	Knotweed, Smartweed	S		
		SC	Late winter	Climbers, nodal (2 buds)
		RC		
		D	Spring, fall	
		SC	Summer	Soft tip
Petalostemon: see *Dalea*				
Petasites sp.	Butterbur	D		Rhizomes
Petrocallis pyrenaica		S		Lime soil, like *Draba*
		SC	Late summer	Lower, lateral shoots
Petrocoptis sp.	Catchfly	S	Early spring	Lime soil, like *Lychnis*
		D		
Petrophytum sp.	Rock Spiraea	S		
		D		
Petrorhagia sp.		S	Early spring	Species
		SC	Early summer	Softwood, non-flw shoots
		D		
Petroselinum crispum	Parsley	S		May be slow
Peucedanum sp.		S		Sow fresh, self sows
Phacelia sp.	Scorpion Weed	S	Spring	
Phalaris sp.	Canary Grass	D	Spring	
Pharium: see *Bessera*				
Phegopteris sp.	Beech Fern	D		Usual method
		S	Summer	Ripe spores
Phlomis sp.		SC	Summer	Shrubby sp.
		SC	Fall	Semi-ripe, sandy mix
		L		
		D	Spring, fall	Use care, *P. tuberosa*
		S	Spring	
Phlox sp.	Garden Phlox	RC	Fall	Not *P. divaricata, stolonifera*; younger roots best; may not bloom well
		D	Fall, spring	Easy
		SC	Spring	Before budding
		S	Early fall	Select strains
Phlox stolonifera	Creeping Phlox	SC	Early summer	After flw
		D	Late summer	Stems root readily
Phlox subulata	Moss Phlox	SC	Late spring, fall	Tips
		D	Spring	After flw
		L		Less common
Phoenicaulis cheiranthoides		S		As *Draba*

See footnotes on page 144

continued on next page

Table A-1. Propagation methods for herbaceous perennials (continued)

Scientific name	Common name[1]	Methods of propagation[2]	Period[3]	Comments/requirements[4]
Phormium sp.	Flax Lily	D		Well-drained soil
		S		
Phragmites australis	Common Reed	D		Rhizome, very invasive
		S		Species
Phuopsis stylosa		L		Remove rooted stems
		S	Fall	
		SC		Semi-ripe
		D		
Phygelius sp.		S	Spring	Easy, self sows
		SC	Spring, late summer	Semi-ripe
		D		
Phyla sp.	Frogfruit	D, S		
Phyllitis: see *Asplenium*				
Phyllostachys sp.	Bamboo	D	Spring	Difficult, large divisions, mist often
Physalis sp.	Ground Cherry	S		
		D	Early spring, fall	Underground stems
Physoplexis comosa		S		Difficult, like *Phyteuma*
Physostegia sp.	Obedient Plant	SC	Early summer	Basal–spring, stem
		D	Spring, fall	May be invasive, rhizomes
		S	Fall	
Phyteuma sp.	Horned Rampion	D	Spring	Or after flw
		S	Fall	Best sow direct
Phytolacca sp.	Pokeweed	S	Spring, fall	
		D	Spring	Some sp. roots poisonous
		SC		
Pilosella sp.		S		
		D		
Pimpinella sp.		S	Spring	Sow fresh
Pinellia sp.		S		As *Arum*
Pinguicula sp.	Butterwort	LC	Summer	Lay on sand, keep warm & moist
		S		May be difficult
		D	Spring, fall	Winter buds at leaf bases
Piptatherum: see *Oryzopsis*				
Pistia stratiotes	Water Lettuce	S	Spring	Keep wet
		D	Summer	Plantlets
Plantago sp.	Plantain	S		
		D		
Platanthera bifolia		S		Like *Orchis*
		D		Tubers
Platycodon grandiflorus	Balloon Flower	S	Spring	Easiest
		D	Spring	May be difficult, woody roots
		SC	Summer	Tip after flw, basal with attached root
Pleioblastus sp.		D		Easy
Pleione sp.	Indian Crocus	S		
		D		Corm-like offset pseudobulblets
Plumbago sp.	Leadwort	S		*P. auriculata*
		SC		Non-flw laterals with heel
		RC		*P. indica*

See footnotes on page 144

continued on next page

Scientific name	Common name[1]	Methods of propagation[2]	Period[3]	Comments/requirements[4]
Poa sp.	Meadow Grass	D	Spring	Usual method most sp.
Podophyllum sp.	Mayapple, Mandrake	S	Summer	Fresh, ripe, or stratify; slow; sandy mix
		RC		Rhizome
		D	Spring, late summer	Stolons root at nodes
Polemonium sp.	Jacob's Ladder	SC		
		S	Fall	Species
		D	Spring, fall	Clumps, cvs
Polianthes sp.	Tuberose	D		Rhizomes
Polygala sp.	Milkwort	S	Spring	Ripe
		SC	Late summer	Bottom heat, semi-ripe or softwood
		D		Rooted shoots
Polygonatum sp.	Solomon's Seal	S	Fall	Stratify, overwinter, slow
		D	Spring, fall	Rhizomes, leave at least one bud per
		RC		May lie dormant one year
Polygonum: see *Fallopia, Persicaria*				
Polypodium sp.	Polypody Fern	S		Spores, not for cvs
		D		
Polystichum sp.	Holly Fern	S	Summer	Spores
		D	Late summer	Bulbils, some sp.
		D	Spring	Cvs
		LC		Gemma at frond tips of some cvs
Pontederia sp.	Pickerel Weed	D	Spring	
		SC	Summer	Stolons
		S	Summer	Green, submerge
Potamogeton sp.	Pondweed	SC	Summer	Or scaly resting buds
		D		May invade streams
Potentilla sp.	Cinquefoil	S	Fall, early spring	Species only, some self sow
		D	Spring, fall	Cvs, after flw
		D		Rooted runners, alpine sp.
		SC	Summer	Shrubby sp., stem tip, for cvs
		SC	Spring, fall	Rooted
Poterium: see *Sanguisorba*				
Pratia sp.		D		Rooted shoots
		S	Fall	Sandy mix
Prenanthes purpurea	Rattlesnake Root	D		Acidic soil, as *Cicerbita*
		S		
Preslia: see *Mentha*				
Primula sp.	Primrose	S		
		RC		*P. denticulata*
		SC		Also leaf bud
		TC		
		D	Summer	After flw
Pritzelago: see *Hutchinsia*				
Prometheum: see *Sedum*				
Prunella sp.	Heal All	S		
		D	Late summer	Remove rooted stems
		SC	Fall	
Pseudofumaria: see *Corydalis*				
Pseudolysimachion: see *Veronica*				

See footnotes on page 144

continued on next page

Scientific name	Common name[1]	Methods of propagation[2]	Period[3]	Comments/requirements[4]
Pseudomuscari: see *Muscari*				
Pseudosasa sp.	Arrow Bamboo	D		
Psilostemon: see *Trachystemon*				
Pteridium aquilinum	Bracken Fern	D		Hardy, invasive
		S		Spores, cvs true
Pteridophyllum racemosum		S	Fall	Slow
		D		After flw
Pterocephalus sp.		S		
		SC	Late summer	Softwood or semi-ripe
Ptilostemon sp.		S		Self sows, as *Carduus*
Ptilotrichum: see *Alyssum*				
Pulmonaria sp.	Lungwort	S		Hybridize, not true
		D	Spring, fall	After flw
		TC		
		RC	Winter	Some cvs
		SC		Basal
Pulsatilla sp.	Pasque Flower	S		Most common
		D	Spring, fall	Transplants poorly, slow
		RC		Some *P. vulgaris* cvs
Puschkinia scilloides		D	Late summer	Bulbils
		S	Fall	Self sows
Pycnanthemum (Koellia) sp.	American Mountain Mint	D		Invasive where warm
		S	Spring, fall	
Pygmaea: see *Chionohebe*				
Pyrethrum: see *Tanacetum*				
Pyrola sp.	Wintergreen	D		Use care, keep moist
		S		In native soil, difficult
Pyrrocoma sp.		S		
		SC		Semi-ripe, sandy mix
		D		As *Haplopappus*
Raffenaldia primuloides		S		Deep pots
Ramischia: see *Orthilia*				
Ramonda sp.	Pyrenean Primrose	S		Seedlings slow
		SC		
		LC		As *Saintpaulia*
		D		Old clumps
Ranunculus sp.	Buttercup	S		Fresh, not of selections
		D	Fall, early spring	Requires constant moisture
Ranzania japonica		D		Difficult to transplant
		S		4 years to flw
Raoulia sp.		D		Of rooted tufts
		SC		Softwood, loamy mix
		S		Must be fresh, low germ
Ratibida sp.	Prairie Coneflower	S		Best sown direct
		D		Deep tap roots, difficult
Rehmannia sp.		S		Biennials where cool
		RC		
		SC		Basal shoots

See footnotes on page 144

continued on next page

Scientific name	Common name[1]	Methods of propagation[2]	Period[3]	Comments/requirements[4]
Reineckea carnea		S D		
Reseda sp.	Mignonette	S SC	Spring Summer	Also fall where warm, direct
Reynoutria: see *Fallopia*				
Rhaponticum: see *Leuzea*				
Rhazya: see *Amsonia*				
Rheum sp.	Rhubarb	S D	Fall Spring	Hybrids likely Ensure a dormant crown bud per
Rhexia sp.	Meadow Beauty	D S	Spring	
Rhinopetalum: see *Fritillaria*				
Rhodiola sp.		SC LC D S	Summer Summer	Non-flw, basal, spring Also offsets Species only
Rhodohypoxis sp.	Red Star	D S	Early spring	Or by offsets Variable seedlings
Riccia fluitans	Crystalwort	D		
Rindera sp.		S		Short-lived plants, dry site
Rodgersia sp.		D S	Early spring Spring	 Hybrids likely
Rohdea japonica	Lily of China	D S		Rhizomes, difficult Rare, not of clones
Romanzoffia sp.		D S		Separate dormant tuberous rhizomes
Romneya sp.	California Tree Poppy	S D RC	Early spring Late winter	Slow, sow ripe Difficult, suckers with roots Pencil-thick, use care
Romulea sp.		D S	Fall	Offsets Spring for *R. macowanii*
Rorippa sp.	Great Yellowcress	SC		Keep wet
Roscoea sp.		D S	Early spring	Peaty mix
Rosmarinus officinalis	Rosemary	SC	Summer	Softwood or semi-ripe
Rosularia sp.		D		Some sp. prefer dry soil
Rubia tinctorum	Madder	S D		As *Galium*
Rubus sp.	Brambles	S D SC L	Spring Spring, fall	Ripe, stratify, some hybridize Suckering sp. Some sp.
Rudbeckia sp.	Coneflower	S SC D	 Spring Spring, fall	Species, 'Goldsturm,' *hirta* With root pieces attached, or as stems lengthening Also rooted basal stems
Ruellia sp.		S SC, D		Bottom heat

See footnotes on page 144

continued on next page

Scientific name	Common name[1]	Methods of propagation[2]	Period[3]	Comments/requirements[4]
Rumex sp.	Dock, Sorrel	S	Spring	
		D		Also flw stem offshoots
Rupicapnos africana		S		Self sows, collect early
		D	Early spring	Use care
Ruta sp.	Rue	SC	Early fall	Photodermititis from sap
		S		Ripe
		L		Old plants
Rydbergia: see *Hymenoxys*				
Saccharum (Erianthus) sp.	Plume Grass	D, S, SC		
Sagina sp.	Pearlwort	S	Fall	Usual
		D	Spring, fall	
		D	Early summer	Offshoots some sp.
Sagittaria sp.	Arrowhead	D		Stolons, invasive
		S		Self sows, ripe
Salvia sp.	Sage	S		Not cvs
		SC		Softwood, non-flw, spring easiest
		D	Spring, fall	
		RC	Spring	
Salvinia sp.		D		May be invasive
Sambucus ebulus	Dwarf Elder	D		Root-crown or suckers
		SC		Heel, hardwood
		S		
Sandersonia aurantiaca	Chinese Lantern Lily	S	Late winter	Sandy mix
		D	Spring	Use care, or offsets
Sanguinaria canadensis	Bloodroot	S		Single flw sp. only, ripe, slow
		D	Early spring, fall	After flw
		L	Late spring	Before flw under mist
Sanguisorba sp.	Burnet	D	Spring, fall	Rhizomes
		S	Spring, fall	
Sanicula europaea	Snakeroot	S		Self sows
		D		
Santolina sp.	Lavender Cotton	SC	Summer	Preferred method, semi-ripe
		S		
		D		*S. elegans,* may be difficult
Saponaria sp.	Soapwort	S		Usual, species only
		D	Spring, summer	*S. officinalis*
		SC		Terminal before budding or sterile shoots after flw
Sarcocopnos enneaphylla		S	Spring	
Sarracenia sp.	Pitcher Plant	S		3–4 years to bloom
		D		Use care
Sasa sp.	Bamboo	D	Early spring	5+ culms per division
Sasaella sp.		D		As *Sasa*
Sasamorpha sp.		D		As *Sasa*
Satureja sp.	Savory	S		Some sp. self sow
		SC	Summer	Softwood
		D	Spring	Stolons, rooted shoots
Saururopsis: see *Saururus*				

See footnotes on page 144   *continued on next page*

Table A-1. Propagation methods for herbaceous perennials *(continued)*

Scientific name	Common name[1]	Methods of propagation[2]	Period[3]	Comments/requirements[4]
Saururus sp.	Lizard's Tail	S		Ripe, keep moist
		D	Spring	
Saussurea sp.		S, D, RC		
Saxifraga sp.	Saxifrage	S		Some sp., monocarpic
		D	Spring, summer	Rooted offsets also
		SC	Spring	Basal
Scabiosa sp.	Pincushion Flower	SC		Basal
		S		Requires well-drained
		D	Spring	Slow, difficult
Scaevola sp.	Fan Flower	SC		Semi-ripe, bottom heat
		D		Rooted shoots
		S		Ripe, sow fresh
Schivereckia (Bornmuellera) sp.		S		As *Ptilotrichum*
		SC, D		
Schizachyrium sp.	Bluestem	D	Spring	
		S		
Schizocodon: see *Shortia*				
Schizostylis coccinea	Kafir Lily	D		
		S		
Schoenoplectus (Scirpus)		D	Spring	As *Carex*
Scilla sp.	Squill	D		Offsets where produced
		S		Ripe
		D	Summer	Clumps, after foliage dies
Scirpus sp.	Bulrush	D	Spring	As *Carex*
Scleranthus sp.	Knawel	S		
		D	Spring, fall	
		SC	Summer	
Scoliopus sp.	Foetid Adder's Tongue	S		As *Trillium*
		D		
Scolopendrium: see *Asplenium*				
Scopolia sp.		S		
		D	Spring	Fleshy rhizomes, toxic
Scorzonera sp.	Salsify	S	Late summer	
		D		Older plants
Scrophularia sp.	Figwort	D		
		S	Spring	
Scutellaria sp.	Skullcap	D		
		S	Spring	Outside, *S. altissima* self sows
Sedum sp.	Stonecrop	SC	Summer	Non-flw, no mist; basal, spring
		LC		
		D	Summer	Also offsets
		S		Species only
Selaginella sp.	Little Club Moss	D		
		L		
		S		Spores

See footnotes on page 144

continued on next page

Herbaceous Perennials Production

Scientific name	Common name[1]	Methods of propagation[2]	Period[3]	Comments/requirements[4]
Selinum sp.		S	Late summer	Fresh
		D		Use care
Selliera radicans		D		Rooted stem segments
Semiaquilegia sp.		S	Early fall	May be slow–2 years
		D	Spring	
Semiarundinaria sp.	Bamboo	D		
Sempervivella: see *Rosularia*				
Sempervivum sp.	Houseleek	S		Seldom in U.S., hybridizes
		D		Offsets
		SC		
Senecio sp.	Groundsel	S, D		
		SC		Seldom
Senna (Cassia) hebecarpa		SC		Semi-ripe, bottom heat
		S		
Seriphidium (Artemisia) sp.		D	Fall, early spring	
		SC	Summer	Remove from mist as roots, woody sp.
Serratula sp.		S, D		
Seseli sp.	Moon Carrot	S		
		D	Late summer	Use care
Sesleria sp.		D	Spring	
		S		Species only
Setaria sp.	Bristle Grass	D		
		S		Cool, under glass
Shibataea sp.	Bamboo	D		
Shortia sp.		D	Spring	Use care, rooted plantlets, runners or after flw
		L		Rooted runners
		S		Fresh, keep moist, slow
		SC	Early summer	Heel cuttings
		TC		
Sibbaldia sp.		S		
		D		Cool, shade, moist, acid
Sibbaldiopsis: see *Potentilla*				
Sibthorpia sp.	Cornish Moneywort	SC	Spring	
		D		
		S		Not variegated form
Sida hermaphrodita	Virginia Mallow	S		Slow, erratic
		D		
Sidalcea sp.	Prairie Mallow	S	Spring	Species only
		D	Spring, fall	Use vigorous outer sections, hybrids
Sideritis sp.		S	Spring	
		D		Mature plants
		SC	Summer	Softwood, shrubby sp.

See footnotes on page 144   continued on next page

Scientific name	Common name[1]	Methods of propagation[2]	Period[3]	Comments/requirements[4]
Sieversia (Fallugia, Geum) *reptans*		SC, S		
Silene sp.	Campion, Catchfly	S		Species
		SC	Summer	Basal, *S. acaulis* soft tip
		D	Spring, fall	
		TC		
Siler: see *Laserpitium*				
Silphium sp.	Rosinweed	S	Spring, fall	Usual, ripe
		D	Spring, fall	Difficult, deep roots
Silybum sp.	Holy Thistle	S	Summer, early fall	May self sow
Sinarundinaria sp.	Bamboo	D	Early spring	Small, multi-stemmed plants
Sinobambusa sp.	Bamboo	D		Invasive roots
Sisyrinchium sp.	Blue-Eyed Grass	D	Early spring	
		S	Spring, fall	
Sium sp.	Water Parsnip	RC	Early spring	
		S	Spring, early fall	
Smilacina sp.	False Solomon's Seal	S		
		D	Spring, fall	Replant all root pieces
Smyrnium sp.	Black Lovage	S	Early fall, spring	Ripe, slow
Solanum sp.	Nightshade	S	Spring	Some sp. toxic
		SC	Summer	Softwood or greenwood, bottom heat, mist
Soldanella sp.	Alpine Snowbell	S		Fresh, section *Soldanella*
		D	Spring	Or after flw
Soleirolia (Helxine) soleirolii	Baby's Tears	D		
		SC, S		
Solenanthus sp.		S		As *Anchusa*
		D		
Solenopsis: see *Isotoma*				
Solidago sp.	Goldenrod	S		Species, 'Golden Baby'
		SC	Spring, fall	Spring tip, fall basal
		D	Spring	
x *Solidaster luteus*		D		
		SC		Basal
Sonchus sp.	Milk Thistle	D		Invasive
		SC		Semi-ripe
		S		
Sorghastrum sp.		S	Early spring	
		D		
Sparaxis sp.	Wandflower	S	Fall	Flw 3rd or 4th year
		D		Offsets, flw 2nd year
Sparganium sp.	Bur Reed	D, S		
Spartinia pectinata	Cord Grass	D	Spring	
Speirantha convallarioides		D	Spring	As *Convallaria*
Spenceria ramulana		S		
		D	Spring	Use care

See footnotes on page 144

continued on next page

Scientific name	Common name[1]	Methods of propagation[2]	Period[3]	Comments/requirements[4]
Sphaeralcea sp.	Globe Mallow	S		
		D		
		SC		Softwood, bottom heat
Spigelia marilandica	Indian Pink	D, S		
		SC	Summer	Tips, after flw, use hormone, difficult
Spiraea: see *Aruncus, Filipendula*				
Spodiopogon sibiricus		D	Spring	
		S		
Stachys sp.	Betony	SC	Spring, summer	Basal, shrubby sp.
		S		
		D	Spring	
Statice: see *Limonium, Goniolimon*				
Steironema: see *Lysimachia*				
Stellaria holostea, pubera	Stitchwort	D, S		
Stenanthium sp.		S		Ripe, fresh
Stenotus sp.		S		
		SC		Semi-ripe, sandy mix
		D		As *Haplopappus*
Sternbergia sp.	Autumn Daffodil	D		Remove dormant offset bulblets
		S		Ripe
		RC		Bulb scales
Stipa sp.	Feather Grass	S		Cold to germinate
		D	Spring	Often lacks vigor
Stokesia laevis	Stoke's Aster	S		Species
		RC	Late winter	
		D	Spring, fall	Cvs, may be difficult
		SC	Fall	
Stratiotes aloides	Water Soldier	RC		Stolons or budlike roots
		SC	Spring	Young rosettes, buds onto water
		S		Less common
Streptopus sp.	Twisted Stalk	D		
		S		Fresh, ripe
Strobilanthes sp.	Mexican Petunia	S		
Struthiopteris: see *Blechnum, Matteuccia*				
Stylophorum sp.	Celandine Poppy	S		Transplant early
		D	Early spring, fall	Transplants easily
Subularia aquatica	Awlwort	SC		Keep wet
Succisa pratensis		D		
		S		Sow into cells/plugs
Succisella inflexa	Devil's Bit	SC	Spring	Basal
		S		
		D	Spring	
Swertia sp.		S		Transplant early
		D	Spring	Use care, taproots

continued on next page

Scientific name	Common name[1]	Methods of propagation[2]	Period[3]	Comments/requirements[4]
Symphyandra sp.	Ring Bellflower	D		Use care
		S	Fall	Easy, often self sows
Symphytum sp.	Comfrey	D	Spring	Fleshy roots
		RC		
		S	Fall	Species, some self sow, invasive
Symplocarpus foetidus	Skunk Cabbage	S	Late summer	Fresh, ripe
		D		Dormant, older plants, difficult
Syndesmon: see *Anemonella*				
Synthyris sp.		S	Spring	
		D		Clumps, after flw
Talinum sp.	Fameflower	S, D, SC		
Tamus communis		D, S		
Tanacetum (Pyrethrum) sp.	Tansy	S		
		D	Spring, early fall	
		SC	Spring	Basal
		SC	Summer	Softwood, with heel, alpines
Tanakaea radicans		D		Rooted runners
Taraxacum sp.	Dandelion	S		
		RC		
Telekia sp.		S		
		D		Difficult for *T. speciosissima*
Tellima grandiflora	Fringe Cups	S	Spring	
		D	Fall	
		SC		
Tephrosia sp.	Hoary Pea	SC		Semi-ripe, heel, lateral shoots
		RC, S		
		D		Remove suckers
Tetragonolobus: see *Lotus*				
Teucrium sp.	Germander	S		Species only
		SC		Young tips, avoid excess water
		D	Spring	May be difficult
Thalia sp.		S	Spring	
		D	Summer	
Thalictrum sp.	Meadow Rue	S	Summer, fall	
		D	Early spring	May be difficult
Thamnocalamus sp.	Bamboo	D		
Thelypteris sp.	Marsh Fern	D		
		S	Late summer	Spores
Themeda triandra		D	Spring	As *Chloris*
Thermopsis sp.	False Lupine	S		Faster
		D		May be difficult
		SC	Summer	
Thladiantha sp.		S		
		D		Tubers may be invasive
Thlaspi sp.	Pennycress	S		
		D	Fall	Use care
		SC		Some sp.

See footnotes on page 144

continued on next page

Scientific name	Common name[1]	Methods of propagation[2]	Period[3]	Comments/requirements[4]
Thymus sp.	Thyme	S	Spring	
		D	Spring	
		SC	Spring, summer	Semi-ripe, heel
		L		
Tiarella sp.	False Mitrewort	S, TC		
		D	Summer	After flw
		SC		Avoid high temps
Tithymalopsis: see *Euphorbia*				
Tofieldia sp.	False Asphodel	D		Rhizomes
		S		Use native soil
Tolmiea menziesii	Piggyback Plant	D		Plantlets on leaves
Tommasinia: see *Peucedanum*				
Tonestus sp.		S		As *Townsendia*
Tormentilla: see *Potentilla*				
Tovara: see *Persicaria*				
Townsendia sp.		S		Ripe, sandy mix, avoid disturbing taproot
Trachelium sp.	Throatwort	S		
		SC	Spring	Bottom heat
Trachomitum: see *Apocynum*				
Trachystemon orientalis		S		
		D		As *Brunnera*
Tradescantia sp.	Spiderwort	S		Hard to find, hybridizes
		SC	Summer	Quick, easy
		D	Spring, fall	Non-flw best
Tragopogon sp.	Goat's Beard, Salsify	S		
Trapa natans	Water Chestnut	S		Must keep seeds moist
Trautvetteria sp.	False Bugbane	D		
Trichophorum: see *Eleocharis*				
Trichosanthes kirilowii	Snake Gourd	S		Bottom heat
		SC		Softwood, if no seeds
Tricyrtis sp.	Toad Lily	D	Early spring	
		S		Best sown fresh
		SC		When not flw
Trientalis sp.	Wintergreen	S	Spring	Very acid mix, slow
		D	Spring, fall	Best method but difficult
Trifolium sp.	Clover	S		Species only
		D		
Trillium sp.	Wake Robin, Wood Lily	D		Difficult, after foliage gone
		S		Cleaned, fresh, 5 yrs to flw
Triosteum sp.	Horse Gentian	D	Spring	
		S		May self sow
Tripleurospermum (Matricaria) sp.	Scentless False Chamomile	S		
		D		Not cvs, as *Chamaemelum*
Tripsacum dactyloides		D	Spring	
		S		

See footnotes on page 144   *continued on next page*

Scientific name	Common name[1]	Methods of propagation[2]	Period[3]	Comments/requirements[4]
Tripterocalyx: see *Abronia*				
Trisetum flavescens		S		Naturalizes
Triteleia sp.		S		Species
		D		Cormlets, as *Brodiaea*
Tritoma: see *Kniphofia*				
Tritonia sp.	Montbretia	D		Cormlets, as *Gladiolus*
		S		
Trollius sp.	Globe Flower	S		Species only, slow
		RC		
		D	Spring, fall	Cvs, spring best
Tropaeolum sp.	Nasturtium	S		Slow, difficult some sp.
		D		Of tubers
		SC		Of long stems
Tulipa sp.	Tulip	D		Bulb offsets
		S		Species only
Tunica: see *Petrorhagia*				
Tussilago farfara	Coltsfoot	S		
		D, RC		
Tweedia (Oxypetalum) caerulea		S		
Typha sp.	Bullrush	D		
		S		Keep seeds moist to wet
Ulmaria: see *Filipendula*				
Umbilicus sp.		S, LC		
Unifolium: see *Maianthemum*				
Uniola: see *Chasmanthium*				
Urospermum dalechampii		S, D		
Utricularia sp.	Bladderwort	D	Summer	Submerge aquatic sp.
Uvularia sp.	Merry Bells	D	Spring	Best method
		S		Ripe, slow
		RC	Spring	Two years for new plants
Valeriana sp.	Valerian	S, SC		
		D		Use care
Vallisneria sp.	Eel Grass	D		Runners from parent plants
Vancouveria sp.	Inside-Out Flower	D	Spring, fall	As *Epimedium*
		S		Ripe, slow
Veratrum sp.	False Hellebore	S		Ripe, erratic, keep moist & cool
		D	Early spring, fall	
		RC		Sandy mix, with buds, toxic sap
Verbascum sp.	Mullein	S		Hybridizes
		RC	Late winter	Many cvs
		D	Spring	Secondary rosettes, may be difficult
		SC	Late summer	Laterals, semi-ripe, subshrub sp.

See footnotes on page 144   *continued on next page*

Scientific name	Common name[1]	Methods of propagation[2]	Period[3]	Comments/requirements[4]
Verbena sp.	Vervain	SC	Late summer	Bottom heat
		RC	Spring	
		S	Spring, fall	
		D		Rooted stems some sp.
Verbesina sp.	Crown Beard	S		
		D		
Vernonia sp.	Ironweed	S		Species only
		SC	Early summer	
		D	Spring	
Veronica sp.	Speedwell	S	Fall	
		SC		Tips early, laterals later
		D	Spring, fall	Clumps
Veronicastrum virginicum	Culver's Root	SC	Spring	Before budding
		D	Spring, fall	
		S		Hard to find
Vicia sp.	Vetch	S	Spring, fall	Most common
		D		
Villarsia: see Nymphoides				
Vinca sp.	Periwinkle	SC	Late spring	Terminal may be difficult
		D	Spring, fall	Easily root at nodes
Vincetoxicum sp.		SC		Semi-ripe, bottom heat
		L		
Viola sp.	Violet	S		Usual
		D	Early spring, fall	Or rooted runners
		SC		Terminal
		RC		*V. labradorica, pedata*
Viorna: see Clematis				
Viscaria: see Lychnis				
Vitaliana primuliflora		S		Fresh, ripe, slow
Wahlenbergia sp.	Rock Bell	S		May self sow
		D		
Waldsteinia sp.	Barren Strawberry	D	Spring, fall	Rhizomes, rooted runners
		S		Uncommon in U.S.
		SC	Spring	Terminal
Watsonia beatricis	Bugle Lily	S		
		D		Offsets
Weingaertneria: see Corynephorus				
Weldenia candida		S, D, RC		
Woodsia sp.		D		
		S		Spores
Woodwardia sp.	Chain Fern	D		
		S		Spores
Wulfenia sp.		S, D	Spring	
Wyethia sp.		D		Crowns, use care, taproot
		S		Several years to flw
Xerophyllum sp.	Bear Grass	S		5–7 years to flw
		D		

See footnotes on page 144

continued on next page

Scientific name	Common name[1]	Methods of propagation[2]	Period[3]	Comments/requirements[4]
Yucca sp.		D		Also suckers
		RC	Winter	
		S		May need to hand pollinate
Yushania sp.	Bamboo	D		
Zannichellia palustris	Horned Pondweed	D		Creeping rhizome, submerge
Zantedeschia sp.	Calla Lily	D	Spring	Cormels or suckers
		S		Germinates slowly
Zauschneria sp.	California Fuchsia	S	Spring	
		D	Summer	Rooted runners
		SC	Spring, fall	Alpine sp.
Zephyranthes sp.	Zephyr Lilies	D	Fall	Bulbils or offsets
		S		Ripe
Zigadenus sp.	Death Camus	D		Toxic sap
		S	Spring	Or ripe
Zizania sp.	Wild Rice	D		
		S	Early spring	Submerge
Zizia sp.	Golden Alexanders	S		
Zwackia: see *Halacsya*				

[1] Most plants in this table are perennials in U.S. Department of Agriculture plant hardiness zones 9 or less (colder zones). However, some may be listed in *Hardy Herbaceous Perennials* by Jelitto and Schacht or the Dutch *Namelist (Naamlijst van Vaste Planten)* as a perennial in zone 10 (in which case they are actually tropical plants and not perennials in zones 9 or less). Names were verified using the British publication *The Plant Finder* as the primary authority, then the Dutch *Namelist (Naamlijst van Vaste Planten)*, then the *New Royal Horticulture Society Dictionary of Gardening*, and finally *Hardy Herbaceous Perennials*; if discrepancies occurred among sources, then the best agreement among the most sources was used. (For complete citations for sources, see the recommended reading section beginning on page 203.) In general, information is available only for the genus. Sp. = species (+ cultivars and hybrids for most, unless noted otherwise)

[2] Method of propagation: S = seed; SC = stem cutting; RC = root cutting; D = division; LC = leaf cutting; L = layering; TC = tissue culture. The preferred method depends on many factors; see text. Vegetative methods tend to be best for cultivars.

[3] In the South: spring = March, fall = October; in the North: spring = April, fall = September

[4] Flw = flowering, cvs = cultivars; sp. = species; use care = often a taproot, roots resent disturbance. For specific germination requirements, see appendix B.

APPENDIX B

Optimum Germination Conditions for Perennials and Biennials

Table B-1. Optimum germination conditions for perennials and biennials

Name	Seeds/oz[1] (x 1,000)	Germination medium temp. (˚F)	Days to germination	Light (L) or dark (D) require- ments	Seed to sale (weeks)[2]	Comments[3]
Abronia sp.	–	60	–	–	–	Remove husk, soak 24 hrs
Acaena sp.	–	50–60	30–100	–	–	–
Acantholimon sp.	–	65–70	–	–	–	Moist, sandy mix
Acanthus sp.	<1	50–75	14–28	–	10	Stratify, D may help
Achillea filipendulina	200	60–70	10–21	L	12	–
Achillea millefolium	140–173	60–70	7–14	L	10	–
Achillea ptarmica	90	60–70	7–14	L	10	–
Aconitum sp.	–	55–60	21–28+	L	9	Prechill 6 wks, old seed slow
Actaea sp.	–	50–70	30+	–	–	70˚ 3 wks, then <32˚ 5 wks, germ at 40˚, then 55˚; sow fresh
Actinidia sp.	–	50	60+	–	–	–
Adenophora sp.	–	50–75	14–21+	L	14	Transplants poorly, surface sow
Adonis sp.	–	60–65	30+	–	–	Sow fresh, prechill, low germ from empty seeds
Aethionema sp.	–	60–70	30+	–	12	–
Agapanthus sp.	–	60–65	30–90	–	–	–
Agastache sp.	–	55–70	30+	L	–	GA may help, DS 1 yr may help *A. scrophulariaefolia*
Agave sp.	–	55–60	30–90	–	–	–
Alcea ficifolia	–	70	10–21	D	–	–
Alcea rosea	3–6	60–75	10–21	L	8	Can sow direct, DS may help
Alchemilla sp.	95	60–75	21–28	–	12	Treat old seed as *Actaea*, 70/ 40˚ may help
Allium sp.	–	50–70	14–42	L	–	Prechill 4 wks, D for *A. schubertii*

See footnotes on page 158

continued on next page

Name	Seeds/oz[1] (x 1,000)	Germination medium temp. (°F)	Days to germination	Light (L) or dark (D) require- ments	Seed to sale (weeks)[2]	Comments[3]
Alstroemeria aurantiaca	–	55–70	14–21+	–	–	Presoak
Althaea sp.	–	65–70	4–21	–	–	DS may help
Alyssum murale	–	55–75	7–21	–	12	Lower night temp after germ, L or prechill 5 days may help
Amsonia sp.	–	65–70	7–14	D	–	Soak or scarify; prechill 6 wks
Anacyclus pyrethrum	50	55–70	7–14	–	12	Prechill 3 wks old seed
Anagallis sp.	–	60–65	4–42	–	–	D for A. linifolia
Anaphalis sp.	600	55–70	10–21	L	10	Light helps
Anchusa azurea italica	1–2	70–75	7–10	–	10	Alternate temp, DS may help other sp., possible low germ
Androsace sp.	–	50–55	30+	–	–	Stratify, up to 2 yrs
Anemone sp.	–	65–75	21–28+	–	14+	Use fresh seed or stratify
Anemonella sp.	–	65–75	30+	–	–	Prechill or may take yr
Anemonopsis macrophylla	–	50–60	30+	L	–	Use low-pH soil
Angelica sp.	–	65–70	10–21	L	14	Sow fresh or prechill
Antennaria dioica	65	55–75	7–10	–	12	Moist, 60° after germ
Anthemis sp.	60	70–75	7–21	–	9	Easy
Anthericum sp.	–	50	14–30+	–	–	Stratify, GA, erratic
Anthriscus sp.	–	55–65	14–21	–	–	Sow direct
Anthyllis sp.	–	50	30+	–	–	Presoak
Aphyllanthes sp.	–	55–60	21+	–	–	–
Aquilegia sp.	15–22	65–75	21–28+	L	12+	Prechill old seed 6 wks, GA or DS helps some sp.
Arabis sp.	70–105	65–70	7–28	L	10+	Can sow direct
Arctotis sp.	–	60–70	7–35	–	–	–
Arenaria sp.	–	55–65	7–35	–	–	DS all except A. norvegica (GA)
Arisaema sp.	–	55–70	14–30+	–	–	D may help, as Actaea helps
Aristolochia sp.	–	70–85	21+	L	–	Stratify unless ripe, 2-day warm water soak
Armeria maritima & cvs	12–20	60–70	7–28	–	16+	Prechill 2 wks, presoak, DS 1 year may help
Arnica sp.	–	55	21–28	–	–	–
Artemisia sp.	–	60–65	4–10	L/D	16+	Store well dry
Arum sp.	–	55–65	30+	–	–	Clean pulp off
Aruncus sp.	–	50–75	14–21+	L	16+	Sow fresh or 4 wks, 40° after sow; dioecious
Asarum sp.	–	60–65	7–30+	–	–	Sow fresh, needs cold, may take yr
Asclepias tuberosa & cvs	3–4	50–75	21–28+	–	12	Stratify old seed; sow fresh transplant early
Asphodeline sp.	–	65–75	14–35	–	12+	Variable germ
Asphodelus sp.	–	70–75	7–28	–	–	Stratify may help

See footnotes on page 158

continued on next page

Name	Seeds/oz[1] (x 1,000)	Germination medium temp. (°F)	Days to germination	Light (L) or dark (D) require- ments	Seed to sale (weeks)[2]	Comments[3]
Aster alpinus	12–24	65–70	7–21	L/D	6	Sow fresh or prechill
Aster novae-angliae	70–80	65	4–21	–	10	Water soak
Aster novi-belgii	–	65–75	10–21	–	10	Prechill 2 wks
Astilbe sp.	380	60–70	14–28	L	12+	70° 2 wks; then 40° 4 wks after sow
Astrantia sp.	–	55–65	30+	L	–	Prechill 4 wks, sow fresh
Asyneuma limonifolium	–	55–70	14–21	–	–	Better in D
Atropa sp.	–	50	21–30	–	–	–
Aubretia deltoidea & cvs	85	55–75	14–21	L	10	60° may help poor germ
Aubretia grandifolia	–	70	7–14	–	–	Sow fresh
Aurinia (Alyssum) saxatilis	30	60–75	7–21	L	10	Can sow direct, prechill 4 wks if slow
Azorina vidallii	–	65–75	7–28	–	–	L may help
Balsamorhiza sp.	–	60–65	14–42	–	–	–
Baptisia sp.	2	70–75	7–30+	–	15	Soak, sow fresh or scarify, transplants poorly
Belamcanda sp.	–	70–90	14–60	–	26+	Prechill 7 days
Bellis perennis	140–160	70–75	7–14	L	9	–
Bergenia sp.	110	60–75	7–30	–	12+	Prechill 2 wks, sow fresh
Blandfordia grandiflora	–	60–70	30+	–	–	–
Bocconia sp.	–	65–75	–	–	–	Now *Macleaya*
Boltonia asteroides	–	70–75	4–14	–	12	–
Borago sp.	–	65–70	7–21	–	–	DS one year or GA helps
Brunnera sp.	–	55	14–21	–	11	Fall seed direct outside
Buphthalmum sp.	30	70–75	7–28	L	10	–
Calamintha sp.	–	60–70	7–21	–	–	–
Callirhoe sp.	–	50	30+	L	–	Can sow direct
Caltha sp.	–	55–70	14–90	–	16	Sow fresh, prechill or GA
Campanula carpatica	200–300	60–70	14–28	L	12	50° after 3 wks at 70°
Campanula lactiflora	–	55–75	14–21	–	13	–
Campanula latifolia	–	70	7–14	–	13	–
Campanula medium	79–105	60–70	14–21	–	14	See *C. carpatica*
Campanula persicifolia	340	55–90	7–21	–	12	L may help, can sow exposed
Campanula pyramidalis	250	65–75	7–21	–	10	Can sow exposed
Campanula rotundifolia	700	60–70	7–10	–	7	–
Canna x generalis, cvs	–	70–75	10–14+	–	–	Presoak or scarify
Carlina sp.	7	55–70	7–28+	–	13	Prechill 6 wks or sow fresh
Cassia sp.	–	65–75	–	–	–	Soak or scarify, now *Senna*
Catananche caerulea	12	50–75	7–28	–	12	Can sow exposed
Cautleya spicata	–	50–55	30+	–	–	–
Centaurea sp.	2–3	60–75	7–28	D	10	Can sow exposed

See footnotes on page 158

continued on next page

Name	Seeds/oz[1] (x 1,000)	Germination medium temp. (°F)	Days to germination	Light (L) or dark (D) require-ments	Seed to sale (weeks)[2]	Comments[3]
Centaurium sp.	–	50–70	7–14	–	–	Stores well
Centranthus sp.	70	60–70	7–42	–	10	Can sow direct, shallow
Cephalaria sp.	–	55–75	7–60	–	10	Prechill 6 wks
Cerastium sp.	80	60–75	7–28	L	10+	DS may substitute for L
Ceratostigma sp.	–	70–75	–	–	–	Prechill 6 wks
Chaenorhinum sp.	–	55–60	10–14	–	–	–
Chaerophyllum sp.	–	65–75	–	–	–	Sow ripe or stratify
Chamaemelum sp.	–	70–75	7–10	–	–	May need DS
Cheiranthus (Erysimum) sp.	–	55–65	7–21	L	–	–
Chelidonium sp.	–	55–65	30+	–	–	–
Chelone sp.	–	55–65	14–42	–	10	Prechill 6 weeks, erratic
Chiastophyllum oppositifolium	55–75	30–60	–	–	60–70° 3 wks, 40° 6 wks	–
Chrysanthemum leucanthemum	60–70	7–21	–	–	10	Now *Leucanthemum*
Chrysanthemum x morifolium	70	70–75	7–14	–	10	Now *Dendranthema*
Chrysanthemum x superbum	15–35	65–70	7–14	D	12	Now *Leucanthemum*
Chrysogonum virginianum	–	70–75	14–21	–	–	–
Chrysopsis sp.	–	65–75	7–14	–	10	Sow fresh, easy, now *Heterotheca*
Cimicifuga sp.	–	55–70	21+	–	16+	Germ slow, erratic; stratify as *Actaea* or sow fresh
Cirsium sp.	–	70–75	15–18	–	–	–
Clematis sp.	–	70–75	30+	–	–	Prechill 4 wks, may need DS or GA, sow fresh
Clintonia sp.	–	55–60	30–90	–	–	Keep moist, one year?
Codonopsis sp.	–	60–75	14–42	D	–	DS may help
Convallaria sp.	–	50–60	60+	L	–	Can sow direct
Coreopsis grandiflorum	10–13	65–75	7–21	–	11	'Sunray', 'Sunburst' year prior; L may help
Coreopsis verticillata	–	65–70	14–21	–	11	Not named cvs
Cornus sp.	–	65–70	–	–	–	Prechill
Cortaderia sp.	–	60–75	14–21	L	10	–
Corydalis sp.	–	50–75	30–60	L	–	Germ erratic; after 8 wks, 32° 8wks; GA may help
Crambe sp.	–	50–75	7–60	–	–	Sow direct, fresh
Crepis sp.	–	65–75	7–21	–	–	Sow fresh, possible low germ
Crocosmia sp.	–	55–70	30–90	–	–	L may help, stores 1 yr

See footnotes on page 158

continued on next page

Herbaceous Perennials Production

Name	Seeds/oz[1] (x 1,000)	Germination medium temp. (˚F)	Days to germination	Light (L) or dark (D) require- ments	Seed to sale (weeks)[2]	Comments[3]
Cyananthus sp.	–	60–65	14–60	L	–	–
Cyclamen sp.	–	55–70	21–30	D	–	Soak may help, not high temp
Cynara sp.	–	50–55	14–28	–	–	Can sow direct
Cynoglossum amabile	–	65–75	7–21	D/L	–	–
Cynoglossum grande	–	40	30–90	–	–	3 months at 70˚ prior helps
Cypripedium sp.	–	65–70	30+	L	–	Very difficult
Dactylorhiza sp.	–	65–70	–	–	–	Presoak
Darlingtonia californica	–	75–80	30+	–	–	Keep moist, slow, irreg.
Delosperma sp.	–	75	14–42	L	–	Surface sow
Delphinium consolida	–	40	21–35	–	–	3 months at 70˚ prior, low germ
Delphinium elatum	8–13	50–75	14–21	D	10	Prechill 2 wks, grow on 45˚; old seed of Pacific Giants 80/ 70˚ F, of Belladonnas 65–75˚ F constant; high temps cause dormancy
Dendranthema sp.	70	70–75	7–14	–	10	Formerly *Chrysanthemum*
Dianthus arenarius	–	65–75	7–14	–	12	DS first
Dianthus armeria	–	70	7–14	L	10	No DS needed
Dianthus barbatus	23–25	60–70	4–21	–	10	DS first, grow on 45˚
Dianthus caryophyllus	14	65–70	7–14	–	12	DS first
Dianthus deltoides	48	65–75	7–14	–	10	12 wks some cvs, DS first
Dianthus superbus	–	70	7–14	L	10	L when fresh or DS
Dicentra sp.	–	55–65	21–28+	–	15	65˚ 4 wks, 40˚ 6 wks, sow fresh, erratic, DS may help
Dicranostigma sp.	–	65–70	7–21	–	–	–
Dictamnus sp.	–	55–60	30+	–	–	Prechill 4–6 wks or stratify; sow fresh
Dierama sp.	–	60–65	30+	L	–	Surface sow
Digitalis sp.	125–300	60–75	7–21	L	9	Grow on 45˚
Dioscorea sp.	–	70–75	21–35	–	–	–
Diplarrhena sp.	–	55–65	30–90	–	–	Sow shallow
Dipsacus sp.	–	70–80	7–28	L	–	Sow direct, fresh, GA
Disporum sp.	–	55–65	30+	L	–	Sow shallow, prechill 6 wks
Dodecatheon sp.	56	60–75	21–28+	–	–	Stratify 3 wks or sow fresh
Doronicum sp.	17–26	70–75	4–21	L	9	Low germ, use fresh seed
Draba sp.	–	55	30+	–	–	Sow shallow, stratify
Dracocephalum sp.	–	55–70	14–30+	–	–	Slow germ possible, erratic
Dracunculus sp.	–	55–70	30+	–	–	Sow shallow, keep moist
Dryas sp.	–	60–70	7–28	–	–	Sow shallow, fresh
Duchesnea sp. (*Fragaria*)	–	55–65	7–28	L	–	Sow shallow
Eccremocarpus sp.	–	40–60	14–60	D	–	–

See footnotes on page 158

continued on next page

Table B-1. Optimum germination conditions for perennials and biennials *(continued)*

Name	Seeds/oz[1] (x 1,000)	Germination medium temp. (°F)	Days to germination	Light (L) or dark (D) require-ments	Seed to sale (weeks)[2]	Comments[3]
Echinacea sp.	8–73	65–75	14–28	–	10	Cooler at night, can sow exposed, DS helps
Echinops ritro	2–3	65–75	4–60	L	12	Sow direct, fresh
Echium sp.	–	65–70	7–14	–	–	–
Edraianthus sp.	–	55–65	30–60	L	–	–
Epigaea sp.	–	65–70	–	L	–	Sow fresh best
Epilobium sp.	–	50–70	14–28	–	–	–
Epimedium sp.	–	55–65	7–14	–	19	Sow fresh, if difficult stratify
Eranthis sp.	–	65–70	–	–	–	Store moist
Eremurus sp.	3–6	40–55	30+	D/L	–	Stratify
Erigeron sp.	99	55–70	7–21	–	9	Sow shallow, stores well
Erinus sp.	–	65–75	21–28	L	–	*E. alpinus* may need D
Eriophyllum lanatum	70	65–75	7–42	–	10	Can sow exposed
Eritrichium sp.	–	45–55	–	–	–	Prechill
Eryngium sp.	4–14	65–80	14–30+	–	12	Use fresh seeds, low germ
Erysimum sp.	–	65–75	14–21	–	7	Germ erratic
Erysium (Barbarea)	–	–	14–28	–	–	Best sown direct outdoors
Erythronium sp.	–	70–75	50–90	–	–	After 4 wks, 35° 6 wks
Eupatorium sp.	–	55–70	14–28+	L	12	Prechill 4–6 wks or sow fresh, GA may help
Euphorbia myrsinites	3–4	65–80	7–30	L	9	Sow fresh or prechill 4–6 wks or GA, soak
Euphorbia wulfenii	–	70	7–21	–	–	Sow fresh
Festuca sp.	–	65–75	–	–	9+	–
Fibigia clypeata	–	55–60	10–14	–	–	–
Filipendula sp.	–	50–75	7–28+	–	13	Germ erratic; after 2 wks try 40° 6 wks; sow fresh
Foeniculum vulgare	–	65–70	10–14	–	–	Sow direct, GA or L may help
Freesia cultivars	–	65–70	–	–	–	Presoak
Fritillaria sp.	–	55–65	–	–	–	Sow fresh or stratify
Gaillardia aristata	8	70–75	7–10	L	6	–
Gaillardia x grandiflora	7–10	70–75	7–14	L	10+	Transplanting keeps stocky
Galega sp.	–	–	14–60	–	–	Sow direct, presoak, DS
Galium verum	–	65–70	7–14	–	10	–
Gaura lindheimeri	1–2	65–75	7–28	–	10	–
Gentiana sp.	–	55–85	14–30+	–	16+	Prechill 8 wks, erratic, L or GA
Geranium sp.	–	50–70	21–42+	–	12+	DS may help, prechill may help
Gerbera cvs	–	70–75	14–28	–	–	–
Geum sp.	7–10	65–70	7–28+	L	10	Cover upon germ; 80/70° may help; D for *G. montanum*
Gillenia trifoliata	–	40–70	30–90	–	–	GA or DS may help

See footnotes on page 158

continued on next page

Name	Seeds/oz[1] (x 1,000)	Germination medium temp. (˚F)	Days to germination	Light (L) or dark (D) require- ments	Seed to sale (weeks)[2]	Comments[3]
Glaucidium palmatum	–	50–55	30–90	–	–	Sow shallow
Glaucium sp.	–	50–55	21–30+	–	–	Sow direct, stores for 2 yrs
Globularia sp.	–	55	10–28	L	–	Prechill 3 wks
Gnaphalium sp.	–	60–70	14–21	L	–	Surface sow
Goniolimon sp.	22	65–75	14–21	–	16	Formerly *Limonium tataricum*
Gunnera sp.	–	70–80	14–60	–	–	Slow, erratic, sow fresh, soak
Gypsophila paniculata	26–35	70–80	7–14	L	10+	Sow shallow
Gypsophila repens	45	70–80	7–14	L	10+	Sow shallow
Hacquetia epipactis	–	55	30+	–	–	Sow shallow, stratify
Haplopappus sp.	–	60–70	21–28	–	–	–
Hedysarum sp.	–	55–65	14–30+	–	–	–
Helenium sp.	140	60–75	7–21	L	10	Germ slow, erratic and slower for *H. hoopesii*
Helianthemum sp.	14	70–75	14–21	–	15	Sow fresh
Helichrysum sp.	–	65–70	10–21	–	–	–
Heliopsis sp.	8	65–70	7–21	–	9	Easy, grow warm
Helleborus sp.	–	60–75	30+	–	16+	Stratify 3 wks; as *Actaea*, or sow fresh
Hemerocallis sp.	–	60–70	10–60	–	16+	Stratify 6 wks, slow germ, sow fresh
Hepatica sp.	–	50–55	30+	L	–	Sow fresh, warm/prechill 3 wks
Heracleum sp.	–	–	30+	–	–	Best sown direct
Herniaria glabra	–	70	10–14	–	–	Sow shallow, DS first
Hesperis matronalis	14–18	65–85	7–28	L	10	Reduce night temp., can sow direct
Heterotheca sp.	–	65–75	7–14	–	10	Sow fresh, easy, was *Chrysopsis*
Heuchera sanguinea	500–700	65–75	10–28+	L	12	Prefers peat-lite mix, cool to 50˚ and sp. 60˚ after 3 wks
Hibiscus moscheutos	2	70–80	7–14	D	7	Sow fresh, presoak, scarify
Hieracium sp.	–	50–70	14–28			Sow shallow
Hippocrepis comosa	–	65–70	–	–	–	Scarify
Hosta sp.	–	50–75	14–30+	D	16+	Stratify if dormant
Humulus lupulus	–	70–75	7–28	–	–	Can sow direct
Hutchinsia (Pritzelago) alpina	–	–	14–28	–	–	Best sown direct
Hydrastis sp.	–	65–70	–	–	–	Prechill
Hyoscyamus sp.	–	–	14–42	–	–	Sow direct, fresh, prechill 3 wks
Hypericum sp.	26	60–70	14–28	–	13	Sow fresh or stratify, nonuniform, L or GA may help
Hyssopus officinalis	–	60–70	14–42	–	–	–

See footnotes on page 158

continued on next page

Name	Seeds/oz[1] (x 1,000)	Germination medium temp. (°F)	Days to germination	Light (L) or dark (D) require- ments	Seed to sale (weeks)[2]	Comments[3]
Iberis sempervirens, sp.	10	60–70	7–21	L/D	11	Grow on 45°
Iliamna sp.	–	55–65	30+	L	–	Prechill 3 wks
Incarvillea delavayi, sp.	–	55–70	7–60	L	–	–
Inula sp.	42	55–65	7–42	L	–	Alternate temps 90/70°
Ipomopsis sp.	–	60	7–10	–	–	–
Iris sp.	–	60–70	7–30+	–	16+	Presoak, sow fresh, prechill, slow, L may help
Isatis sp.	–	40–50	14–42	–	–	Sow direct or DS to 2 yrs
Jasione perennis	–	65–70	10–21	–	–	Sow shallow
Jeffersonia diphylla	–	65–70	–	–	–	Collect before pods open, prechill
Kalimeris (Asteromoea) sp.	–	70	4–7	D	–	Stores one year dry
Kirengeshoma sp.	–	55–65	30+	–	–	Sow shallow, keep moist
Knautia sp.	–	70	7–21	L	–	Sow direct, GA or L
Kniphofia uvaria	9–20	65–75	10–28	–	9	Erratic; sow fresh or prechill 6 wks; reduce night temp.
Lamium sp.	–	65–70	30+	–	–	Sow shallow
Lathyrus latifolius	<1	55–70	10–28	–	10	Soak or scarify, sow direct
Lavandula sp.	–	55–75	7–30+	–	13	Fungicide soak; prechill 4 wks
Lavatera sp.	–	70	7–21	–	–	Sow direct
Leontopodium alpinum	268–310	50–75	7–42	L	11	Sow fresh or stratify
Leonurus sp.	–	70	–	–	–	DS first
Leucanthemum sp.	–	60–70	7–21	–	10	Formerly *Chrysanthemum*
Leucanthemum x superbum	15–35	65–70	7–14	D	12	Formerly *Chrysanthemum*
Lewisia sp.	–	50–70	21–30+	L	–	Stratify 3–6 wks, erratic
Liatris sp.	7–9	55–75	21–28	L	13	55° helps poor germ
Libertia sp.	–	50–70	30+	–	–	Slow, irreg. germ
Ligularia sp.	–	55–65	14–42	–	12	Use fresh seed, cold after warm
Lilium sp.	–	65–75	21–30+	–	–	Prechill 6 wks if slow, varies with sp., D may help; warm 3 months prior to prechill *L. canadense*
Limonium latifolium	28	65–75	14–21	–	10	Now *Platyphyllum*
Limomium tataricum	22	65–75	14–21	–	16	Now *Goniolimon*
Linaria sp.	–	55–60	10–14	–	–	Prechill 3 wks, sow shallow
Linum sp.	9–24	55–75	7–28	–	12	Self sows, 50–60° may help
Liriope muscari	–	70–75	14–30+	–	–	Presoak, erratic, chill 4 wks if dormant
Lithodora diffusa	–	70–75	–	–	–	Presoak 48 hrs or scarify

See footnotes on page 158

continued on next page

Name	Seeds/oz[1] (x 1,000)	Germination medium temp. (°F)	Days to germination	Light (L) or dark (D) require- ments	Seed to sale (weeks)[2]	Comments[3]
Lobelia sp.	–	65–70	7–21	L	10	Prechill 3 months, keep seeds moist, GA may help
Lunaria sp.	1–2	65–75	10–28	–	10	Sow within first year
Lupinus sp., hybrids	1–2	55–75	4–28+	D	7+	Presoak, scarify, or stratify old seed; 100/80° may help
Lychnis sp.	12–13	65–70	7–28	–	12	Prechill 2 wks, no bottom heat, L for *L. alba*
Lysichiton sp.	–	55–70	14–30+	–	–	Keep wet, L improves germ
Lysimachia sp.	–	55–70	7–30	L	9	Keep moist
Lythrum salicaria	2	65–70	7–28	–	8	Sow shallow
Macleaya cordata	–	70–75	14–28	–	16	Sow shallow
Malva alcea	–	70–75	7–10	–	10	Prechill 6 wks, scarify
Malva moschata	–	70–75	7–10	–	–	Presoak, DS well
Mandragora sp.	–	55–60	30–60	–	–	Slow, prechill may help
Marrubium vulgare	–	65–70	28	–	–	Erratic, DS may help
Matricaria sp.	–	65–75	7–21	L	9	L or DS
Meconopsis sp.	–	55–70	14–28	–	–	Keep moist, sow fresh
Mertensia sp.	–	55–60	7–30+	L	12+	Prechill 3 wks
Mimulus sp.	–	55–75	7–21	–	–	Prechill 3 wks; L/DS some sp.
Miscanthus sp.	–	65–75	–	–	10	–
Monarda didyma	56	60–70	7–42	–	8	Sow shallow, reduce night temp
Monarda menthifolia	–	70	7–14	–	–	–
Monarda sp.	–	70	7–21	L	–	L or DS often helps
Moricandia arvensis	–	65–70	7–21	–	–	Low germ
Morina sp.	–	50–70	4–42	–	–	–
Myosotis sp.	45	65–75	7–28	–	9	Surface sow
Myrrhis odorata	–	55–65	14–42	–	–	Can be sown direct
Nelumbo sp.	–	75–95	7–14	–	–	Scarify, submerge pots/keep wet
Nepeta sp.	–	60–70	7–28	–	–	Can be sown direct, L some sp.
Nierembergia sp.	–	60–75	14–28	–	–	–
Oenothera missouriensis	6–7	65–75	7–28	L	10	Stretches at higher temps
Oenothera sp.	–	70	7–21	L/D	–	L or DS *O. argillicola* and *O. biennis*
Omphalodes sp.	–	65–75	4–42	–	–	–
Onopordon (Onopordum) sp.	–	55–65	30–60	–	–	Can sow direct, low germ
Onosma sp.	–	50	30–60	–	–	–
Ophiopogon japonicus	–	70–75	28–42	–	–	Soak berries 24 hrs to remove pulp
Origanum sp.	–	65–70	21–28	–	–	–

See footnotes on page 158

continued on next page

Name	Seeds/oz[1] (x 1,000)	Germination medium temp. (°F)	Days to germination	Light (L) or dark (D) require-ments	Seed to sale (weeks)[2]	Comments[3]
Osmunda sp.	–	65–70	–	L	–	Sow spores very fresh
Osteospermum sp.	–	60–65	10–14	L	–	Sow shallow
Paeonia hybrids	–	50–60	42+	L	–	Slow, erratic, sow fresh and ripe
Paeonia suffruticosa	–	50–60	30+	–	–	Sow fresh, as *Actaea*, 40° or GA for leaves
Pancratium maritimum	–	75	30+	–	–	–
Papaver nudicaule	165	65–70	10–28	D/L	9	Best sown direct
Papaver orientale	95–110	55–75	7–28	L	10+	Grow on 45°
Papaver somniferum	–	55	10–28	L	9	DS may help
Papaver sp.	–	70	7–21	L	–	L or GA most sp., D okay for *P. pilosum*
Paradisea sp.	–	50–70	30+	–	–	Low germ, GA may help
Parnassia sp.	–	55–65	30+	–	–	Keep moist, GA may help
Parochetus communis	–	50	30+	–	–	Presoak
Peltiphyllum (Darmera) peltatum	–	50–60	14–30+	–	–	Keep moist, L improves germ
Pennisetum sp.	–	70	14–21	–	–	–
Penstemon barbatus	15	65–70	7–14	–	10	Can sow exposed
Penstemon confertus	–	55–60	7–21	L	–	Sow shallow
Penstemon sp.	–	70	7–42	L/D	–	L or DS or both may help; 40° for *P. monoensis, P. retroceus, P. scapoides;* GA for *P. pachypyllus*
Penstemon strictus	37	55–75	7–21	–	11	Sow shallow
Perovskia sp.	–	65–70	7–21	–	–	L may improve germ
Persicaria sp.	–	70–75	21–60	–	–	Formerly *Polygonum*
Petrorhagia sp.	–	50	14–60	–	–	–
Phacelia purshii	–	70	90	–	–	–
Phlomis sp.	–	60–70	14–42	–	–	Sow shallow
Phlox paniculata	2–3	60–70	14–28	D	11	Prechill 3–4 wks or stratify, poor germ, sow fresh
Phlox sp.	–	70	7–30+	–	–	Sow fresh, GA may help or as *Actaea*
Phormium sp.	–	60–70	30+	–	–	Sow shallow, low germ
Phuopsis stylosa	–	50–60	30+	L	–	Surface sow
Phygelius sp.	–	60–75	10–14	–	–	Sow shallow
Physalis sp.	17	65–75	7–28+	L	10	Sow within first year or prechill, remove from fruit
Physostegia sp.	18	55–75	7–28	–	10	Reduce night temp, stratify if erratic
Phyteuma sp.	–	55–65	30+	–	–	Sow shallow
Phytolacca sp.	–	65–70	30–60	–	–	–

See footnotes on page 158

continued on next page

Herbaceous Perennials Production

Name	Seeds/oz[1] (x 1,000)	Germination medium temp. (°F)	Days to germination	Light (L) or dark (D) require-ments	Seed to sale (weeks)[2]	Comments[3]
Platycodon sp.	32	60–75	7–28	–	10	Can sow exposed
Podophyllum sp.	–	55–65	30+	L	–	Prechill 3 wks, keep moist
Polemonium sp.	32	65–70	7–28	–	10	Reduce night temp, L or prechill may help
Polygonatum sp.	–	50–75	21–60	–	–	Sow fresh as *Trillium,* when blue fruit is soft
Polygonum sp.	–	70–75	21–60	–	–	Very low germ, now *Persicaria*
Potentilla atrosanguinea	–	65–70	14–21	–	–	Sow shallow
Potentilla nepalensis	75	65–70	7–14	–	10	Can sow exposed
Potentilla recta	–	70	7–14	–	–	GA or DS and L
Potentilla tridentata	–	65–70	7–28	–	–	Acid soil, prechill 2–4 wks
Primula sp.	25–35	60–75	14–42	L	12+	Prechill 2–4 wks may help
Prunella sp.	–	55–70	14–60	–	–	Sow fresh
Pulmonaria sp.	–	60–70	14–42	–	11	Sow shallow
Pulsatilla sp.	–	60–75	30+	–	–	Use fresh seed, old seed as *Actaea*
Pyrethrum coccineum	–	–	–	–	–	See *Tanacetum*
Ramonda sp.	–	55–60	30–60	L	–	Surface sow, very small seed
Ranunculus sp.	–	50–70	7–30+	–	16+	As *Actaea,* GA may help some sp.
Raoulia sp.	–	55–60	30+	L	–	Surface sow
Ratibida sp.	–	65–75	21–42	–	–	Reduce night temp, stores well
Rehmannia sp.	–	60–75	7–42	–	–	–
Reseda sp.	–	55–70	7–21	–	–	Sow direct
Rheum sp.	–	60–65	21–42	–	–	–
Rhodohypoxis sp.	–	50	30+	–	–	Acidic medium
Rodgersia sp.	–	55–75	14–60	L	–	50–60° after germ
Romneya sp.	–	65–75	14–60	–	–	DS and GA may help
Roscoea sp.	–	50–55	30+	L	–	Surface sow, slow
Rudbeckia fulgida	25	70–95	14–21	–	11	Prechill 2 wks
Rudbeckia hirta	27–80	65–70	7–10	L	10	No bottom heat, can sow exposed
Ruella sp.	–	65–75	30+	–	–	Sow shallow
Rumex sp.	–	65–70	–	–	–	Cold stratify
Ruta sp.	–	60–70	4–30+	–	–	Sow shallow
Sagina sp.	–	70	14–60	–	–	L may help
Sagina subulata	1,000	55–70	7–21	–	8	Sow shallow
Salvia sp.	–	70	4–7	–	–	–
Salvia superba	25	70–80	7–14	–	10	Prechill 3–4 weeks, can sow exposed
Sandersonia aurantiaca	–	70–75	30+	–	–	70/40°

 continued on next page

Name	Seeds/oz[1] (x 1,000)	Germination medium temp. (°F)	Days to germination	Light (L) or dark (D) require- ments	Seed to sale (weeks)[2]	Comments[3]
Sanguinaria canadensis	–	50–55	30+	–	–	4 wks 68°, 4 wks 40° after sow, or sow fresh
Sanguisorba sp.	–	50–70	7–30+	–	–	Stores well
Santolina chamaecyparissus	56	65–75	7–14	–	10	Irreg. germ, 40° 4 wks may help
Saponaria sp.	16	60–70	10–28	D/L	10	Prechill 3–4 weeks or sow fresh, GA may help
Sarracenia sp.	–	70–80	30+	L	–	Prechill 1 wk, keep moist, sow fresh
Saxifraga sp.	700	60–75	7–60	–	16+	Sow fresh or stratify, GA may help, or as *Actaea*
Scabiosa sp.	2–3	65–75	7–21	–	10	Cool night temps
Scilla sp.	–	50–70	21–60	–	–	Erratic germ
Scutellaria sp.	–	50–70	14–30+	–	–	L or GA may help
Sedum sp.	400	50–70	7–28	–	11	85/75° or fresh seed, L some sp.
Sempervivum sp.	368	50–75	7–28	–	15	Stretches at higher temps/ grow on warm
Senecio sp.	–	65–75	7–14	L	–	L some sp., sow fresh
Senna sp.	–	65–75	–	–	–	Soak or scarify
Shortia sp.	–	60–65	30–60	L	–	Prechill 3 wks, sow fresh
Sidalcea malviflora, hybrids	9	50–65	14–42	–	10	2 wks 40–50° after sow or sow fresh
Sideritis syriaca	–	65–70	14–21	–	–	–
Silene sp.	–	70	4–21	–	9	Can be sown direct
Silphium perfoliatum	–	70–75	7–14	–	15	Sow shallow, fresh, can sow exposed
Sisyrinchium sp.	–	40–50	30+	–	–	Prechill 3 wks, slow
Sisyrinchium striatum	–	70–75	21–28	–	–	–
Smilacina racemosa	–	60–75	30+	L	–	Sow when red fruit soft, or stratify
Smyrnium perfoliatum	–	50–70	60+	–	–	As *Actaea*, low germ
Soldanella sp.	–	55–70	21–30+	L/D	–	Prechill 4 wks may help
Solidago sp.	220	50–70	7–42	–	10	Sow shallow
Sphaeralcea sp.	–	70	4–30+	L	–	Softly scarify *S. remota*
Stachys (lanata) byzantina	16	65–70	7–28	L	12	Reduce night temp, grow dry
Stachys sp.	–	70	–	–	–	Sow fresh, possible low germ
Stipa sp.	–	70	21–28	–	–	–
Stokesia sp.	3	70	7–28+	–	11	Prechill 6 wks if erratic
Stylophorum sp.	–	65–70	–	–	–	Collect as capsules open, prechill 3 wks then sow fresh

See footnotes on page 158

continued on next page

Name	Seeds/oz[1] (x 1,000)	Germination medium temp. (°F)	Days to germination	Light (L) or dark (D) require-ments	Seed to sale (weeks)[2]	Comments[3]
Succisa sp.	–	65–70	14–60	L	–	–
Symphyandra sp.	–	60–65	21–28	L	–	–
Tanacetum coccineum	17–35	55–70	14–30+	–	10	Doubles seldom from seed
Tanacetum parthenium	200	65–75	7–14	–	10	Prechill 2–4 wks if slow
Tellima grandiflora	–	55–60	30+	–	–	Surface sow
Tephrosia sp.	–	65–70	21–42	–	–	Scarify, water soak
Teuchrium chamaedrys	–	65–70	21–28	–	–	Surface sow
Thalictrum aquilegifolium	10–12	50–80	7–30+	–	12	Scarify or soak, stratify if erratic, or sow fresh
Thalictrum sp.	–	70	14–21	–	–	Sow fresh, GA often helps
Thermopsis caroliniana	6	70–80	14–28	–	–	Scarify old seed or sow fresh
Thymus sp.	–	55–75	7–28	L	9	–
Tiarella sp.	–	50–70	14–30+	L	15	Sow fresh, cold stratify old seed
Townsendia sp.	–	60	30+	–	–	–
Tradescantia sp.	10	70–75	7–42	–	14	Presoak, prechill 12 wks may help
Tricyrtis sp.	–	65–70	30+	–	–	Sow fresh or stratify
Trientalis sp.	–	65–70	–	L	–	–
Trifolium sp.	–	65–70	4–28	–	–	Scarify
Trillium sp.	–	60–70	365+	–	–	2 periods of 3 months 40°, 3 months 70° between, GA helps some sp.
Trollius sp.	–	50–70	7–30+	–	9	Prechill 2 wks, sow fresh or GA, poor germ
Tunica (Petrorhagia)	–	50	14–60	–	–	–
Urospermum dalechampii	–	60–65	14–28	L	–	Sow shallow
Uvularia sp.	–	55–60	30+	–	–	Sow shallow, fresh, prechill
Valeriana officinalis	–	55–75	21–28	L	–	–
Veratrum sp.	–	55–70	14–90+	–	–	Stratify, GA may help
Verbascum sp.	200	55–85	4–28	–	10	Slow, 85° best, L often helps
Verbena sp.	–	60–70	14–90	D/L	–	Sow fresh, prechill 4 wks, L or GA some sp.
Veronica incana	221	65–75	7–28	L	13	60° after germ, difficult
Veronica longifolia	200	65–75	14–28	–	12	Reduce night temp
Veronica sp.	–	70	4–14	–	9	Prechill 12 wks
Veronica spicata	221	65–75	7–28	L	12	Reduce night temp
Veronicastrum virginicum	–	55–75	7–42	L	–	Sow fresh, 60° after germ
Vicia sp.	–	65–70	21–42	–	–	Scarify, sow shallow

See footnotes on page 158

continued on next page

Table B-1. Optimum germination conditions for perennials and biennials *(continued)*

Name	Seeds/oz[1] (x 1,000)	Germination medium temp. (°F)	Days to germination	Light (L) or dark (D) require-ments	Seed to sale (weeks)[2]	Comments[3]
Viola sp.	20–40	60–75	7–21	D	9+	Prechill 2 wks or GA, sow fresh
Vitaliana primuliflora	–	65–70	–	–	–	Cold stratify
Waldsteinia sp.	–	70–75	14–35	L	–	60–65° after germ, stratify old seed
Xerophyllum sp.	–	55–60	30–60	–	–	Sow shallow
Yucca sp.	–	65–75	30–60	–	–	Slow
Zantedeschia sp.	–	70–80	–	–	–	Presoak
Zephyranthes sp.	–	70–75	21–28	–	–	–

[1] Seed weights may be for one or more species of a genus.

[2] + = 4 weeks or more; otherwise, ± 1 to 2 weeks; sale = green pack, as most do not flower the first year.

[3] Grow on at 50–60°F unless noted otherwise. Time to germination, sale is dependent on the cultivar, temperature, etc. Prechill = chill seeds at 40° and keep moist; best to sow on/near surface after chilling for light. Stratify = store seeds moist at 32° for 6+ weeks. Scarify = abrade seed (for example, with sandpaper). Presoak = pour lukewarm water on seeds, leave 24 hrs. DS = dry store seeds at 70°F and 50% or higher relative humidity for 6 months unless noted. GA = gibberellic acid (GA3) presoak. Day/night temperatures may be listed. wks = weeks, hrs = hours, temp = temperature, germ = germination. Temperatures in °F. D = dark, L = light.

Herbaceous Perennials Production

Pests, Diseases, and Problems of Herbaceous Perennials

Table C-1. Pests, diseases, and problems of herbaceous perennials

Scientific name[1]	Diseases and physiological problems	Insects and other pests
Abronia	Damping-off, downy mildew (Peronospora), leaf spot (Heterosporium), rust (Puccinia)	
Acantholimon	Root rots in poor drainage	
Acanthus sp.	Root rots in wet soil	Slugs, snails
Achillea sp.	Crown gall, powdery mildew, rot (Rhizoctonia), stem rot, rust, dodder, root rots	Root-knot nematode, Asiatic garden beetle, caterpillars, oriental beetle
Aciphylla sp.	Root rots in poor drainage	
Aconitum sp.	Crown rot, root rot, stem rot, Verticillium wilt, mosaic, bacterial leaf spot (Pseudomonas), downy mildew (Plasmopara), powdery mildew, root rots, rusts, leaf and stem smut	Mites (especially cyclamen mite), root-knot nematodes
Acorus sp.	Leaf spots, rusts	
Actaea sp.	Leaf spots, rust, smut (Urocystis)	
Actinidia sp.	Damping-off, powdery mildew	
Actinomeris: see Verbesina		
Adenophora sp.	Damping-off	
Adiantum sp.	Dead leaf spots from high humidity and poor ventilation	
Adoxa moschatellina	Leaf gall (Synchtrium), leaf spot (Phyllosticta), rusts	
Adoxa sp.	Leaf gall, leaf spot, rusts	
Aegopodium sp.	Leaf blight (when hot and humid)	In greenhouse: two-spotted mites
Aethiopappus: see Centaurea		
Agapanthus sp.	Phythophthora root or stem rot, virus, Pythium, bacterial blight (Erwinia)	Slugs, snails
Agastache sp.	Powdery mildew, downy mildew, leaf spots, rust, viruses	

See footnotes on page 186   continued on next page

Table C-1. Pests, diseases, and problems of herbaceous perennials *(continued)*

Scientific name[1]	Diseases and physiological problems	Insects and other pests
Agave sp.	Cucumber mosaic virus, anthracnose, leaf spot, bacterial blight *(Erwinia)*, *Botrytis* blight, leaf scorch *(Stagnospora)*	Scales, yucca moth stalk borer, yucca weevil, mealybugs
Agrimonia sp.	Stem blight *(Phoma)*, downy mildew, leaf spots, powdery mildews, root rot, rusts, viruses	
Agrostemma: see *Lychnis, Silene*		
Ajuga sp.	Rot *(Sclerotium)*, crown rot, leaf spot *(Corynespora,* South), leaf spot *(Myrothecium,* South)	Southern root-knot nematode
Alcea (Althaea) sp.	Leaf spot *(Cercosporella)*, rust, anthracnose, crown gall, *Pythium* root rot	Mallow flea beetle, capsid bugs, caterpillars, two-spotted mites, Japanese beetle, slugs, stalk borer
Allionia: see *Mirabilis*		
Allium sp.	Smut, rust, smudge *(Colletotrichum)*, onion white rot *(Sclerotium)*, bacterial soft rots *(Erwinia);*	Onion flies *(Delia)*, stem nematode *(Ditylenchus)*, onion thrips
Alonsoa sp.		Aphids (esp. in greenhouse)
Alopecurus sp.	Roots rot from wet winters	
Aloysia sp.	Leaf spots, anthracnose *(Sphaceloma)*, black mildew *(Meliola)*, blight *(Pellicularia)*, root rot *(Phymatotrichum)*	Southern root-knot nematode
Alsine: see *Minuartia*		
Alstroemeria sp.		Slugs, swift moth larvae, two-spotted mites, spider mites (in greenhouse)
Alternanthera sp.	Leaf spot *(Phyllosticta)*, root rots, *Fusarium* wilt	Root-knot nematode
Althaea sp.	Anthracnose, rust, leaf spots, bacterial wilt and blight, canker *(Nectria)*, powdery mildew, root and crown rots, viruses	Lesion and root-knot nematode, potato leafhopper, Japanese beetle, oriental beetle, abutilon moth, hollyhock leaf-skeletonizer, two-spotted mite, leafminer, melon aphid, green peach aphids
Alyssum murale, sp.	Black root rot *(Thielaviopsis)*, club root *(Plasmodiophora)*, damping-off, root and basal rots *(Pythium* and *Rhizoctonia)*, downy mildew and white blister *(Albugo)*	
Amaracus: see *Origanum*		
Amaranthus sp.	Damping-off, leaf spot, root rot, viruses, white rust	Root-knot nematode
Amaryllis belladonna	*Botrytis* blight, cucumber mosaic virus, rot *(Sclerotium)*, bulb rot if poor drainage, narcissus leaf scorch *(Stagonospera)*	Slugs, snails, eelworm *(Ditylenchus)*, narcissus flies *(Merodon, Eumerus)*, bulb scale mite *(Steneotarsonemus)*, Spanish moth caterpillar *(Xanthopastis)*, black blister beetle *(Epicauta)*, spotted cutworm *(Amathes)*, lesion nematode; in greenhouse: aphid, mealybug, whiteflies, spider mites
Ampelopsis sp.	*Nectria* canker, downy mildew, leaf spots, powdery mildew, root rot *(Helicobasidium)*	Dagger nematode
Amsonia sp.	Leaf spot *(Mycosphaerella)*, rusts	
Anagallis sp.	Leaf spot *(Septoria)*, aster yellows	Nematode *(Meloidogyne)*, aphids (in green house), aster leafhopper
Anaphalis sp.	Leaf spot *(Septoria)*, rust *(Uromyces)*	

See footnotes on page 186

continued on next page

Scientific name[1]	Diseases and physiological problems	Insects and other pests
Anchusa sp.	Crown rot, damping off, leaf spot *(Stemphyllium)*, rusts, viruses	
Andropogon sp.	Rust *(Chelone* alternate host)	
Androsace sp.	Downy mildew *(Peronospora)*, leaf spot *(Mycosphaerella)*, rust *(Puccinia)*	Aphid, root mealybug, root aphid, spider mites (in greenhouse), birds pecking rosettes
Anemone sp.	Impatiens necrotic spot virus, collar rot *(Botrytis)*, leaf spots, rhizome rot *(Pellicularia* and *Sclerotium)*, spot disease *(Synchytrium)*, powdery mildew, plum rust *(Tranzschelia)*, anemone and cucumber mosaic viruses, downy mildew, anemone smut *(Urocystis)*	Flea beetle *(Phyllotreta)* on seedlings, aphids, black blister beetle *(Epicauta)*, cutworms *(Agrotis)*, stem and bulb nematode *(Ditylenchus)*, scabious bud nematode *(Aphelenchoides)*, root lesion nematode *(Pratylenchus)*, symphilids (in greenhouse), green peach aphid *(Myzus)*, thrips
Anemonella sp.	Leaf spot *(Cercospora)*, root rot *(Phymatotrichum)*, rusts	
Angelica sp.	Leaf spots, rusts, root rot *(Phymatotrichum)*	
Anoda sp.	Powdery mildew, rust	
Antennaria sp.	Leaf spots, white rust	
Anthemis sp.	Damping off, viruses, root rot *(Phymatotrichum)*	Root-knot nematode
Antirrhinum sp.	Impatiens necrotic spot virus, cucumber mosaic virus, rust *(Puccinia)*, downy mildew on seedlings and young plants, leaf spot *(Phyllosticta)*, leaf spot *(Corynespora,* South), leaf spot *(Cercospora)*, leaf spot *(Myrothecium,* South), frog-eye leaf spot *(Colletotrichum)*, shot-hole *(Heteropatella)*, anthracnose, *Botrytis* blight, powdery mildew, *Verticillium* wilt, rots *(Pellicularia* and *Sclerotinia)*, rot *(Sclerotium)*, *Pythium* root rot	Aphids, bumble bees (eat corolla tube), strawberry mite *(Tarsonemus)*, greenhouse leaf tier *(Oeobia)*, caterpillars, two-spotted mite *(Tetranychus)*, cyclamen mite *(Steneotarsonemus)*, stinkbug *(Cosmopepla)*, verbena bud moth *(Endothenia)*, southern root-knot nematode *(Meloidogyne)*, thrips
Apocynum sp.	Leaf spots, root rot, rusts	
Aquilegia sp.	*Botrytis* blight, *Alternaria* blight, impatiens necrotic spot virus, powdery mildew, leaf spots, crown rot and root rot, rust, cucumber mosaic virus, damping off, leaf and stem smut	Aphids, columbine leafminer *(Phytomyza)*, bumble bees (eat corolla tubes), columbine skipper caterpillar *(Erynnis)*, columbine borer *(Papaipema)*, whiteflies (in greenhouse), spider mites, foliar nematode, columbine sawfly, thrips
Arabis sp.	*Botrytis* blight, damping off, rot *(Rhizoctonia)*, downy mildew, leaf spot *(Septoria)*, club root *(Plasmodiophora)*, root rot *(Phymatotrichum)*, rusts	Green peach aphid *(Myzus)*, arabis midge *(Dasyneura)*
Arachniodes sp.	Leaf spots, sooty mold (indoors or South), rusts, damping-off (of prothalli)	Nematodes, aphids, whiteflies and fern moth caterpillar in greenhouse; thrips, scales, mealybugs, scales, black vine weevil, fern snail *(Deroceras)*, armyworms, Japanese beetle, crickets, grasshoppers, caterpillars
Arctostaphylos sp.	Black mildew *(Asterina* or *Meliola)*, red leaf spot gall *(Exobasidium)*, leaf spots, rots, rust	
Arctotis sp.	Rot *(Sclerotium)*, leaf spot and blotch *(Cercospora)*, root rots, crown rot, stem rot	Root-knot nematode

continued on next page

Table C-1. Pests, diseases, and problems of herbaceous perennials *(continued)*

Scientific name[1]	Diseases and physiological problems	Insects and other pests
Arenaria sp.	Leaf spot *(Hendersonia)*, powdery mildew, anther smut *(Ustilago)*, rusts, root rot *(Phymatotrichum)*	
Arisaema sp.	Rust *(Uromyces)*, blight *(Streptotinia)*, leaf spots *(Cladosporium* and *Volutella)*	Slugs
Aristolochia sp.	Leaf spots, *Botrytis* blight, root rot *(Diplodia)*	Spider mites, aphids
Armeria sp.	Crown rots *(Sclerotium)* from winter wet and poor drainage, rust *(Uromyces)*	
Armoracia rusticana	Excess nitrogen causing root forking and excess top growth, pale leaf spot *(Ramularia)*, black rot, clubroot, white blister, turnip mosaic virus	
Arnica sp.	Leaf spots *(Ovularia* and *Phyllosticta)*, powdery mildews *(Erysiphe* and *Sphaerotheca)*, rusts *(Puccinia* and *Uromyces)*, white smut *(Entyloma)*	
Artemesia sp.	White rust, downy mildew, leaf blights, leaf gall *(Synchytrium)*, leaf spots, powdery mildew, rusts, *Botrytis* blight, stem blight *(Sclerotium)*, stem gall *(Syncarpella)*, dodder, root rots *(Phymatotrichum* and others)	Root-knot nematode
Aruncus sp.	Leaf spot *(Ramularia* or *Cercospora)*, stem canker *(Leptosphaeria)*	
Arundinaria: see *Pleioblastus, Sasa,* and other bamboo genera		
Arundo sp.	Leaf spots, *Armillaria* root rot, rusts	
Asarum sp.	Impatiens necrotic spot virus, leaf gall *(Synchytrium)*, leaf spots, rhizome rot *(Sclerotinia)*, rust	Slugs, thrips
Asclepias sp.	Leaf spots *(Cercospora* and *Phyllosticta)*, rusts, cucumber mosaic virus, stem blight *(Phoma)*, root rot *(Phymatotrichum)*	Aphids, serpentine leaf miner, San Jose scale, western flower thrips, whiteflies (in greenhouse), aphids
Asparagus sp.	Blight *(Ascochyta)*, root rot *(Fusarium)*, crown gall, yellows	Onion thrips, asparagus beetles *(Crioceris)*, garden fleahopper *(Halticus)*, variegated cutworm *(Peridroma)*, two-spotted mite, scales, asparagus fern caterpillar *(Laphyama)*
Asparella: see *Hystrix*		
Aspidium: see *Polystichum*		
Asplenium sp.	Tip blight *(Phyllosticta)*, leaf spots, sooty mold (if sap-sucking insects are present – greenhouse or South), rusts, damping-off (of prothalli)	In greenhouse: aphids, whiteflies and fern moth caterpillar; thrips, scales, mealybugs, black vine weevil, fern snail *(Deroceras)*, armyworms, Japanese beetle, crickets, grasshoppers, caterpillars, nematodes
Aster sp.	Impatiens necrotic spot virus, aster yellows, stem canker *(Phomopsis, Rhizoctonia)*, rots *(Fusarium* and *Sclerotinia)*, *Botrytis* blight, leaf spots, aster wilt *(Phialaophora)*, *Verticillium* wilt, powdery mildew *(Erisyphe)*, anthracnose, downy mildew, rusts, crown gall, black knot *(Gibberidea)*, dodder *(Cuscuta* sp.), leaf gall *(Synchytrium)*, white smut	Aphids, Japanese beetle, chrysanthemum lace bug *(Corythucha)*, green peach aphid (in greenhouse), western flower thrips, rosy blister gall *(Asteromyzia)*, aster leafhopper, leaf and root-knot nematodes

See footnotes on page 186

continued on next page

Scientific name[1]	Diseases and physiological problems	Insects and other pests
Astilbe sp.	Bacterial blights, powdery mildew *(Erisyphe)*, wilt *(Fusarium)*	Japanese beetle, whiteflies (in greenhouse), tarnished plant bug, water stress injury
Athyrium sp.	*Botrytis* blight, leaf spots, sooty mold (indoors or South), rusts, damping-off (of prothalli)	Nematodes, aphids, whiteflies, and fern moth caterpillar in greenhouse; thrips, scales, mealybugs, black vine weevil, fern snail *(Deroceras)*, armyworms, Japanese beetle, crickets, grasshoppers, caterpillars
Aubrieta sp.	Black root rot *(Thielaviopsis)*, club root *(Plasmodiophora)*, damping-off, root and basal rots *(Pythium* and *Rhizoctonia)*, downy mildew, white blister *(Albugo)*	Nematodes *(Ditylenchus)*, aphids
Aurinia (Alyssum) saxatilis (saxatile)	Black root rot *(Thielaviopsis)*, club root *(Plasmodiophora)*, damping-off, root and basal rots *(Pythium* and *Rhizoctonia)*, downy mildew and white blister *(Albugo)*	
Avena: see *Helictotrichon*		
Avenastrum: see *Avenula*		
Avenella: see *Deschampsia*		
Avenula: see *Helictotrichon*		
Balsamorhiza sp.	Leaf spot *(Septoria)*, powdery mildew, rust	Leaf gall nematode *(Anguina)*
Bambusa sp.	Leaf spots, smut *(Ustilago)*, rusts in South, black mildew *(Meliola)*, tip blight *(Diplodia)*, leaf mold *(Cladosporium)*, viruses	Burrowing nematode *(Radophlolus)*, powder-post beetles *(Dinoderus* and *Lyctus)*, aphids, scales, mites, squirrels, deer, rabbits
Baptisia sp.	Leaf spots, powdery mildews *(Erysiphe* and *Microsphaera)*, rust *(Puccinia)*, root rots	
Barbarea sp.	Bacterial black rot *(Xanthomonas)*, dodder, downy mildew *(Peronospora)*, leaf spots, stem rot *(Sclerotium)*, viruses, white rust	
Batrachium: see *Ranunculus*		
Belamcanda chinensis	Bacterial blight *(Erwinia)*, scorch, leaf spots, rust	Borers
Bellidiastrum: see *Aster*		
Bellis sp.	*Botrytis* blight, leaf spots, root rots, aster yellows, crown rot *(Sclerotinia)*	Southern root-knot nematode, aphids, aster leafhopper
Bergenia sp.	Viruses, leaf spots *(Colletotrichum, Alternaria)*, anthracnose	Black vine weevil damage, foliar nematode
Betonica: see *Stachys*		
Bistorta: see *Polygonum*		
Blechnum sp.	Leaf spots, sooty mold (indoors or South), rusts, damping-off (of prothalli)	Nematodes, aphids, whiteflies, and fern moth caterpillar in greenhouse; thrips, scales, mealybugs, black vine weevil, fern snail *(Deroceras)*, armyworms, Japanese beetle, crickets, grasshoppers, caterpillars
Bocconia: see *Macleaya*		
Bolax: see *Azorella*		
Boltonia	Leaf spot, powdery mildew, smut, rusts	Mites
Brasenia sp.	Leaf spot *(Dichotomophothoropsis)*	
Brauneria: see *Echinacea*		

See footnotes on page 186

continued on next page

Scientific name[1]	Diseases and physiological problems	Insects and other pests
Brevoortia (Brodiaea): see *Dichelostemma*		
Brunella: see *Prunella*		
Buddleia sp.	Stem canker, root rot, scab	Root-knot nematode, aphids, mites
Bupleurum sp.		Root-knot nematode
Butomus umbellatus		Waterlily aphid
Cacalia: see *Adenostyles*		
Calceolaria sp.	Root and basal rots, *Botrytis* blight, tomato spotted wilt virus, stem rot, wilt *(Verticillium),* boron deficiency	Leaf nematode, aphids, whiteflies, greenhouse leafhopper *(Hauptidea),* chrysanthemum nematode *(Aphelanchoides),* spider mites (alpine sp.), slugs
Calimeris: see *Kalimeris*		
Callendrinia: see *Lewisia*		
Callirhoe sp.	Leaf spots, root rot *(Phymatotrichum),* rusts, *Verticillium* wilt	
Calluna sp.	Rot *(Phytophthora),* chlorosis (iron deficiency)	
Caltha sp.	Leaf gall, leaf spots, powdery mildew, rusts	
Campanula sp.	Crown rot, rot *(Sclerotium),* impatiens necrotic spot virus, aster yellows, leaf spots, powdery mildew, root rots, rust, damping-off, *Botrytis* blight, *Verticillium* wilt	Aphids, onion thrips, slugs, snails, western flower thrips, spider mites, aster leafhopper, leaf and root-knot nematodes
Canna generalis	Rot *(Sclerotium),* rust, leaf spots, bean yellow mosaic virus, bacterial bud rot *(Xanthomonas),* stem rot, canna mosaic virus, aster yellows, *Fusarium* rhizome rot	Burrowing nematode *(Radopholus),* Japanese beetle, caterpillars, scales, aster leafhopper
Cardiocrinum sp.	As *Lilium*	Voles, mice, slugs
Carex sp.	Rust *(Puccinia,* alternate host *Oenothera)*	
Carpogymnia: see *Gymnocarpium*		
Carum sp.	Dodder *(Cuscuta),* stem rot, viruses	Root-knot nematode
Cassia: see *Senna*		
Castilleja sp.	Powdery mildews, rusts	
Cathcartia: see *Meconopsis*		
Caulophyllum sp.	*Botrytis* leaf blight, leaf spot *(Cercospora)*	
Cedronella canariensis		Whiteflies (in greenhouse)
Celsia: see *Verbascum*		
Centaurea sp.	Rot *(Sclerotium),* impatiens necrotic spot virus, aster yellows, rust, white rust, stem rots, downy mildew, powdery mildew, *Fusarium* wilt, dodder *(Cuscuta),* root rots, *Verticillium* wilt	Root-knot nematode, aphids, stalk borer *(Papaipema),* aster leafhopper, thrips
Centaurium sp.		Aphids
Centranthus sp.	Leaf spot *(Ramularia)*	
Centrosema sp.	Leaf spots	
Ceterach: see *Asplenium*		
Chamaenerion: see *Chamerion*		
Chamaepericlymenum: see *Cornus*		
Chamaepeuce: see *Ptilostemon*		
Chartolepis: see *Centaurea*		

See footnotes on page 186

continued on next page

Scientific name[1]	Diseases and physiological problems	Insects and other pests
Cheilanthes sp.	Root rots from excessive winter wetness	
Cheiranthus: see *Erysimum*		
Chelidonium majus	Leaf spot, root rot	
Chelone sp.	Leaf spot *(Septoria)*, powdery mildews, rust *(Andropogon* alternate host)	
Cherleria: see *Minuartia*		
Chimaphila sp.	Leaf spots, rust *(Pucciniastrum)*	
Chimonobambusa sp.	Leaf spots, smut *(Ustilago)*, and rusts in South	Powder-post beetles *(Dinoderus* and *Lyctus)*, aphids, scales, mites, squirrels, deer, rabbits
Chionodoxa sp.		Stem and bulb nematode *(Ditylenchus)*
Chondrosum: see *Bouteloua*		
Chrysanthemum: see *Leucanthemum*		
Chrysopsis: see *Heterotheca villosa*		
Cimicifuga sp.	Leaf spot *(Ascochyta)*, rust, smut	Southern root-knot nematode
Cirsium sp.	Leaf spots, rusts, root rots, smut, powdery mildews, white rust, flower smut *(Thecaphora)*	Aphids, plant bugs, caterpillars
Claytonia sp.	Downy mildew, leaf gall *(Physoderma)*, leaf spot *(Ramularia)*, root rot, rusts	
Clematis sp.	Leaf spots *(Ascochyta* and others), powdery mildew, smut, rusts, leaf blight *(Phleospora)*, bacterial wilt, stem rot, bacterial crown gall *(Agrobacterium)*	Root knot nematode, blister beetle, tarnished plant bug, cyclamen mite
Clintonia sp.	Leaf gall *(Synchytrium)*, leaf rot *(Ceratobasidium)*, rust	
Cniscusi sp.	Southern blight	
Colchicum sp.	Leaf smut, *Botrytis* blight	
Collinsonia canadensis	Smut, rusts, leaf spot *(Septoria)*, root rot *(Pythium)*, stem black spot *(Phyllachora)*	
Colocasia sp.	Soft rot *(Pectobacterium*, South), rots *(Diplodia, Fusarium)*, *Sclerotium* blight	Southern root nematode
Comarum: see *Potentilla*		
Commelina sp.	Bacterial blight *(Erwinia)*, cucumber mosaic virus	
Convallaria sp.	Anthracnose, leaf spots, leaf streak *(Colleocephalus)*, stem rot *(Botrytis paeoniae)*, leaf blotch *(Ascochyta)*, crown gall	Weevil, nematodes
Convolvulus sp.	Rust, leaf spots	
Coptis sp.	Leaf spots	
Corbularia: see *Narcissus*		
Coreopsis sp.	Rot *(Sclerotium, Alternaria, Rhizoctonia)*, *Botrytis* blight, bacterial blight *(Pseudomonas)*, viruses, aster yellows, *Verticillium* wilt, leaf spots, powdery mildew, rust, dodder *(Cuscuta)*, scab *(Cladosporium)*	Root knot nematodes, aphids, plant bugs, spotted cucumber beetle, leafminer, western flower thrips, aster leafhopper, chrysomela leaf beetle *(Calligrapha)*
Coronaria: see *Lychnis*		
Coronilla sp.	Stem rots	Southern root knot nematode
Cortaderia sp.	Leaf spots	

See footnotes on page 186

continued on next page

Table C-1. Pests, diseases, and problems of herbaceous perennials *(continued)*

Scientific name[1]	Diseases and physiological problems	Insects and other pests
Corydalis sp.	Downy mildew, rusts, leaf spot *(Septoria)*	Southern root nematode
Cosmos atrosanguineus	*Botrytis* blight, aster yellows, bacterial wilt *(Pseudomonas)*, canker *(Diaporthe)*, leaf spots, powdery mildew, root and stem rots, viruses	Aphids, beetles, aster leafhopper, bugs, European corn borer, two-spotted mite
Cossonia: see *Morisia*		
Cotyledon: see *Rosularia*		
Crambe sp.	Black leaf spot *(Alternaria)*, root rot *(Aphanomyces)*, virus, *Fusarium* wilt	
Craspedia sp.	Root rots from overwatering especially in winter	
Crassula sp.	Anthracnose, root rot, leaf spot	Cyclamen mite, mealybugs
Crepis sp.	Leaf spots, powdery mildew, rusts	
Crinum sp.	as *Amaryllis*	
Crocosmia sp.		Mites
Crocus sp.	Scab *(Pseudomonas)*, dry rot *(Stromatinia)*, corm rot *(Fusarium)*, blue mold rot *(Penicillium)*, iris mosaic virus, rusts, other diseases as for *Narcissus*	Green peach aphid, bulb mite, mice, voles, chipmunks, squirrels
Crucianella: see *Phuopsis*		
Cryptogramma sp.	Leaf spots, sooty mold (indoors or South), rusts, damping-off (of prothalli)	Nematodes, aphids, whiteflies, and fern moth caterpillar in greenhouse; thrips, scales, mealybugs, black vine weevil, fern snail *(Deroceras)*, armyworms, Japanese beetle, crickets, grasshoppers, caterpillars
Currania: see *Gymnocarpium*		
Curtonus: see *Crocosmia*		
Cyclamen sp.	*Botrytis* blight, stunt *(Ramularia)*, tuber rot, root rot *(Thielaviopsis)*, and wilt *(Fusarium)* in greenhouse; bud and leaf blights, leaf spots,	Nematodes, black vine weevil, aphids, cyclamen mite, and spider mites in greenhouse; mice, squirrels, slugs, snails
Cyclobothra: see *Calochortus*		
Cymbopogon sp.	Leaf spot *(Helminthosporium)*, tangle top *(Myriogenospora)*	
Cynara sp.	*Botrytis* blight, leaf spots, powdery mildew, root and stem rots, viruses	Root-knot nematode, aphids, slugs
Cynoglossum sp.	Leaf spots, downy mildew, stem decay, powdery mildew, root rots	Southern root nematode
Cypripedium sp.	*Botrytis* blight	Slugs
Cyrtomium sp.	Leaf spots, sooty mold (indoors or South), rusts, damping-off (of prothalli)	Nematodes, aphids, whiteflies, and fern moth caterpillar in greenhouse; thrips, scales, mealybugs, black vine weevil, fern snail *(Deroceras)*, armyworms, Japanese beetle, crickets, grasshoppers, caterpillars
Cystopteris sp.	Leaf blister *(Taphrina)*	Slugs
Dactylorchis: see *Dactylorhiza*		
Dahlia hybrids	Rot *(Sclerotium)*, bacterial blight *(Erwinia, Pseudomonas)*, *Botrytis* blight, impatiens necrotic spot virus, cucumber and dahlia mosaic virus, tomato spotted wilt virus, powdery mildew, stem rots, crown gall, smut, *Verticillium* wilt, *Fusarium* wilt, leaf spots, scab *(Streptomyces)*	Aphids, European corn borer, stalk borers, bugs, thrips, whiteflies, mites, nematodes, spider mites, plant leafhopper

See footnotes on page 186

continued on next page

Herbaceous Perennials Production

Scientific name[1]	Diseases and physiological problems	Insects and other pests
Dalea (Petalostemon) sp.	Root rot *(Phymatotrichum)*, rusts	
Davallia sp.	Leaf spots, sooty mold (indoors or South), rusts, damping-off (of prothalli)	Nematodes, aphids, whiteflies, and fern moth caterpillar in greenhouse; thrips, scales, mealybugs, black vine weevil, fern snail *(Deroceras)*, armyworms, Japanese beetle, crickets, grasshoppers, caterpillars
Dedronella: see *Meehania*		
Delphinium sp.	Impatiens necrotic spot virus, viruses, aster yellows, *Verticillium* wilt, bacterial blight *(Pseudomonas)*, stem canker *(Fusarium)*, damping-off, smut, crown rots, *Botrytis* blight, black leg *(Erwinia)*, crown gall, leaf spots, powdery mildew, rusts, chlorosis (low temperature, wet soil)	Aphids, borers, leaf miner, mites (cyclamen, brood, two-spotted spider), lily aphid, green peach aphid *(Myzus)* in greenhouse, beetles, cutworm, sowbugs, slugs, nematodes, aster leafhopper, thrips
Dendranthema sp.	Rot *(Sclerotium)*, bacterial blight *(Pseudomonas, Erwinia)*, leaf spots *(Septoria, Alternaria, Myrothecium*–South*)*, aster yellows, impatiens necrotic spot virus, mosaic viruses, tomato spotted wilt virus, crown gall, fasciation *(Corynebacterium)*, rust, powdery mildew *(Erysiphe)*, *Verticillium* wilt, *Fusarium* wilt, *Acremonium* wilt, *Botrytis* blight, ray blight *(Mycosphaerella)*, ray speck, damping-off *(Stemphylium)*, stem rots *(Fusarium, Pellicularia)*, wilt *(Pythium)*, phloem necrosis	Aphids, whiteflies, leafminer, western flower thrips, beetles, stalk borer *(Papaipema)*, plant bugs, caterpillars, gall midge, leaf miner, leaf tier, lace bug, mealybug, cutworms, mites, foliar nematode, aster leafhopper, European corn borer
Dendrocalamus sp.	Leaf spots, smut *(Ustilago)*, and rusts in South	Powder-post beetles *(Dinoderus* and *Lyctus)*, aphids, scales, mites, squirrels, deer, rabbits
Dennstaedtia punctilobula		Slugs, birds
Dentaria: see *Cardamine*		
Dianthus sp.	Rots, impatiens necrotic spot virus and others, bacterial blights and wilts, fungal wilts *(Alternaria* and others*)*, *Fusarium* wilt *(D. barbatus)*, *Botrytis* blight, leaf spot, rust, root rot *(Pythium)*, crown rot *(Rhizoctonia)*, crown gall, stem rot	Aphids, cabbage looper, cutworm, mites, fungus gnat larvae (in greenhouse), green peach aphid (in greenhouse), caterpillars, southern root nematode, thrips
Dicentra sp.	Rot *(Sclerotium)*, stem rot *(Pellicularia)*, downy mildew and rust *(D. canadensis)*, virus, *Verticillium* and *Fusarium* wilts	Aphids, fungus gnat larvae (in greenhouse), whiteflies (in greenhouse)
Didissandra: see *Corallodiscus*		
Dielytria: see *Dicentra*		
Digitalis sp.	Crown and root rots, anthracnose, wilt, viruses, fungal leaf spots, powdery mildew, downy mildew	Foxglove and lily aphids, melon aphids, western flower thrips, mealybug, beetles, stem and bulb nematodes
Diopogon: see *Jovibarba*		
Diosphaera: see *Trachelium*		
Diplazium sp.	Leaf spots, sooty mold (indoors or South), rusts, damping-off (of prothalli)	Nematodes, aphids, whiteflies, and fern moth caterpillar in greenhouse; thrips, scales, mealybugs, black vine weevil, fern snail *(Deroceras)*, armyworms, Japanese beetle, crickets, grasshoppers, caterpillars
Dipsacus sp.	Southern blight, downy mildew *(Peronospora)*, leaf spot *(Cercospora)*, powdery mildew	Leaf and stem nematodes
Dodecatheon sp.	Rust, leaf spot	

See footnotes on page 186

continued on next page

Scientific name[1]	Diseases and physiological problems	Insects and other pests
Doronicum sp.	Powdery mildew	Aphids, sawflies, lily aphid, fern and southern root-knot nematode
Doryopteris sp.	Leaf spots, sooty mold (indoors or South), rusts, damping-off (of prothalli)	Nematodes, aphids, whiteflies, and fern moth caterpillar in greenhouse; thrips, scales, mealybugs, black vine weevil, fern snail *(Deroceras)*, armyworms, Japanese beetle, crickets, grasshoppers, caterpillars
Draba sp.	Rots from overwatering when not in growth, downy mildew, white rust *(Albugo)*, rust *(Puccinia)*	
Dracocephalum sp.	Downy mildew, sclerotium blight, leaf spots	
Drepanostachyum sp.	Leaf spots, smut *(Ustilago)*, and rusts in South	Powder-post beetles *(Dinoderus* and *Lyctus)*, aphids, scales, mites, squirrels, deer, rabbits
Dryopteris sp.	Leaf blister *(Taphrina)*, leaf spots, sooty mold (indoors or South), rusts, damping-off (of prothalli)	Nematodes, aphids, whiteflies, and fern moth caterpillar in greenhouse; thrips, scales, mealybugs, black vine weevil, fern snail *(Deroceras)*, armyworms, Japanese beetle, crickets, grasshoppers, caterpillars
Duchesnea sp.	Downy mildew *(Peronospora)*, leaf gall *(Synchytrium)*, leaf spot *(Pezizella)*, rust *(Frommea)*	
Echinacea sp.	Damping-off, *Botrytis* blight, bacterial leaf spot *(Pseudomonas, Xanthomonas)*, *Rhizopus* (gray fuzz on flowers), mosaic virus, fungal leaf spots, leaf spot *(Myrothecium*, South), root rot	Japanese beetle
Echinops sp.	Rot *(Sclerotium)*, crown rot *(Pellicularia)*	Melon and green peach aphids, four-lined plant bug
Echioides: see *Arnebia*		
Echium sp.	Leaf spot *(Cercospora)*, root rot *(Rosellinia)*	
Eichhornia sp.	Leaf spot *(Cercospora)*, root and crown rot *(Mycoleptodiscus)*	
Elisma: see *Luronium*		
Endymion: see *Hyacinthoides*		
Epilobium sp.	*Botrytis* blight, southern blight *(Sclerotium)*, downy mildew, leaf spots, powdery mildew, root rot, rusts, leaf smut *(Doassansia)*, viruses	Root-knot nematode
Eranthis sp.		Aphids and sooty mold, birds (peck flowers)
Eremurus sp.	Leaf spots	
Erianthus: see *Saccharum*		
Erica sp.	Powdery mildew, collar *(Phytophthora)* and stem *(Asochyta)* rots, rust *(Pucciniastrum)*	
Erigeron sp.	Rot *(Sclerotium)*, downy mildews, leaf spots, powdery mildews, rusts, aster yellows, white smut *(Entyloma)*, viruses, *Verticillium* wilt, *Botrytis* blight, leaf gall *(Synchytrium)*	Aphids, aster leafhopper
Eriophyllum sp.	Rusts	Southern root-knot nematode
Erodium sp.	Leaf spot *(Pseudomonas)*, fungal crown and stem rots, curly top virus, *Sclerotium* blight, downy mildew, leaf gall *(Synchytrium)*, root rot	Aphids (in greenhouse)
Eryngium sp.	Smut, fungal leaf spots, stem rot *(Macrophomina)*, root rots, white smut *(Entyloma)*	

 continued on next page

Scientific name[1]	Diseases and physiological problems	Insects and other pests
Erysimum (Cheiranthus) sp.	Cucumber mosaic virus, bacterial wilt *(Xanthomonas)*, club root, white rust, *Botrytis* blight, leaf spots, *Rhizoctonia* crown rot, aster yellows virus, downy mildew *(Peronospora)*, powdery mildew *(Erysiphe)*, rusts	Aphids, diamondback moth caterpillar, beetles
Erysium: see *Barbarea*		
Erythraea: see *Centaurium*		
Erythronium sp.	Leaf blights, black spot *(Asteroma)*, rust *(Uromyces)*, leaf smuts	Nematodes, green peach aphid
Eulalia: see *Miscanthus*		
Eunomia: see *Aethionema*		
Eupatorium sp.	Impatiens necrotic spot virus, powdery mildew *(Erysiphe)*, *Botrytis* blight, downy mildew, leaf spots, root and stem rots, rusts, white smut *(Entyloma)*, *Fusarium* wilt	Aphids, leafminer, western flower thrips, chrysanthemum leaf miner, scales, southern root-knot nematode
Euphorbia sp.	Stem and root rots, *Botrytis* blight, leaf spots, powdery mildew *(Microsphaera)*, rusts, anthracnose, stem smut *(Tilletia)*, leaf mold *(Cercosporidium)*	Aphids, mealybug, mites, scales
Euthamia: see *Solidago*		
Fallopia (Polygonum) sp.	Impatiens necrotic spot virus	Japanese beetle, thrips
Fargesia sp.	Leaf spots, smut *(Ustilago)*, and rusts in South	Powder-post beetles *(Dinoderus* and *Lyctus)*, aphids, scales, mites, squirrels, deer, rabbits
Felicia rosulata: see *Aster natalensis*		
Festuca sp.	Rot *(Sclerotium)*	
Ficaria: see *Ranunculus*		
Filipendula sp.	Powdery mildew *(Sphaerotheca)*, leaf spots, rust *(Triphragmium)*	
Fragaria sp.	Anthracnose, bacterial leaf spot and rots, *Botrytis* blight, leaf blight *(Dendrophoma)*, southern blight, downy mildew *(Peronospora)*, leaf gall, leaf spots and scorches, powdery mildew *(Sphaerotheca)*, crown rot, fungal root and crown rots, slime molds, sooty mold, viruses, *Verticillium* wilt	Nematodes, aphids (in greenhouse)
Freesia cultivars	Bacterial scab *(Pseudomonas)*, leaf spot, *Fusarium* wilt, dry rot, iris mosaic virus, blue mold *(Penicillium)*	Green peach aphid *(Myzus)*, bulb mite, thrips, southern root-knot nematode
Fritillaria sp.	Leaf spot *(Phyllostricta)*, rust *(Uromyces)*, mosaic virus	
Fuchsia sp.	*Botrytis* leaf spot and blight, rust, *Verticillium* wilt, dieback *(Phomopsis)*, leaf spot *(Septoria)*, root rots, tomato spotted wilt virus, sun scorch	Aphids, beetles, mealybugs, mites, scales, greenhouse thrips, whiteflies, southern root-knot nematode
Funkia: see *Hosta*		
Gaillardia sp.	Bacterial blight *(Pseudomonas)*, viruses, aster yellows, leaf spot *(Septoria)*, smut *(Entyloma)*, powdery mildews, rust, root rots	Aster leafhopper, plant bugs, green peach aphid (in greenhouse), thrips, beetles, stalk borer, nematode *(Naccobus)*
Galanthus sp.	Gladiolus dry rot *(Stromatinia)*, narcissus leaf scorch *(Stagonospora)*, *Botrytis* mold	Narcissus bulb fly, stem and bulb nematode

See footnotes on page 186

continued on next page

Scientific name[1]	Diseases and physiological problems	Insects and other pests
Galega sp.	Leaf spots, powdery mildew	Aphids, cutworms, pea and bean weevils
Galeobdolon: see *Lamium*		
Galium sp.	Leaf scorch in hot climates, dodder *(Cuscuta)*, downy mildew, leaf spots, powdery mildews, root rot, rusts	
Galtonia sp.	*Ornithogalum* mosaic virus	
Gaura sp.	Downy mildew, leaf gall *(Synchytrium)*, leaf spots, powdery mildew, root rot, rusts, viruses	
Gazania sp.	Bacterial blight *(Pseudomonas)*, crown rot *(Rhizoctonia)*	
Gentiana sp.	*Botrytis* blight, damping-off, leaf spots, rusts, *Fusarium* root rot	Aphids, spider mites, slugs, snails
Geranium sp.	Bacterial blight and leaf spots, fungal leaf spots, cucumber mosaic virus, *Botrytis* blight, downy mildew *(Plasmopara)*, rusts, powdery mildews, leaf gall *(Synchytrium)*, root rots	Asiatic garden beetle, plant bugs, fungus gnat larvae (in greenhouse), foliar nematodes
Geum sp.	Downy mildew *(Peronospora)*, leaf gall *(Synchytrium)*, leaf spots, powdery mildew, root rots, rust, leaf smut *(Urocystis)*, viruses	Sawfly larva, leafminer *(Mettalus)*, strawberry rhynchites weevil *(Caenothinus)*, root-knot nematodes
Gillenia sp.	Rust *(Gymnosporangium)*	
Gladiolus sp.	Corm and dry and hard rots, leaf blights *(Stemphylium)*, *Fusarium* yellows and wilt, mosaic viruses, ringspot viruses, aster yellows, leaf spots, smut *(Urocystis)*, blue mold *(Penicillium)*, bacterial leaf spot and blight *(Xanthomonas)*, scab *(Pseudomonas)*, soft rot *(Pectobacterium)*	Thrips, aphids, caterpillars, mites, slugs, wireworms, grape mealybug, plant bugs, white grubs, corn earworm, root-knot nematodes among others, aster leafhopper
Gloriosa superba	Rot *(Sclerotium)*, cucumber mosaic virus	
Gnaphalium sp.	Stem canker *(Phoma)*, downy mildew, leaf spots, root rot, rusts, white smut *(Entyloma)*, viruses	Root-knot nematodes
Gromania: see *Sedum*		
Gymnocarpium sp.	Leaf spots, sooty mold (in greenhouse or South), rusts, damping-off (of prothalli)	Nematodes, aphids, whiteflies, and fern moth caterpillar in greenhouse; thrips, scales, mealybugs, black vine weevil, fern snail *(Deroceras)*, armyworms, Japanese beetle, crickets, grasshoppers, caterpillars
Gymnothrix: see *Pennisetum*		
Gynerium: see *Cortaderia*		
Gypsophila sp.	Damping-off, bacterial fasciation, aster yellows, *Botrytis* blight, crown gall	Aster leafhopper and others, root-knot nematode
Harpalium: see *Helianthus*		
Hebe sp.	Leaf spots, downy mildew *(Peronospora)*, root rots *(Armillaria* and *Phytophthora)*, *Fusarium* wilt	
Hedyotis: see *Houstonia*		
Hedysarum sp.	Black mildew *(Parodiella)*, leaf spots, rusts	Root-knot nematode
Helenium sp.	Leaf spots, rusts, smut, powdery mildew, aster yellows, root rot	Snout beetle, aster leafhopper
Heleocharis: see *Eleocharis*		

continued on next page

Scientific name[1]	Diseases and physiological problems	Insects and other pests
Helianthemum sp.	Leaf spots, root rots *(Phymatotrichum)*	
Helianthus sp.	Rots, bacterial blight and leaf spot and wilt, crown gall, fungal leaf spots, powdery mildew *(Erysiphe)*, rusts, wilt, stem rot, *Botrytis* blight, southern blight, dodder, downy mildew *(Plasmopara)*, viruses, leaf smut	Aphids, bugs, beetles, caterpillars, sunflower maggot, citrophilus mealybug, cottony-cushion scale
Helichrysum sp.	Rot *(Sclerotium)*, *Fusarium* stem rot, *Verticillium* wilt, aster yellows, downy mildew *(Plasmopara)*, viruses	Root-knot nematode, aster leafhopper, leaf miners
Heliopsis helianthoides	Black knot *(Gibberidea)*, leaf spots, powdery mildew, root rot, rusts, viruses	Aphids, leafminer
Heliosperma: see *Silene*		
Helleborus sp.	Black spot *(Coniothyrium)*, blights, crown rot *(Sclerotium)*	
Hemerocallis sp.	Rot *(Sclerotium)*, crown rot, bacterial blight *(Erwinia)*, root rot *(Armillaria)*, leaf streaks *(Colletotrichum, Colleocephalus)*, fungal leaf spots, *Botrytis* blight, leaf blight *(Kabatiella)*, "spring sickness" (distortion, sideways growth in spring)	Slugs and snails (young foliage), gall midge *(Contarinia)*, daylily aphid, spider mites, thrips, nematodes, cutworm, Japanese beetle, grasshoppers, southern root-knot nematode
Hepatica sp.	Rust *(Tranzschelia)*, downy mildew *(Plasmopara)*, leaf spot *(Septoria)*, leaf and stem smut *(Urocystis)*	
Hertia: see *Othonna*		
Hesperis sp.	Club root *(Plasmodiophora)*, downy mildew *(Peronospora)*, white rust, viruses	
Heterotheca (Chrysopsis) sp.	Bacterial blight *(Pseudomonas)*, leaf spots, rusts, powdery mildew *(Erysiphe)*	
Heuchera sp.	*Botrytis* blight, leaf spots *(Colletotrichum* and others), powdery mildews, anthracnose, bacterial leaf spot *(Pseudomonas, Xanthomonas)*, stem rot, leaf and stem smut, leafy gall *(Corynebacterium)*, root rots, rust, sunburn (purple foliage cultivars)	Mealybugs, root weevils, fungus gnat larvae (in greenhouse), foliar nematode, four-lined plant bug
x *Heucherella* sp.	as *Heuchera*	
Hexastylis: see *Asarum*		
Hibanobambusa tranquillans	Leaf spots, smut *(Ustilago)*, and rusts in South	Powder-post beetles *(Dinoderus* and *Lyctus)*, aphids, scales, mites, squirrels, deer, rabbits
Hibiscus sp.	Root and stem rot, bacterial blight and wilt, canker, leaf spots, crown gall, rust, molybdenum deficiency, bud drop (dry conditions or low temperatures)	Nematodes; in greenhouse: aphids, Japanese beetle, scales, whiteflies, mealybugs, caterpillars, thrips
Hieracium sp.	Stem blight *(Phoma)*, downy mildew, leaf spots, powdery mildew, root rot, rusts	
Hoorebekia: see *Grindelia*		
Hosta sp.	Rot *(Sclerotium)*, bacterial blight *(Erwinia)*, *Botrytis* blight and leaf spots, leaf spots *(Colletotrichum)*, anthracnose, mottle virus, crown rots, water deficiency	Slugs and snails, grasshoppers, black vine weevil, thrips, spider mites, deer, rabbits
Houstonia (Hedyotis) sp.	Downy mildew *(Peronospora* sp.), leaf spots, rusts	

See footnotes on page 186 *continued on next page*

Scientific name[1]	Diseases and physiological problems	Insects and other pests
Humulus sp.	Downy mildew, powdery mildew, leaf spot anthracnose, bacterial crown gall, leaf spots, *Armillaria* root rot, rust, sooty mold, viruses, *Verticillium* wilt, leaf tatter (wind)	Spider mites, aphids, potato leafhopper, root-knot nematode
Hyacinthus orientalis	Yellow rot (*Xanthomonas*), soft rot, black slime (*Sclerotinia*), *Fusarium* root rot, *Botrytis* blight and rot, rust (*Uromyces*), mosaic virus, bulb and root rots	Aphids, bulb mite (*Rhizoglyphus*), lesser bulb fly (*Eumerus*), yellow woolybear, white grubs, stem and bulb nematode
Hydrastis canadensis	*Botrytis* leaf spot, blight (*Alternaria*), stem rots, *Fusarium* wilt and root rot, viruses	Root-knot nematode
Hydrocharis sp.		Waterlily leaf cutter (*Synclita*), snails
Hydrophyllum sp.	Downy mildew, leaf spots, powdery mildew, leaf and stem rots, rusts	
Hylotelephium: see *Sedum*		
Hymenocallis sp.	Leaf scorch, leaf spots, leaf blotch (*Stagonospora*), mosaic virus	Spiral nematode (*Rotylenchus*), Spanish moth caterpillar, lesser snow scale (*Pinnaspis*), thrips
Hymenopappus sp.	Downy mildew, root rot (*Phymatotrichum*), rust	
Hypericum sp.	Rusts, root rot (*Rosellia*), powdery mildew (*Erysiphe*), fungal leaf spots, stem black knot (*Gibberidea*), bacterial leaf spot (*Pseudomonas*), leaf blight (*Rosellina*)	Caterpillars, southern root-knot nematode
Hypoxis sp.	Leaf spots, rusts, flower smut (*Urocystis*)	Slugs and snails
Hyppolytia: see *Hippolytia*		
Hyssopus sp.		Root-knot nematode
Iberis sp.	Rot (*Sclerotium*), club root (*Plasmodiophora*), damping-off, downy mildew (*Peronospora*), powdery mildew (*Erysiphe*), white rust, *Botrytis* blight, dodder (*Cuscuta*), root rots, viruses	Diamondback moth caterpillar, oystershell scale, southern root-knot nematode
Inula sp.	Powdery mildew, leaf spot (*Ramularia*), rust (*Puccinia*)	
Ipheion sp.		Slugs, snails
Iris sibirica	Fungal leaf spots, rust, *Botrytis* blight	Thrips, aphids
Iris sp. (Germanica type)	Bacterial blight (*Erwinia*, *Xanthomonas*), bacterial soft rot (*Pectobacterium*), mosaic viruses, fungal leaf spots (*Didymellina* and others), leaf "fire" and spots (*Mycosphaerella*), blossom blights, rust (*Puccinia*), rhizome rot (*Botryotinia*), crown rot (*Pellicularia*), black rot (*Sclerotinia*), ink spot (*Mystrosporium*), *Fusarium* basal rot, blue mold (*Penicillium*)	Iris borers, thrips, slugs, snails, aphids, lesser bulb fly, Florida red scale (*Chrysomphalus*), caterpillars, iris weevil, bulb mite, nematodes
Jussiaea: see *Ludwigia*		
Kelseya uniflora	Molds and rots under wet situations	
Kentranthus: see *Centranthus*		
Kniphofia (*Tritoma*) sp.	Rot (*Sclerotium*), leaf spot (*Alternaria*)	Root-knot nematode, thrips, aphids, mites
Koellia: see *Pycnanthemum*		
Korolkowia: see *Fritillaria*		
Lachenalia sp.	*Ornithogalum* mosaic virus	
Lactuca sp.	Rots	Aphids
Lamiastrum: see *Lamium galeobdolon*		

See footnotes on page 186

continued on next page

Scientific name[1]	Diseases and physiological problems	Insects and other pests
Lamium sp.	Impatiens necrotic spot virus	Slugs, snails, western flower thrips, spider mites
Lamyra: see *Ptilostemon*		
Lasiagrostis: see *Stipa*		
Lastrea: see *Dryopteris, Thelypteris* et al.		
Lathyrus sp.	Anthracnose *(Glomerella)*, basal and root rots, damping-off, downy mildew *(Peronospora)*, fungal leaf spots, powdery mildews, *Fusarium* wilt, *Botrytis* blight, white mold *(Ramularia)*, crown gall, bacterial streak *(Erwinia)* and fasciation *(Corynebacterium)*, tomato spotted wilt virus, mosaic viruses, bud drop (improper nutrition and watering)	Aphids, greenhouse leaf tier *(Oeobia)*, corn earworm, plant bugs, thrips, serpentine leaf miner, mites, sowbugs, fungus gnat larvae, slugs and snails, southern root-knot nematode
Lavandula sp.	Damping-off, leaf spot *(Septoria)*, root rot *(Armillaria)*	Caterpillars, northern root-knot nematode, whiteflies, four-lined plant bug
Lavatera sp.	Root rot, damping-off, leaf spot anthracnose, rust, viruses	
Leonurus sp.	Black mildew *(Dimerosporium)*, leaf spots, mosaic virus	
Lepachys: see *Ratibida*		
Lepidium sp.	Damping-off, downy mildew *(Peronospora)*, root rots, crown rot, rust, virus, white rust	
Leptandra: see *Veronicastrum*		
Leptosyne: see *Coreopsis*		
Leucanthemopsis sp.	as *Leucanthemum*	
Leucanthemum sp.	Leaf spots, stem rots, crown gall, viruses, powdery mildew, leaf blotch *(Septoria)*, root rots	Root knot nematode and others, four-lined plant bug, leaf miner, caterpillars
Leucojum sp.	Leaf scorch *(Stagonospora)*, *Botrytis* rot	Meadow nematode *(Pratylenchus)*
Levisticum officinale		Leaf-mining and celery flies
Lewisia sp.	Rots (overwatering), rust	
Liatris sp.	Rots, root rot *(Rhizoctonia)*, bacterial blight *(Pseudomonas)*, leaf spot *(Corynespora*, South), leaf spots, rusts, *Verticillium* wilt, dodder *(Cuscuta)*	Root nematodes (South), rodents
Ligularia sp.	Leaf scorch (sun, dark-leaved forms), wilt (lack of water in sun)	
Lilium sp. and hybrids	Rot *(Sclerotium)*, bacterial blight *(Erwinia)*, bacterial soft rot *(Pectobacterium)*, *Botrytis* "fire" on leaves and blight on flowers, stem canker, rusts, ringspot and mosaic viruses, bud spots *(Sclerotinia)*, basal rots, bulb rots, damping-off, leaf spots, leaf and bulb mold *(Cladosporium)*, bud blast, bud and lower leaf drop (insufficient light), chlorosis (iron deficiency)	Aphids, brown scale, weevils, beetles, stalk borer *(Papaipema)*, thrips, mites, nematodes
Limnanthemum: see *Nymphoides*		
Limonium sp.	Rot *(Sclerotium)*, anthracnose, bacterial blight *(Erwinia)*, *Botrytis* blight, leaf spots, rust *(Uromyces)*, aster yellows, crown rots, turnip mosaic virus	Foliar nematode, root-knot nematode, aster leafhopper

See footnotes on page 186

continued on next page

Scientific name[1]	Diseases and physiological problems	Insects and other pests
Linaria sp.	Rot, anthracnose *(Colletotrichum)*, downy mildew *(Peronospora)*, powdery mildew, leaf spots, foliar and root and stem rots, *Botrytis* blight, rusts, white smut *(Entyloma)*, viruses	Root nematodes, aphids, flea beetles
Linosyris vulgaris: see *Aster linosyris*		
Linum sp.	Rot *(Sclerotium)*, damping-off *(Pellicularia)*	Cutworm, grasshoppers, root-knot nematode
Lippia (Phyla, Aloysia) sp.	Leaf spots, anthracnose *(Sphaceloma)*, black mildew *(Meliola)*, blight *(Pellicularia)*, root rot *(Phymatotrichum)*	Southern root-knot nematode
Liriope sp.	Rot *(Sclerotium)*	
Lithophragma sp.	Rust, leaf and stem smut *(Urocystis)*	
Lithospermum sp.	*Septoria* leaf spot, powdery mildew, rusts	
Lobelia sp.	*Botrytis* blight, damping-off *(Pythium)*, root rots, rust *(Puccinia)*, smut *(Entyloma)*, crown rot, leaf spots, viruses	Fungus gnat larvae (in greenhouse), plant bugs, red-banded leaf roller *(Argyrotaenia)*, wireworms, southern root-knot nematode, slugs, thrips
Lomara: see *Blechnum*		
Ludwigia (Jussiaea) sp.	Leaf spots, rusts	
Lunaria sp.	White blister rust, club root, virus, leaf spots, stem canker *(Leptothyrium)*, root rot, damping off *(Aphanomyces)*	
Lupinus sp.	Root and stem rots, impatiens necrotic spot virus, cucumber mosaic virus, leaf blight *(Hadotrichum)*, leaf spots, crown rot *(Pellicularia)*, downy mildew, powdery mildews, anthracnose *(Colletotrichum)*, rusts, seedling blights, damping-off	Nematodes, aphids, plant bugs, whiteflies (in greenhouse), western flower thrips
Luzula sp.	Rust *(Puccinia)*, flower smut *(Cintractia)*	
Lychnis sp.	Impatiens necrotic spot virus, ringspot virus, leaf spots, root rots, rust, anther smut, *Botrytis* blight	Whiteflies, thrips
Lycopus sp.	Leaf gall *(Synchytrium)*, leaf spots, rusts	
Lycoris sp.	Leaf scorch *(Stagonospora)*	Nematodes
Lygodium palmatum	Leaf spots, sooty mold (indoors or South), rusts, rots (from winter injury, overwatering), damping-off (of prothalli)	Nematodes, aphids, whiteflies, and fern moth caterpillar in greenhouse; thrips, scales, mealybugs, black vine weevil, fern snail *(Deroceras)*, armyworms, Japanese beetle, crickets, grasshoppers, caterpillars
Lymanthiemum: see *Nymphoides*		
Lysimachia sp.	Rots, leaf and stem blight *(Ceratobasidium)*, leaf gall *(Synchytrium)*, leaf spots, rusts	Root-knot and stem nematodes
Lythrum sp.	Stem canker *(Coniothyrium)*, blight *(Rhizoctonia)*, leaf spot, root rot, leaf gall *(Synchytrium)*	Melon aphid *(Aphis)*
Macleaya (Bocconia) sp.	Anthracnose	
Macrochloa: see *Stipa*		
Maianthemum sp.	*Botrytis* blight, leaf spots, rusts	
Majorana: see *Origanum*		
Malva sp.	Crown gall, viruses, rusts, leaf spots, stem canker *(Colletotrichum)*, powdery mildew *(Erysiphe)*, root rots	Japanese beetle, whiteflies (in greenhouse), thrips

See footnotes on page 186

continued on next page

Table C-1. Pests, diseases, and problems of herbaceous perennials *(continued)*

Scientific name[1]	Diseases and physiological problems	Insects and other pests
Manfreda sp.		Spider mites
Marrubium sp.	Leaf gall *(Synchytrium),* leaf spot *(Cercospora)*	Root-knot nematode
Matteuccia sp.	Leaf blister *(Taphrina),* leaf spots, sooty mold (in greenhouse or South), rusts, damping-off (of prothalli)	Nematodes, aphids, whiteflies, and fern moth caterpillar in greenhouse; thrips, scales, mealybugs, black vine weevil, fern snail *(Deroceras),* armyworms, Japanese beetle, crickets, grasshoppers, caterpillars
Matthiola fruticulosa	Bacterial rot and stem canker *(Xanthomonas),* damping-off, downy mildew *(Peronospora), Botrytis* blight, club root, wilts, white rust, leaf spot *(Alternaria, Myrothecium),* fungal rots, cucumber mosaic virus and others	Aphids, diamondback moth caterpillar, flea beetles, garden springtails *(Bourletiella),* cabbage root fly *(Delia)*
Meconopsis sp.	Downy mildew *(Peronospora)*	
Megasea: see *Bergenia*		
Melandrium: see *Silene*		
Melissa sp.	*Botrytis* blight, leaf spot *(Phyllosticta)*	
Mentha sp.	Bacterial blight *(Pseudomonas),* bacterial blight *(Erwinia),* rust, powdery mildew, leaf spot, stem canker, spot anthracnose *(Sphaceloma), Verticillium* wilt, viruses	Nematodes, whiteflies (in greenhouse), thrips
Mertensia sp.	Downy mildew *(Peronospora),* powdery mildew *(Erysiphe),* leaf spot *(Septoria),* stem rot *(Sclerotinia),* smut *(Entyloma),* rusts, cucumber mosaic virus	
Mesembryanthemum: see *Delosperma*		
Microderis: see *Leontodon*		
Microglossa: see *Aster albescens*		
Micromeria sp.	Rust *(Puccinia)*	
Microseris: see *Leontodon*		
Milla uniflora: see *Ipheion uniflorum*		
Mimulus sp.	*Botrytis* blight	
Mindium: see *Michauxia*		
Mirabilis sp.	Downy mildew, leaf spots, root rot, rust, white rust	
Mitchella sp.	Black spot *(Meliola),* stem rot	
Mitella sp.	Leaf spots, powdery mildew, leaf rot *(Sclerotium),* rusts	
Monarda sp.	Rot *(Sclerotium),* impatiens necrotic spot virus, mosaic virus, leaf spots, powdery mildew, rusts, crown rot *(Pellicularia),* leaf gall *(Synchytrium),* southern blight *(Sclerotium)*	Leafminer, melon aphid *(Aphis),* stalk borer, thrips
Monardella sp.	Leaf spot *(Phyllosticta),* rust *(Puccinia)*	
Moneses uniflora	Rust *(Chrysomyxa)*	
Montbretia: see *Crocosmia*		
Moraea sp.	Rust *(Puccinia)*	
Muscari sp.	Smut, bulb rot *(Sclerotium)*	Northern root-knot nematode *(Meloidogyne),* stem and bulb nematode *(Ditylenchus)*

See footnotes on page 186

continued on next page

Scientific name[1]	Diseases and physiological problems	Insects and other pests
Myosotis sp.	Powdery mildew, aster yellows, rust *(Puccinia)*, wilts, downy mildew *(Peronospora)*, *Botrytis* blight, smut, root rots	Spider mites, aphids, potato flea beetle, caterpillars, aster leafhopper
Narcissus sp.	Bacterial blight *(Erwinia)*, crown rot, leaf spot *(Didymellina)*, *Fusarium* basal rot, leaf scorch *(Stagonospora)*, *Botrytis* blight, narcissus fire *(Sclerotinia)*, white mold *(Ramularia)*, bulb rot *(Rhizoctonia)*, streak and mosaic viruses, blue mold *(Penicillium)*, root rots	Aphids, bulb flies, bulb and bulb scale mites, slugs, millipedes, mice, stem and bulb nematodes
Nasturtium sp.	Crook root *(Spongospora)*, turnip mosaic virus, downy mildew *(Peronospora)*, leaf spots *(Septoria)*	Aphids, flea beetles, mites, beetles, diamondback moth caterpillar
Naumbergia: see *Lysimachia*		
Nelumbo sp.	Leaf spots *(Alternaria, Cercospora)*	Aphids, Japanese beetle
Neopaxia: see *Claytonia*		
Nepeta sp.	Rot *(Sclerotium)*, powdery mildew *(Erysiphe)*, leaf spots, bacterial leaf spot *(Pseudomonas)*, stem and root rots, mosaic virus, *Fusarium* wilt	
Nerine sp.	Leaf scorch *(Stagospora)*	Lance nematode *(Hoplolaimus)*
Nitholaena: see *Cheilanthes*		
Nothoscordum sp.	Anthracnose *(Colletotrichum)*, rusts, nothoscordum mosaic virus	
Nuphar sp.	as *Nymphaea*	
Nymphaea sp.	Rot *(Sclerotium)*, leaf spots, white smut *(Entyloma)*, leaf and stem rot *(Pythium)*, crown rot	Waterlily leaf beetle *(Galerucella)*, waterlily aphid *(Rhopalosiphum,* eggs overwinter on *Prunus)*, false leafmining midge *(Cricotopus)*, waterlily leaf cutter *(Synclita)*, caddis fly, China mark moth *(Nymphula)*
Nymphoides sp.	Rust *(Puccinia)*, leaf smut *(Burrillia)*	
Oenothera sp.	Impatiens necrotic spot virus, root rot, leaf spots, rusts, downy mildew *(Peronospora)*, powdery mildew *(Erysiphe)*, *Botrytis* blight, dodder, leaf gall *(Synchytrium)*, mosaic virus	Aphids, thrips
Olymposciadium: see *Seseli*		
Onoclea sensibilis	Dodder *(Cuscuta)*, leaf blister *(Taphrina)*, leaf spots, sooty mold (in greenhouses or South), rusts, damping-off (of prothalli)	Nematodes, aphids, whiteflies, and fern moth caterpillar in greenhouse; thrips, scales, mealybugs, black vine weevil, fern snail *(Deroceras)*, armyworms, Japanese beetle, crickets, grasshoppers, caterpillars
Onopordum sp.		Slugs and snails
Ophiopogon sp.	Rot *(Sclerotium)*	
Opuntia sp.	Anthracnose *(Mycosphaerella)*, charcoal spot *(Stevensea)*, dry rot *(Phyllosticta)*, rots, sunscald *(Hendersonia)*, leaf spot *(Stemphylium)*, crown rot *(Sclerotinia)*, viruses	Cactus fruit gall midge, mites, mealybugs, cactus scale *(Diaspis,* in greenhouse, Southwest), corky scab (high humidity, low light)
Oreobroma: see *Lewisia*		
Oreopteris sp.	Leaf spots, sooty mold (indoors or South), rusts, damping-off (of prothalli)	Nematodes, aphids, whiteflies, and fern moth caterpillar in greenhouse; thrips, scales, mealybugs, black vine weevil, fern snail *(Deroceras)*, armyworms, Japanese beetle, crickets, grasshoppers, caterpillars

See footnotes on page 186

continued on next page

Scientific name[1]	Diseases and physiological problems	Insects and other pests
Ornithogalum sp.	Leaf spots, stem rot *(Pellicularia)*, mosaic virus, southern blight *(Sclerotium)*	
Orobus: see *Lathyrus*		
Osmunda sp.	Leaf blister *(Taphrinia)*, leaf spots, sooty mold (indoors or South), rusts, damping-off (of prothalli)	Nematodes, aphids, whiteflies, and fern moth caterpillar in greenhouse; thrips, scales, mealybugs, black vine weevil, fern snail *(Deroceras)*, armyworms, Japanese beetle, crickets, grasshoppers, caterpillars
Othonna sp.		Aphids
Othonnopsis: see *Othonna*		
Oxalis sp.	Rot *(Sclerotium)*, leaf spots, rust *(Puccinia,* alternate host corn), red rust *(Puccinia,* alternate host *Mahonia)*, root rot *(Thielaviopsis)*, seed smut *(Ustilago)*, viruses	
Oxypetalum: see *Tweedia*		
Oxyria sp.	Rust *(Puccinia)*, floral smut *(Ustilago)*	
Pachistima: see *Paxistima*		
Pachysandra sp.	Rot and leaf spot *(Rhizoctonia)*, leaf spot and leaf stem blight *(Volutella)*, leaf spots, sunburn	Leaf tier *(Archips)*, scale *(Enonymus)*, mites, northern root-knot nematode
Paeonia hybrids	Impatiens necrotic spot virus, peony ringspot virus, leaf spots, red spot *(Cladosporium)*, stem rots *(Sclerotinia)*, *Verticillium* wilt, *Botrytis* blight, *Phytophthora* blight, rot *(Sclerotium)*, peony blotch *(Septoria)*, root rot *(Armillaria,* tree peonies), stem wilt *(Leptosphaeria,* tree peonies), anthracnose *(Gleosporium)*, bacterial crown gall *(Agrobacterium)*, powdery mildew, bud blast (improper culture, climate), oedema	Nematodes, Japanese beetles, rose chafer and rose leaf beetles, ants, scales, flower thrips, southern root-knot nematode
Panax sp.	Blights, damping off, leaf spots, sunscald, rhizome and root rots, downy mildew, rust, *Verticillium* wilt	Root-knot nematode
Papaver sp.	Bacterial blight *(Xanthomonas)*, impatiens necrotic spot virus and others, leaf spots, *Botrytis* blight, powdery mildew *(Erysiphe)*, root rots, smut *(Entyloma)*, downy mildew *(Peronospora)*, *Verticillium* wilt, anthracnose *(Gleosporium)*	Aphids, capsid bugs, plant bugs, aster leafhopper, grape mealybug, northern root-knot nematode, thrips
Parathelypteris: see *Thelypteris*		
Pardanthus: see *Belamcanda*		
Passiflora sp.	Rot *(Sclerotium)*, cucumber mosaic virus, leaf spots, blight *(Pellicularia)*, collar rot *(Sclerotinia)*, root rot *(Phymatotrichum)*	Caterpillars, mealybugs, scales, root-knot nematode
Paxistima canbyi	Leaf spots	
Pedicularis sp.	Leaf gall *(Synchytrium)*, leaf spots, powdery mildew *(Sphaerotheca)*, rusts	
Pelargonium endlicherianum	*Botrytis* blight, black leg rot	
Pellaea sp.	Leaf spots, sooty mold (indoors or South), rusts, damping-off (of prothalli)	Nematodes, aphids, whiteflies, and fern moth caterpillar in greenhouse; thrips, scales, mealybugs, black vine weevil, fern snail *(Deroceras)*, armyworms, Japanese beetle, crickets, grasshoppers, caterpillars

See footnotes on page 186

continued on next page

Scientific name[1]	Diseases and physiological problems	Insects and other pests
Peltandra sp.	Leaf spots, rust *(Uromyces)*	
Peltiphyllum: see *Darmera*		
Pennisetum sp.	Leaf spot *(Helminthosporium),* seed smut *(Ustilago),* viruses	
Penstemon sp.	Rot *(Sclerotium),* impatiens necrotic spot virus, leaf spots, rusts, root rots, powdery mildew *(Erysiphe),* black mildew *(Dimerium)*	Aphids, nematode *(Aphelenchoides),* Fuller rose beetle, caterpillars, thrips
Percidium: see *Leibnitzia*		
Persicaria (Polygonum) sp.	Impatiens necrotic spot virus	Japanese beetle, thrips
Petalostemon: see *Dalea*		
Petasites sp.	Leaf gall *(Synchytrium),* leaf spots, rusts	
Petroselinum crispum	Bacterial soft rot *(Erwinia), Botrytis* blight, leaf blights, damping off, dodder, leaf spots, root and stem rots, viruses	Carrot fly, aphids, nematodes
Phalaris sp.	Iris rust *(Puccinia,* alternate host), ergot *(Claviceps),* leaf spots	
Pharium: see *Bessera*		
Phegopteris sp.	Leaf spots, sooty mold (indoors or South), rusts, damping-off (of prothalli)	Nematodes, aphids, whiteflies, and fern moth caterpillar in greenhouse; thrips, scales, mealybugs, black vine weevil, fern snail *(Deroceras),* armyworms, Japanese beetle, crickets, grasshoppers, caterpillars
Phlox paniculata, maculata, sp.	Rot *(Sclerotium),* leaf spots, aster yellows, *Verticillium* wilt, crown rots (seedlings), leafy gall *(Corynebacterium),* crown gall *(P. drummondii),* stem canker, bacterial blight *(Xanthomonas),* leaf spot *(Septoria),* powdery mildews, rusts, stem blight *(Pyrenochaeta),* downy mildew, viruses, leaf blight (older stems, upwards from base)	Beetles, phlox plant bug *(Lopidea),* corn earworm, aster leafhopper, scales, wireworms, foliar nematodes, stem nematode, mites, thrips, rabbits
Phlox subulata	Rust	Spider mites, stem nematodes
Phyllitis: see *Asplenium*		
Phyllostachys sp.	Leaf spots, smut *(Ustilago),* and rusts in South	Powder-post beetles *(Dinoderus* and *Lyctus),* aphids, scales, mites, squirrels, deer, rabbits
Physalis sp.	Rot *(Sclerotium),* bacterial wilt *(Pseudomonas), Verticillium* wilt, leaf spot, white smut *(Entyloma),* mosaic virus, root rot, rusts	Tortoise beetles, striped cucumber beetle, flea beetle, imported long-horned weevil, nematodes
Physostegia sp.	Rust *(Puccinia),* crown rots, fungal rots, bacterial rots, leaf spot, downy mildew *(Plasmopara),* stem rot *(Sclerotinia)*	
Phytolacca sp.	Viruses (alternative host to many affecting Amaryllis, Lily, and Nightshade families)	
Piptatherum: see *Oryzopsis*		
Platycodon grandiflorus	Leaf spot *(Alternaria),* stem canker and blight *(Sclerotinia),* root rots, viruses	Leafminer, western flower thrips, whiteflies, aphids
Pleioblastus sp.	Leaf spots, smut *(Ustilago),* and rusts in South	Powder-post beetles *(Dinoderus* and *Lyctus),* aphids, scales, mites, squirrels, deer, rabbits
Plumbago sp.	Crown gall	
Podophyllum sp.	Leaf spots, rust *(Puccinia), Botrytis,* leaf blight *(Septotinia), Rhizoctonia* stem rot	

See footnotes on page 186

continued on next page

Scientific name[1]	Diseases and physiological problems	Insects and other pests
Polemonium sp.	Leaf spots, powdery mildews, rusts, wilt	Leafminer
Polianthes sp.	Bacterial soft rot *(Erwinia)*, *Botrytis* blight and spots, leaf spots, root rots	Root-knot nematode
Polygala sp.	Anthracnose *(Gleosporium)*, leaf spots, rusts	Whiteflies (in greenhouse)
Polygonatum sp.	Leaf spots, rhizome rot *(Stromatinia)*, rusts, leaf smut, mosaic virus	Sawfly larvae, slugs
Polygonum: see *Fallopia, Persicaria*		
Polypodium sp.	Leaf spots, sooty mold (indoors or South), rusts, damping-off (of prothalli)	Nematodes, aphids, whiteflies, and fern moth caterpillar in greenhouse; thrips, scales, mealybugs, black vine weevil, fern snail *(Deroceras)*, armyworms, Japanese beetle, crickets, grasshoppers, caterpillars
Polystichum sp.	Leaf blister *(Taphrina)*, leaf blotch *(Cylindrocladium)*, leaf spots, sooty mold (indoors or South), rusts, damping-off (of prothalli)	Nematodes, aphids, whiteflies, and fern moth caterpillar in greenhouse; thrips, scales, mealybugs, black vine weevil, fern snail *(Deroceras)*, armyworms, Japanese beetle, crickets, grasshoppers, caterpillars
Potamogeton sp.		Waterlily leaf cutter *(Synclita)*, foliar nematode
Potentilla sp.	Downy mildew *(Peronospora)*, powdery mildews, leaf spots, rust *(Phragmidium)*	Rose aphid, strawberry weevil, spittlebugs
Poterium: see *Sanguisorba*		
Prenanthes sp.	Downy mildew *(Bremia)*, leaf gall *(Synchytrium)*, leaf spots, powdery mildews, rusts	
Preslia: see *Mentha*		
Primula sp.	Bacterial blight *(Erwinia)*, *Botrytis* blight, bacterial leaf spot *(Pseudomonas)*, anthracnose *(Colletotrichum)*, fungal leaf spots, root rots, stem rots, aster yellows, rusts, viruses, powdery mildew *(Erysiphe)*, chlorosis (iron deficiency)	Aphids, flea beetles, beetles, mealybugs, mites, whiteflies, black vine weevil, thrips, millipedes, slugs, nematodes, aster leafhopper
Pritzelago: see *Hutchinsia*		
Prometheum: see *Sedum*		
Prunella vulgaris	Southern blight *(Sclerotium)*, leaf spots, powdery mildews, root rots	
Pseudofumaria: see *Corydalis*		
Pseudolysimachion: see *Veronica*		
Pseudomuscari: see *Muscari*		
Pseudosasa sp.	Leaf spots, smut *(Ustilago)*, and rusts in South	Powder-post beetles *(Dinoderus* and *Lyctus)*, aphids, scales, mites, squirrels, deer, rabbits
Psilostemon: see *Trachystemon*		
Pteridium aquilinum	Leaf spots, sooty mold (indoors or South), rusts, damping-off (of prothalli)	Nematodes, aphids, whiteflies, and fern moth caterpillar in greenhouse; thrips, scales, mealybugs, black vine weevil, fern snail *(Deroceras)*, armyworms, Japanese beetle, crickets, grasshoppers, caterpillars
Pteridophyllum racemosum		Slugs
Ptilotrichum: see *Alyssum*		
Pulmonaria sp.	Powdery mildew, crown rot, *Botrytis* blight	Aphids, slugs

See footnotes on page 186 *continued on next page*

Scientific name[1]	Diseases and physiological problems	Insects and other pests
Pycnanthemum sp.	Leaf gall *(Synchytrium)*, leaf spots, rusts	
Pygmaea: see *Chionohebe*		
Pyrethrum: see *Tanacetum*		
Pyrola sp.	*Botrytis* gray mold, leaf spots, rusts	
Ramischia: see *Orthilia*		
Ramonda sp.	*Botrytis* blight, leaf spots (water on leaves), crown rot	
Ranunculus sp.	Bacterial blight *(Pseudomonas)*, rot *(Sclerotium)*, powdery mildews, downy mildew *(Peronospora)*, leaf spots, root rots, rusts, virus, aster yellows, *Botrytis* blight, leaf galls, leaf and white smuts	Aster leafhopper, nematodes
Ratibida sp.	Downy mildew *(Plasmopara)*, leaf spots, powdery mildew *(Erysiphe)*, root rots, rust *(Uromyces)*, white smut	Aphids
Reseda sp.	Blight *(Cercospora)*, damping-off, root rot, *Verticillium* wilt, leaf spot *(Cercospora)*	Caterpillars, potato flea beetle, corn earworm, aster leafhopper, thrips, mites, nematodes
Reynoutria: see *Fallopia*		
Rhaponticum: see *Leuzea*		
Rhazya: see *Amsonia*		
Rheum sp.	*Armillaria* root rot, crown rot	
Rhexia sp.	Leaf spots	
Rhinopetalum: see *Fritillaria*		
Rosmarinus officinalis	Powdery mildew, root rot *(Phymatotrichum)*	Aphids
Rubus sp.	Powdery mildew *(Sphaerotheca)*, rusts, leaf spot *(Mycosphaerella)*, mosaic viruses	Aphids
Rudbeckia sp.	Rot *(Sclerotium)*, leaf spots, bacterial blight *(Pseudomonas, Xanthomonas)*, *Botrytis* blight, aster yellows, downy mildew *(Plasmopara)*, powdery mildew *(Erysiphe)*, crown rot *(Pellicularia)*, leaf gall *(Synchytrium)*, stem rot *(Sclerotinia)*, smut *(Entyloma)*, rusts, viruses, *Verticillium* wilt	Aphids, sawflies, whiteflies (in greenhouse), thrips, beetles, plant bugs, stalk borers, aster leafhopper
Ruellia sp.	Leaf spot *(Cercospora)*, root rot *(Phymatotrichum)*, rusts	
Rumex sp.	Leaf gall, leaf spots, root rot *(Rhizoctonia)*, rust *(Puccinia)*, aster yellows virus	
Rydbergia: see *Hymenoxys*		
Saccharum (Erianthus) sp.	Anthracnose *(Colletotrichum)*, ergot *(Claviceps)*, leaf spots, rusts	
Sagina sp.		Aphids, spider mites
Sagitarria sp.		Waterlily leaf cutter *(Synclita)*, waterlily aphid
Salvia sp.	Rot *(Sclerotium)*, bacterial blight *(Pseudomonas)*, leaf spots, *Botrytis* blight, damping-off, powdery mildew *(Erysiphe)*, downy mildew *(Peronospora)*, *Verticillium* wilt, stem rot *(Sphaeropsis)*, rusts, root rots, viruses	Scale, whiteflies, spider mites, aphids, beetles, stalk borers, aster leafhopper and others, plant bugs, caterpillars, nematodes, greenhouse leaf tier *(Oeobia)*, greenhouse orthezia *(Orthezia)*
Sambucus ebulus	Cankers, leaf spots, powdery mildews, thread blight *(Pellicularia)*, root rots, *Verticillium* wilt	Borers, potato flea beetle, green stink bug, omnivorous looper, grape mealybug, San Jose scale, madrona thrips

See footnotes on page 186

continued on next page

Scientific name[1]	Diseases and physiological problems	Insects and other pests
Sanguinaria sp.	*Botrytis* gray mold and blight, leaf spots	
Sanguisorba sp.	Leaf spots, powdery mildew, rust *(Xenodochus)*	
Saponaria sp.	Leaf spots, root rot *(Phymatotrichum)*, rust *(Puccinia)*	
Sarracenia sp.	Southern blight *(Sclerotium)*, leaf spots, root rots	
Sasa sp.	Leaf spots, smut *(Ustilago)*, and rusts in South	Powder-post beetles *(Dinoderus* and *Lyctus)*, aphids, scales, mites, squirrels, deer, rabbits
Sasaella sp.	as *Sasa*	
Sasamorpha sp.	as *Sasa*	
Saururopsis: see *Saururus*		
Saururus sp.	Leaf gall *(Physoderma)*, leaf spots	Root-knot nematode
Saxifraga sp.	*Botrytis* blight, leaf spots, powdery mildew *(Sphaerotheca)*, rusts	Aphids
Scabiosa sp.	Rot *(Sclerotium)*, damping-off, blight *(Pellicularia)*, powdery mildew *(Erysiphe)*, root rot *(Phymatotrichum)*, stem rot *(Sclerotinia)*, viruses, aster yellows	Fuller rose beetle *(Pantomorus)*, aster leaf-hopper, chrysanthemum lace bug *(Corythucha)*, slugs, snails, fungus gnat larvae (in greenhouse)
Scaevola sp.	Cucumber mosaic virus	Aphids
Schizocodon: see *Shortia*		
Scilla sp.	Crown rot *(Sclerotium)*, blue mold *(Penicillium)*, flower smut *(Ustilago)*, rust *(Uromyces)*, mosaic virus	Tulip bulb aphid
Scolopendrium: see *Asplenium*		
Scorzonera sp.	White blister rust	
Scrophularia sp.		Figwort weevil
Scutellaria sp.	Leaf spots, powdery mildews, root rots, *Botrytis* blight	
Sedum sp.	Bacterial blight *(Erwinia)*, leaf spots, crown and root rots *(Pellicularia)*, leaf blotch *(Septoria)*, stem rots, rusts, southern blight *(Sclerotium)*, *Fusarium* wilt	Mealybugs, fungus gnat larvae (in greenhouse), aphids, western flower thrips, southern root-knot nematode, slugs
Selaginella sp.	Leaf spot *(Myrothecium,* South)	
Semiaquilegia sp.	*Botrytis* blight, *Alternaria* blight, impatiens necrotic spot virus, powdery mildew, leaf spots *(Actinonema, Haplobasidion,* and more common), crown and root rot *(Sclerotium)*, rust, cucumber mosaic virus	Aphids, columbine leafminer *(Phytomyza)*, bumble bees (eat corolla tubes), columbine skipper caterpillar *(Erynnis)*, columbine borer *(Papaipema)*, green peach aphid *(Myzus)*, melon aphid *(Aphis)*, whiteflies (in greenhouse), spider mites, foliar nematode, thrips
Semiarundinaria sp.	Leaf spots, smut *(Ustilago)*, and rusts in South	Powder-post beetles *(Dinoderus* and *Lyctus)*, aphids, scales, mites, squirrels, deer, rabbits
Sempervivella: see *Rosularia*		
Sempervivum sp.	Crown rot, rust *(Endophyllum)*, leaf and stem rot *(Phytophthora)*, root rot *(Pythium)*	Aphids, birds (uproot rosettes)

See footnotes on page 186

continued on next page

Table C-1. Pests, diseases, and problems of herbaceous perennials *(continued)*

Scientific name[1]	Diseases and physiological problems	Insects and other pests
Senecio sp.	Bacterial blight *(Erwinia)*, rot *(Sclerotium)*, stem rots, powdery mildew, downy mildew *(Plasmopara)*, *Botrytis* blight, root rot, leaf spot, virus, aster yellows, leaf gall *(Synchytrium)*, rusts, white smut, white rust, fungal wilts	Aphids, cutworms, caterpillars, mealybug, spider mites, leaf miner, whiteflies, greenhouse leaf tier, aster leafhopper
Senna (Cassia) hebecarpa	Branch dieback *(Diplodia)*, root rots	Southern root-knot nematode, lace bugs, scales
Seriphidium (Artemisia) sp.	Leaf rust, downy mildew	
Shibataea sp.	Leaf spots, smut *(Ustilago)*, and rusts in South	Powder-post beetles *(Dinoderus* and *Lyctus)*, aphids, scales, mites, squirrels, deer, rabbits
Shortia sp.	Leaf spot *(Pezizella)*	
Sibbaldiopsis: see *Potentilla*		
Sida sp.	Southern blight *(Sclerotium)*, leaf spots, root rots, rusts, virus	Root-knot nematode
Sidalcea sp.	Rusts *(Puccinia)*, leaf spots, blight *(Pellicularia)*, mosaic virus	Japanese beetle, root-knot nematode
Silene sp.	Rot *(Sclerotium)*, damping-off *(Rhizoctonia)*, downy mildew *(Peronospora)*, leaf spots, rusts, flower smuts	
Siler: see *Laserpitium*		
Silphium sp.	Downy mildew *(Plasmopara)*, leaf spots, powdery mildew *(Erysiphe)*, root rots, rusts, white smut	
Silybum sp.		Slugs, snails
Sinarundinaria sp.	Leaf spots, smut *(Ustilago)*, and rusts in South	Powder-post beetles *(Dinoderus* and *Lyctus)*, aphids, scales, mites, squirrels, deer, rabbits
Sinobambusa sp.	as *Sinarundinaria*	
Sisyrinchium sp.	Leaf blight *(Kellermania)*, rusts	Lesion nematode
Smilacina sp.	Leaf spots, rhizome rot *(Stromatinia)*, rusts, leaf smut	
Solanum sp.	*Botrytis* blight, leaf spots, crown gall *(Erwinia)*, *Verticillium* wilt, defoliation *(Phytophthora)*, viruses, magnesium deficiency	Spider mites, aphids, caterpillars, thrips, southern root-knot nematode, oedema,
Soldanella sp.		Slugs (young shoots)
Solenopsis: see *Isotoma*		
Solidago sp.	Scab *(Elsinoe,* young plants), rust, powdery mildew, black knot *(Gibberidia)*, thread blight *(Pellicularia)*, stem canker *(Botryosphaeria)*, dodder *(Cuscuta)*, downy mildew, leaf fall *(Rhodochytrium)*, leaf spots, leaf mold *(Cladosporium)*, root rot, viruses	Chrysanthemum lace bug, orange tortrix *(Argyrotaenia)*, aphids, mites, lesion nematode
x *Solidaster luteus*	as *Solidago*	
Sparaxis sp.	Mosaic virus	
Sphaeralcea sp.	Powdery mildew, rusts	
Spiraea: see *Aruncus, Filipendula*		
Stachys sp.	Leaf gall, leaf spots, powdery mildews, rust	Root-knot nematode
Statice: see *Limonium, Goniolimon*		

See footnotes on page 186

continued on next page

Herbaceous Perennials Production

Scientific name[1]	Diseases and physiological problems	Insects and other pests
Steironema: see *Lysimachia*		
Stellaria holostea, pubera	Downy mildew *(Peronospora)*	
Stokesia laevis	Rot *(Sclerotium)*, leaf spots, *Botrytis* blight, powdery mildew *(Erysiphe)*, viruses	
Struthiopteris: see *Blechnum, Matteuccia*		
Symplocarpus foetidus	*Botrytis* blight, leaf spots	
Syndesmon: see *Anemonella*		
Tanacetum (Pyrethrum) sp.	Leaf spot *(Ramularia)*, powdery mildew *(Erysiphe)*, rust *(Puccinia)*, bacterial fasciation *(Corynebacterium)*, *Botrytis* blight, damping-off, root rots, stem rot *(Sclerotinia)*, aster yellows virus	Root knot-nematode
Telekia sp.		Slugs
Tellima grandiflora	*Botrytis* blight, leaf spots, powdery mildews, anthracnose, bacterial leaf spot *(Pseudomonas, Xanthomonas)*, stem rot, leaf and stem smut, leafy gall *(Corynebacterium)*, rust	Root-knot and foliar nematodes, mealybugs, root weevils, fungus gnat larvae (in greenhouse), four-lined plant bug
Tetragonolobus: see *Lotus*		
Teuchrium sp.	Downy mildew *(Peronospora)*, leaf spots, powdery mildew *(Erysiphe)*, rust *(Puccinia)*	Root-knot nematode, mites (leaf crinkle)
Thalictrum sp.	Powdery mildew *(Erysiphe)*, rusts, smuts, downy mildew, leaf spots	
Thamnocalamus sp.	Leaf spots, smut *(Ustilago)*, rusts in South	Powder-post beetles *(Dinoderus* and *Lyctus)*, aphids, scales, mites, squirrels, deer, rabbits
Thelypteris sp.	Leaf spots, sooty mold (indoors or South), rusts, damping-off (of prothalli)	Nematodes, aphids, whiteflies, and fern moth caterpillar in greenhouse; thrips, scales, mealybugs, black vine weevil, fern snail *(Deroceras)*, armyworms, Japanese beetle, crickets, grasshoppers, caterpillars
Thermopsis sp.	Leaf spots, powdery mildew *(Erysiphe)*	
Thymus sp.	Root rot *(Pellicularia)*, *Botrytis* blight, *Rhizoctonia* root rot	Root mealybug *(Rhizoecus)*
Tiarella sp.	Powdery mildew, rusts	
Tithymalopsis: see *Euphorbia*		
Tolmiea menziesii	Powdery mildew *(Sphaerotheca)*	Mites, mealybugs
Tommasinia: see *Peucedanum*		
Tormentilla: see *Potentilla*		
Tovara: see *Persicaria*		
Trachomitum: see *Apocynum*		
Trachymene sp.	Viruses, root and stem rots	Root-knot nematode
Tradescantia sp.	Bacterial blight *(Erwinia)*, *Botrytis* blight, leaf spots, rust *(Uromyces)*	Caterpillars, mealybugs, scales, greenhouse leaf tier *(Oeobia)*, morning-glory leaf cutter *(Loxostege)*, orange tortrix *(Argyrotaenia)*, southern root-knot nematode
Tragopogon sp.	White blister rust, aster yellows	Aster leafhopper

See footnotes on page 186

continued on next page

Scientific name[1]	Diseases and physiological problems	Insects and other pests
Trautvetteria sp.	Downy mildew *(Peronospora)*, leaf spot *(Septoria)*, rust *(Puccinia)*, leaf and stem smut	
Trichophorum: see *Eleocharis*		
Trientalis sp.	Leaf gall, leaf spots, leaf rot *(Ceratobasidium)*, rust, leaf and stem smut *(Tuburcinia)*	
Trillium sp.	Leaf spots, stem rots, rust *(Uromyces)*, leaf blight *(Ciborinia)*, leaf smut *(Urocystis)*	
Triosteum sp.	Leaf spots, powdery mildew *(Phyllactinia)*, rust *(Aecidium)*	
Tripterocalyx: see *Abronia*		
Tritoma: see *Kniphofia*		
Tritonia sp.	Fungal blights, *Fusarium* yellows, corm rot, iris mosaic virus, southern blight	
Trollius sp.	Powdery mildew, leaf spots, smut *(Uromyces)*	Melon aphid *(Aphis)*
Tropaeolum sp.	Bacterial leaf spot and wilt *(Pseudomonas)*, leaf spots, viruses, aster yellows	Aphids, cabbage looper, corn earworm, western black flea beetle, thrips, two-spotted mite, tarnished plant bug, serpentine leaf miner, greenhouse leaf tier, root-knot and root gall nematodes, aster leafhopper
Tulipa sp.	Rot *(Sclerotium)*, *Botrytis* blight and fire, basal rot *(Fusarium)*, blue mold *(Penicillium)*, crown and gray bulb rots *(Pellicularia)*, stem rot and flower spots *(Phytophthora)*, anthracnose *(Gleosporium)*, soft rot *(Pectobacterium)*, viruses, bacterial soft rot *(Erwinia)*, southern blight, sunscald (dry conditions), frost injury, topple (stem and flower stalk collapse, improper forcing or culture), retarded growth (improper storage)	Tulip bulb aphid, crescent-marked lily aphid, narcissus bulb fly, bulb mite, millipedes, wireworms, root-knot nematodes
Tunica: see *Petrorhagia*		
Tussilago farfara	Leaf spots	
Typha sp.	Leaf spots, leaf mold *(Cladosporium)*, leaf rots, culm rot *(Ophiobolus)*	
Ulmaria: see *Filipendula*		
Unifolium: see *Maianthemum*		
Uniola: see *Chasmanthium*		
Uvularia sp.	Leaf spot *(Sphaeropsis)*, rusts	
Valeriana sp.	Leaf spots, powdery mildew *(Erysiphe)*, root and stem rots, rusts	
Vancouveria sp.	Leaf spots	
Veratrum sp.	Leaf spots, rusts	
Verbascum sp.	Impatiens necrotic spot virus, powdery mildew, downy mildew *(Peronospora)*, leaf spots, root rot *(Phymatotrichum)*	Thrips, root-knot nematode
Verbena sp.	Impatiens necrotic spot virus, bacterial wilt *(Pseudomonas)*, *Botrytis* blight, powdery mildew *(Erysiphe)*, stem rot *(Macrophomina)*, root rots, dodder, downy mildew *(Plasmopara)*, leaf spots, root rot, rusts, virus	Aphids, clematis blister beetle *(Epicauta)*, caterpillars, verbena leaf miner *(Agromyza)*, whiteflies, mites, snapdragon lace bug, tarnished plant bug, morning-glory leaf cutter, greenhouse orthezia, cottony-cushion scale, thrips, nematodes

See footnotes on page 186

continued on next page

Scientific name[1]	Diseases and physiological problems	Insects and other pests
Verbesina sp.	Downy mildew *(Plasmopara)*, leaf spots, powdery mildew *(Erysiphe)*, root rots, rusts, viruses	Root-knot nematode
Veronia sp.	Black mildew *(Stigmella)*, downy mildew, leaf spots, powdery mildew, root rot, rusts	
Veronica sp.	*Botrytis* blight (lower leaves), downy mildew *(Peronospora)*, powdery mildew *(Sphaerotheca)*, leaf spots, leaf galls, root rots, stem rot, leaf smut *(Entyloma)*, rot *(Sclerotium)*, rusts	Tarnished plant bug, caterpillars, southern root-knot nematode
Veronicastrum sp.	Leaf spots, powdery mildew, root rots, rust	
Vicia sp.	Leaf spot *(Erostrotheca)*	
Villarsia: see *Nymphoides*		
Vinca sp.	Rot *(Sclerotium)*, blight *(Phyllosticta)*, *Botrytis* blight, canker and dieback *(Phomopsis)*, leaf spots, root rots, dodder, leaf mold *(Cladosporium)*, rust *(Puccinia)*, aster yellows virus, *Verticillium* wilt	Cyclamen mites, scales, nematodes
Viola sp.	Cucumber mosaic virus, *Botrytis* blight, anthracnose *(Colletotrichum)*, crown rot, root rots, powdery mildews, downy mildew, leaf spots, rusts, scab *(Sphaceloma)*, smut *(Urocystis)*, stem rot *(Myrothecium)*, viruses, aster yellows, blight *(Sclerotinia)*, damping off, southern blight, leaf gall *(Synchytrium)*, sooty mold, oedema	Cutworm, aphids, violet gall midge *(Phytophaga)*, greenhouse leaf tier, mealybugs, violet sawfly *(Ametastegia)*, mites, nematodes, slugs, snails, aster leafhopper
Viorna: see *Clematis*		
Viscaria: see *Lychnis*		
Waldsteinia sp.	Leaf spots, rust, smut *(Urocystis)*	
Watsonia beatricis (pillansii)	Root rot *(Armillaria)*, iris mosaic virus	Gladiolus thrips
Weingaertneria: see *Corynephorus*		
Woodsia sp.	Leaf spots, sooty mold (indoors or South), rusts, damping-off (of prothalli)	Nematodes, aphids, whiteflies, and fern moth caterpillar in greenhouse; thrips, scales, mealybugs, black vine weevil, fern snail *(Deroceras)*, armyworms, Japanese beetle, crickets, grasshoppers, caterpillars
Woodwardia sp.	Leaf spots, sooty mold (indoors or South), rusts, damping-off (of prothalli)	Nematodes, aphids, whiteflies, and fern moth caterpillar (in greenhouse); thrips, scales, mealybugs, black vine weevil, fern snail *(Deroceras)*, armyworms, Japanese beetle, crickets, grasshoppers, caterpillars
Wyethia sp.	Leaf spots, rust *(Puccinia)*	Leaf gall nematode *(Tylenchus)*
Xerophyllum sp.	Rust *(Puccinia)*	
Yucca sp.	Bacterial blight *(Erwinia)*, rot *(Sclerotium)*, leaf spots, fungal leaf blights, leaf molds, rusts	Nematode, plant bug *(Halticotoma)*, mealybug, stalk borer *(Papaipema)*, scales, yucca weevil *(Scyphophorus)*, yucca bug
Yushania sp.	Leaf spots, smut *(Ustilago)*, and rusts in South	Powder-post beetles *(Dinoderus* and *Lyctus)*, aphids, scales, mites, squirrels, deer, rabbits
Zantedeschia sp.	Bacterial blight *(Erwinia)*, rot *(Sclerotium)*, leaf spots, viruses, bacterial soft rot of tubers, root rot *(Phytophthora)*, crown rot *(Pellicularia)*, storage rot *(Pythium)*	Yellow woolybear, mealybugs, bulb mite, thrips

See footnotes on page 186

continued on next page

Scientific name[1]	Diseases and physiological problems	Insects and other pests
Zauschneria sp.	Rust *(Puccinia)*	
Zephyranthes sp.	Rot *(Sclerotium)*, leaf spot and scorch, rust	
Zigadenus sp.	Rusts, leaf smut	
Zizia sp.	Leaf gall *(Urophlyctis)*, leaf spots, powdery mildew *(Erysiphe)*, rust	
Zwackia: see *Halacsya*		

Note: Some plants listed are generally considered or grown as annuals but are included in this table since they are perennials in at least some nontropical areas. Pests and problems were compiled from various sources listed in the references (see page 193). If a plant is not listed, either it has no major problems or no problems have been reported in the literature consulted. If a pest or problem is listed, the plant may or may not get it depending on many other factors (see chapter 10 for more information on pests). No causal agent is listed when a disease or pest is common, when a problem may be caused by more than one agent, or if the causal agent was not listed in the literature consulted. When a general pest name is listed (for example, *borers* or *aphids)*, that usually means that a specific pest was not listed in the literature, or that there are two or more specific pests of that general type. New pests and diseases are always being observed, and plants not listed in this appendix may also have problems. Corrections and additions are welcome.

[1] Most plants in this table are perennials in U.S. Department of Agriculture plant hardiness zones 9 or less (colder zones). However, some may be listed in *Hardy Herbaceous Perennials* by Jelitto and Schacht or the Dutch *Namelist (Naamlijst van Vaste Planten)* as a perennial in zone 10 (in which case they are actually tropical plants and not perennials in zones 9 or less). Names were verified using the British publication *The Plant Finder* as the primary authority, then the Dutch *Namelist (Naamlijst van Vaste Planten)*, then the *New Royal Horticulture Society Dictionary of Gardening,* and finally *Hardy Herbaceous Perennials;* if discrepancies occurred among sources, then the best agreement among the most sources was used. (For complete citations for sources, see the recommended reading section beginning on page 203.) Pests and diseases may be a problem of one cultivar and not another. In general, information is available only for the genus. Sp. = species (+ cultivars and hybrids for most, unless noted otherwise)

APPENDIX D

Useful Conversions and Calculations

Table D-1. Conversions between Fahrenheit (°F) and Celsius (°C) temperature

Known temperature (in °C or °F)	Converted to °C	Converted to °F	Known temperature (in °C or °F)	Converted to °C	Converted to °F
−40	−40.0	−40.0	25	−3.9	77.0
−35	−37.2	−31.0	26	−3.3	78.8
−30	−34.4	−22.0	27	−2.8	80.6
−25	−31.7	−13.0	28	−2.2	82.4
−20	−28.9	−4.0	29	−1.7	84.2
−15	−26.1	5.0	30	−1.1	86.0
−10	−23.3	14.0	31	−0.6	87.8
−5	−20.6	23.0	32	0	89.6
0	−17.8	32.0	33	0.6	91.4
1	−17.2	33.8	34	1.1	93.2
2	−16.7	35.6	35	1.7	95.0
3	−16.1	37.4	36	2.2	96.8
4	−15.6	39.2	37	2.8	98.6
5	−15.0	41.0	38	3.3	100.4
6	−14.4	42.8	39	3.9	102.2
7	−13.9	44.6	40	4.4	104.0
8	−13.3	46.4	41	5.0	105.8
9	−12.8	48.2	42	5.6	107.6
10	−12.2	50.0	43	6.1	109.4
11	−11.7	51.8	44	6.7	111.2
12	−11.1	53.6	45	7.2	113.0
13	−10.6	55.4	46	7.8	114.8
14	−10.0	57.2	47	8.3	116.6
15	−9.4	59.0	48	8.9	118.4
16	−8.9	60.8	49	9.4	120.2
17	−8.3	62.6	50	10.0	122.0
18	−7.8	64.4	51	10.6	123.8
19	−7.2	66.2	52	11.1	125.6
20	−6.7	68.0	53	11.7	127.4
21	−6.1	69.8	54	12.2	129.2
22	−5.6	71.6	55	12.8	131.0
23	−5.0	73.4	56	13.3	132.8
24	−4.4	75.2	57	13.9	134.6

continued on next page

Table D-1. Conversions between Fahrenheit (°F) and Celsius (°C) temperature *(continued)*

Known temperature (in °C or °F)	Converted to °C	Converted to °F	Known temperature (in °C or °F)	Converted to °C	Converted to °F
58	14.4	136.4	84	28.9	183.2
59	15.0	138.2	85	29.4	185.0
60	15.6	140.0	86	30.0	186.8
61	16.1	141.8	87	30.6	188.6
62	16.7	143.6	88	31.1	190.4
63	17.2	145.4	89	31.7	192.2
64	17.8	147.2	90	32.2	194.0
65	18.3	149.0	91	32.8	195.8
66	18.9	150.8	92	33.3	197.6
67	19.4	152.6	93	33.9	199.4
68	20.0	154.4	94	34.4	201.2
69	20.6	156.2	95	35.0	203.0
70	21.1	158.0	96	35.6	204.8
71	21.7	159.8	97	36.1	206.6
72	22.2	161.6	98	36.7	208.4
73	22.8	163.4	99	37.2	210.2
74	23.3	165.2	100	37.8	212.0
75	23.9	167.0	105	40.6	221.0
76	24.4	168.8	110	43.3	230.0
77	25.0	170.6	115	46.1	239.0
78	25.6	172.4	120	48.9	248.0
79	26.1	174.2	125	51.7	257.0
80	26.7	176.0	130	54.4	266.0
81	27.2	177.8	135	57.2	275.0
82	27.8	179.6	140	60.0	284.0
83	28.3	181.4			

Temperature Conversion Formulas

- To convert °C to °F: (°C x 9/5) + 32 = °F

- To convert °F to °C: (°F – 32) x 5/9 = °C

Type of measurement	To convert:	Into:	Multiply by:
Length	centimeters (cm)	inches (in)	0.394
	feet (ft)	centimeters (cm)	30.48
	feet (ft)	inches (in)	12
	feet (ft)	yards (yd)	0.33
	inches (in)	feet (ft)	0.083
	inches (in)	millimeters (mm)	25.4
	inches (in)	centimeters (cm)	2.54
	meters (m)	inches (in)	39.37
	meters (m)	feet (ft)	3.281
	meters (m)	yards (yd)	1.094
	yards (yd)	feet (ft)	3
	yards (yd)	centimeters (cm)	91.44
	yards (yd)	meters (m)	0.9144
Area	acres	square feet (ft²)	43,560
	acres	square yards (yd²)	4,840
	acres	hectares (ha)	0.4047
	hectares (ha)	acres	2.471
	hectares (ha)	square meters (m²)	10,000
	square inches (in²)	square centimeters (cm²)	6.452
	square centimeters (cm²)	square inches (in²)	0.155
	square feet (ft²)	square centimeters (cm²)	929.09
	square feet (ft²)	square meters (m²)	0.0929
	square meters (m²)	square feet (ft²)	10.76
	square meters (m²)	square yards (yd²)	1.196
Weight	grams (g)	ounces (oz)	0.0353
	kilograms (kg)	pounds (lb)	2.205
	metric tons (megagrams)	short tons	1.1023
	ounces (oz)	pounds (lb)	0.0625
	ounces (oz)	grams (g)	28.35
	pounds (lb)	ounces (oz)	16
	pounds (lb)	grams (g)	453.6
	short tons	metric tons (megagrams)	0.9078
Volume, solids	bushels (bu)	cubic feet (ft³)	1.24
	bushels (bu)	cubic meters (m³)	0.352
	bushels (bu)	liters (L)	35.24
	cubic feet (ft³)	liters (L)	28.32
	cubic feet (ft³)	U.S. gallons (gal)	7.48
	cubic feet (ft³)	cubic inches (in³)	1,728
	cubic feet (ft³)	cubic yards (yd³)	0.037
	cubic feet (ft³)	bushels (bu)	0.804
	cubic inches (in³)	milliliters (ml)	16.39
	cubic meters (m³)	cubic yards (yd³)	1.308
	cubic meters (m³)	U.S. gallons (gal)	264.2

continued on next page

Type of measurement	To convert:	Into:	Multiply by:
Volume, solids (continued)	cubic meters (m³)	cubic feet (ft³)	35.3
	cubic yards (yd³)	cubic feet (ft³)	27
	cubic yards (yd³)	liters (L)	764.6
	cubic yards (yd³)	cubic meters (m³)	0.765
	cubic yards (yd³)	bushels (bu)	21.7
	gallons, U.S. dry (gal)	cubic inches (in³)	269
	liters (L)	cubic inches (in³)	61.02
	milliliters (mL)	cubic inches (in³)	0.0610
	quarts, dry (qt)	cubic inches (in³)	67.2
Volume, liquids	cubic centimeters (cm³ or cc)	milliliters (mL)	1
	cups (c)	fluid ounces (fl oz)	8
	gallons, U.S. (gal)	cups (c)	16
	gallons, U.S. (gal)	cubic inches (in³)	231
	gallons, U.S. (gal)	quarts (qt)	4
	gallons, U.S. (gal)	liters (L)	3.785
	gallons, U.S. (gal)	gallons, Imperial (gal)	0.833
	gallons, Imperial (gal)	cubic inches (in³)	277.42
	gallons, Imperial (gal)	liters (L)	4.546
	gallons, Imperial (gal)	gallons, U.S. (gal)	1.20
	liters (L)	pints (pt)	2.113
	liters (L)	quarts (qt)	1.057
	liters (L)	gallons, U.S. (gal)	0.2642
	milliliters (mL)	fluid ounces (fl oz)	0.0338
	pints (pt)	fluid ounces (fl oz)	16
	pints (pt)	cups (c)	2
	pints (pt)	quarts (qt)	0.5
	pints (pt)	cubic inches (in³)	28.87
	pints (pt)	liters (L)	0.4732
	fluid ounces (fl oz)	cubic inches (in³)	1.805
	fluid ounces (fl oz)	tablespoons (Tbsp)	2
	fluid ounces (fl oz)	teaspoons (tsp)	6
	fluid ounces (fl oz)	milliliters (mL)	29.57
	quarts (qt)	fluid ounces (fl oz)	32
	quarts (qt)	cups (c)	4
	quarts (qt)	pints (pt)	2
	quarts (qt)	U.S. gallons, liquid (gal)	0.25
	quarts (qt)	cubic inches (in³)	57.7
	quarts (qt)	liters (L)	0.9463
	tablespoons (Tbsp)	teaspoons (tsp)	3
	tablespoons (Tbsp)	milliliters (mL)	15
	teaspoons (tsp)	milliliters (mL)	5

continued on next page

Type of measurement	To convert:	Into:	Multiply by:
Weight per volume	grams/cubic centimeter (g/cm^3)	pounds/cubic foot (lbs/ft^3)	62.3
	tablespoons/bushel (Tbsp/bu)	pounds/cubic yard (lbs/yd^3)	1 (approx.)
	pounds/cubic yard (lbs/yd^3)	ounces/cubic foot (oz/ft^3)	0.6
	ounces/cubic foot (oz/ft^3)	pounds/cubic yard (lbs/yd^3)	1.67
	pounds/cubic yard (lbs/yd^3)	grams/liter (g/L)	0.595
	kilograms/cubic meter (kg/m^3)	pounds/cubic yard (lbs/yd^3)	1.6821
Light	lumens/square foot (lm/ft^2)	lumens/square meter (lm/m^2)	10.764
	lumens/square foot (lm/ft^2)	foot-candles (ft-c)	1
	foot-candles (ft-c)	lux (lx)	10.764
	lux (lx)	foot-candles (ft-c)	0.0929

Parts per Million (ppm) Conversions

- 1 milligram/liter = 1 ppm
- 1 ounce/gallon = 7,490 ppm
- 1 ounce/100 gallons = 75 ppm

percent fertilizer element x 75 = ppm of element in 100 gallons of water per ounce of fertilizer

For example, for a 9-45-15 fertilizer, the ppm nitrogen (N) in 100 gallons of water per ounce of fertilizer would be:
    0.09 (percent N) x 75 = 6.75 ppm N in 100 gallons of water per ounce of 9-45-15

If you want 150 ppm N, and each ounce gives 6.75 ppm, then you need:
    150 ÷ 6.75 = 22.22 ounces of 9-45-15 fertilizer in 100 gallons of water

Table D-3. Number of various containers for several volumes of growing media

Container	3.8-cubic-foot compressed bale	3-cubic-foot bag	Cubic yard
Plug Trays			
72	112	50	450
128	55	24	216
288	112	50	450
Flats			
606	40	16	144
804	40	16	144
806	48	19	170
1004	45	18	162
1006	48	19	170
Pots (round unless noted)			
4-inch standard	302	122	1,098
4-inch standard, square	392	157	1,413
4-inch azalea	425	170	1,530
5-inch standard	169	68	498
5-inch azalea	209	84	616
6-inch standard	99	41	369
6-inch azalea	122	49	441
8-inch standard	38	14	126
8-inch azalea	47	19	171
10-inch standard	20	8	72
10-inch azalea	27	11	99
Nursery Pots			
100 classic	220	95	882
200 classic	105	44	396
300 classic	70	30	270
400 classic	54	23	207
600 classic	32	14	126

The number of containers is only approximate, as actual numbers will vary according to factors such as type of medium, compaction when filling, and even container manufacturer.

Calculating the Volume of a Round Planting Container

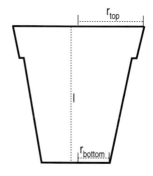

Container volume = $2 \times \pi \times r \times l$

$$r = \frac{r_{top} + r_{bottom}}{2}$$

l = height of container
r = radius
π = 3.14

References

Abbey, T. A. 1996. Key pests of field production perennials. *Connecticut Greenhouse Newsletter* 192 (University of Connecticut, Storrs, Connecticut): 4–12. [For an easier-to-read format, see Abbey, T. A. 1990. Key pests of production perennials. *Yankee Nursery Quarterly* (Summer): 4–9.]

Adam, S. 1988. Nitrogen nutrition of container grown *Hemerocallis*. M. S. thesis, University of Vermont, Burlington, Vermont. [Also see Adam, S. A. 1990. *Journal of Environmental Horticulture* 8 (1 March): 19–21.]

Adam, S. and L. Perry. 1987. *Powdery mildew incidence on phlox.* Leaflet COH 24. Department of Plant and Soil Science, University of Vermont, Burlington, Vermont.

Armitage, A. 1996. Forcing perennials in the greenhouse. *GrowerTalks* (July): 86–97.

Aylsworth, Jean. 1995. Perfecting perennial plugs. *Greenhouse Grower* (Fall): 20–22.

Baldwin, I. and J. Stanley. 1983. Producing perennials. *Florists' Review* 173 (no. 4473): 22–24, 26–28. [Also see *American Nurseryman* 157 (no. 10): 47–52.]

Beam, J. L. 1983. A picture of perennial perfection. *Greenhouse Manager* 2 (no. 2): 87, 90, 92–94, 96.

Beattie, D. J. 1982. Minimum attention helps popularity of herbaceous perennial pot plants. *Florists' Review* 17 (no. 4424): 66, 71–72, 74.

Beattie, D. J. and E. J. Holcomb. 1983. Effects of chilling and photoperiod on forcing *Astilbe. HortScience* 18: 449–450.

Behe, B. and C. Walker. 1995. Sales are up, but prices aren't. *Greenhouse Management and Production* (February): 42–44.

Bilderback, T. 1996. Water management in container nurseries. *NC Nursery Notes* (May–June): 33–34.

Brand, M. 1996a. Fertilization of fountain grass with a controlled release fertilizer. *Yankee Nursery Quarterly*, University of Connecticut 6 (1 Spring): 1–3.

Brand, M. 1996b. Direct potting of ornamental grasses using two division sizes. *Yankee Nursery Quarterly*, University of Connecticut 6 (1 Spring): 8–10.

Cabrera, R. 1996. Monitoring and managing soluble salts in plant production. *Long Island Horticulture News* (July): 1–4.

Cameron, A., R. Heins, and W. Carlson. 1996a. Forcing perennials 102. *Greenhouse Grower* (April): 19–21.

Cameron, A., R. Heins, and W. Carlson. 1996b. Forcing herbaceous perennials. *Professional Plant Growers Association News* (July): 3.

Cathey, H. M. 1966. *Growing flowering perennials.* Home and Garden Bulletin 114, U.S. Department of Agriculture, Washington, DC.

Cumming, R. W. and R. E. Lee. 1960. *Contemporary perennials.* New York: MacMillan.

Daughtrey, M. and M. Semel. 1987. *Herbaceous perennials: Diseases and insect pests.* Information Bulletin 207. Cornell Cooperative Extension,, Ithaca, New York.

Daughtrey, M., M. Macksel, L. Perry, and S. Clark. 1993. Comparison of phlox cultivars for susceptibility to powdery mildew. Biological and Cultural Tests, American Phytopathological Society, vol. 129.

DiSabato-Aust, T. M. 1987. Hardiness of herbaceous perennials and its implication to overwintering container grown plants. M.S. thesis, Ohio State University, Columbus, Ohio.

Duarte, M. 1986. Herbaceous perennial production systems for *Achillea, Gypsophila,* and *Heuchera.* M. S. thesis, University of Vermont, Burlington, Vermont.

Duarte, M. 1989. Perennial plugs could lead to tenfold savings. *Nursery Manager* (July): 92–93.

Duarte, M. and L. P. Perry. 1987. Figuring the costs of seeds and seedlings four ways. *Greenhouse Manager* (March).

Duarte, M. and L. P. Perry. 1988. Field fertilization of *Heuchera sanguinea* 'Splendens'. *HortScience* 23 (6): 1084.

Garber, M. 1996. Perennials are here to stay—and grow. *Greenhouse Grower* (May): 48–49.

German, R. T., Sr. 1980. *Perennial culture.* German Seed Co., Smethport, Pennsylvania.

Hamaker, C., W. H. Carlson, R. D. Heins, and A. C. Cameron. 1995. Influence of daylength delivery on flowering in several herbaceous perennial species. *HortScience* 30 (4): 561. Abstract 739.

Hamaker, C., B. Engle, R. Heins, A. Cameron, and W. Carlson. 1996a. Forcing perennials crop by crop. *Greenhouse Grower* (July): 43–46.

Hamaker, C., B. Engle, R. Heins, A. Cameron, and W. Carlson. 1996b. Using growth regulators to control height of herbaceous perennials. *Grower Talks* (September): 46–53.

Hamaker, C., B. Engle, R. Heins, A. Cameron, and W. Carlson . 1996c. Perennials: Best long-day treatments for your varieties. *Grower Talks* (November): 36–42.

Han, S. and M. Rogers. 1984. Factors affecting flowering in selected herbaceous perennials. Presentation at the American Society of Horticultural Science 81st annual meeting, Vancouver, British Columbia, August 8.

Hanchek, A. 1991. Herbaceous perennials: Growth and flowering. *Professional Plant Growers Association News* (September): 7–8.

Hebb, R. S. 1975. Low maintenance perennials. *Arnoldia* 34 (5) and 35 (1).

Herrick, T. A. 1996. Cold hardiness of herbaceous perennials. M.S. thesis, University of Vermont, Department of Plant and Soil Science, Burlington, Vermont.

Herrick, T. A. and L. P. Perry. 1997. Influence of freeze acclimation procedure on survival and regrowth of container-grown *Campanula takesimana*. *HortTechnology* 7 (1): 43–46.

Holcomb, E. J. and D. J. Beattie. 1991. Proper use of growth retardants important to successful production of perennials as potted plants. *Professional Plant Growers Association News* (September): 9–10.

Iles, J. K. and N. H. Agnew. 1993a. Responses of five container-grown herbaceous perennial species to laboratory freezing. *HortTechnology* 3: 192–194.

Iles, J. K. and N. H. Agnew. 1993b. Determining cold hardiness of *Heuchera sanguinea* Engelm. 'Chatterbox' using dormant crowns. *HortScience* 28: 1087–1088.

Iles, J. K. and N. H. Agnew. 1995. Forcing herbaceous perennials to flower after storage outdoors under a thermoblanket. *HortTechnology* 5 (3): 239–243.

IQDHO. 1994. *Les vivaces la production (Perennial production).* Proceedings from a conference held in February 1994 at Trois-Rivieres, Quebec. Published by IQDHO (Institut québécois du développement de l'horticulture ornementale), 3230 rue Sicotte, B219, Saint-Hyacinthe, Quebec, Canada J2S2M2.

Iverson, R. R. 1989. Greenhouse forcing of herbaceous garden perennials. Ph.D. thesis, Cornell University, Ithaca, New York.

Iverson, R. R. and T. C. Weiler. 1989. Forcing the issue: A guide to forcing garden perennials into bloom for flower show exhibitions. *American Nurseryman* (April): 15.

Iverson, R. R. and T. C. Weiler. 1994. Strategies to force flowering of six herbaceous garden perennials. *HortTechnology* 4: 61–65.

Karlovich, Paul. 1995. Producing perennials from plugs. *Grower Talks* (Winter): 34–39.

Lake, B., C. Noble, and D. C. Hamilton. 1982. Growing herbaceous perennials. *American Nurseryman* 155 (7): 81–85.

Langhans, Robert W. 1990. *Greenhouse management: A guide to structures, environmental control, materials handling, crop programming, and business analysis.* 3rd edition. Ithaca, New York: Halcyon Press.

Lochlear, J. H. and G. D. Coorts. 1982. Container production of herbaceous perennials. *BPI News* 8 (2): 6–7, (7): 3, and (8): 5–7.

Lucas, R. E. and J. K. Davis. 1961. Relationships between pH values of organic soils and availabilities of 12 plant nutrients. *Soil Science* 92: 177–182.

Maqbool, M. 1986. Post-harvest handling and storage of bare-root herbaceous perennials. Master's thesis, Michigan State University.

Pellett, N. and D. Heleba. 1995. Chopped newspaper for weed control in nursery crops. *Journal of Environmental Horticulture* 13 (2): 77–81.

Perry, F., M. Badenhop, and T. Phillips. 1987. *Costs of establishing and operating a small and large size container nursery in USDA climatic zones 7 and 8.* Southern Coop. Series Bulletin 327, Auburn University, Auburn, Alabama.

Perry, L. 1994. Comparison of powdery mildew controls on White Admiral Phlox. Biological and Cultural Tests, American Phytopathological Society, vol. 163.

Perry, L. P. 1990. Overwintering container-grown herbaceous perennials in northern regions. *Journal of Environmental Horticulture* 8 (3): 135–138.

Perry, L. P. 1998. Comparison of powdery mildew resistance among bee balm cultivars. Biological and Cultural Tests, American Phytopathological Society, vol. 13.

Perry, L. P. and S. Adam. 1990. Nitrogen nutrition of container grown *Hemerocallis* x 'Stella de Oro'. *Journal of Environmental Horticulture* 8 (1): 19–21.

Perry, L. P. and A. Bove. 1985. Perennial pressures. *Florists' Review* 176 (4544): 26–29.

Perry, L. P. and A. Bove. 1986. Seed propagation. *Perennial Plants* 4 (Spring): 3–5.

Perry, L. P. and M. Duarte. 1989. Perennial plugs could lead to tenfold savings. *Nursery Manager* (July).

Perry, L. P. and T. A. Herrick. 1996. Freezing date and duration effects on regrowth of three container-grown herbaceous perennials. *Journal of Environmental Horticulture* 14: 214–216.

Perry, L. P., C. Ormsbee, and K. Finley. 1989. Does a floating row cover or black plastic mulch increase production in perennials? *Perennial Plants* 17: 6–7.

Pinnell, M., A. Armitage, and D. Seaborn. 1985. *Germination needs for common perennial seeds.* Research Bulletin 331, University of Georgia, Athens, Georgia.

Pundt, L. 1996. Monitoring for key pests during the greenhouse production of perennials. *Connecticut Greenhouse Newsletter* 191 (University of Connecticut, Storrs, Connecticut): 4–9.

Rhodus, T. 1994. Views on Management. *Perennial Plants* (Summer): 26–34.

Runkle, E. S., R. D. Heins, A. C. Cameron, and W. H. Carlson. 1995. Determining the critical photoperiod for flowering of several herbaceous perennial species. *HortScience* 30 (4): 861. Abstract 715 and poster presentation, Montreal, Canada, August 1–3.

Runkle, E. S., R. D. Heins, A. C. Cameron, and W. H. Carlson. 1996a. Manipulating daylength to flower perennials. *GrowerTalks* (June): 66–70.

Runkle, E. S., R. D. Heins, A. C. Cameron, and W. H. Carlson. 1996b. Forcing perennials crop by crop. *Greenhouse Grower* (September): 41–42.

Ruter, J. M. 1995. Growth of *Coreopsis* and *Plumbago* in plastic and copper hydroxide impregnated fiber containers. *HortTechnology* 5: 300–302.

Scott, Simon W. 1996. Hosts of tomato spotted wilt virus and impatiens necrotic spot virus. *Plant Diagnostic Quarterly* 17 (2): 27.

Senesac, A. and Tsontakis-Bradley. 1996. Managing liverwort and pearlwort in container perennials. Long Island Horticultural Research Laboratory Research Report (Riverhead, New York): 15–20.

Shedron, K. G. and T. C. Weiler. 1982. Producing perennials as bedding plants. *American Nurseryman* 155 (10): 45–47.

Smith, E. M. 1983. *Proceedings from the herbaceous perennial symposium.* Bulletin 717, Ohio State University, Columbus, Ohio.

Still, S. M. 1994. *Herbaceous ornamental plants.* 2nd edition. Champaign, Illinois: Stipes.

Still, S. M., T. DiSabato-Aust, and G. Brenneman. 1987. Cold hardiness of herbaceous perennials. Proceedings from the International Plant Propagators' Society Annual Meeting 37: 386–392.

Taylor, R., H. Kneen, E. Smith, D. Hahn, and S. Uchida. 1986. *Costs of establishing and operating field nurseries differentiated by size of firm and species of plant in USDA plant hardiness zones 5 and 6.* Ohio State University Research Bulletin 1177, Wooster, Ohio.

Taylor, R. S. Smith, D. Beattie, and G. Pealer. 1990. *Requirements and costs of establishing and operating a three-acre herbaceous perennial container nursery.* Ohio State University Special Circular 136.

Tessene, M. 1979. Germinating and timing perennials. Proceedings from the Bedding Plant Conference 12: 274–277.

Truog, E. 1947. U.S. Department of Agriculture yearbook of agriculture, 1943–47. Washington, DC: Superintendent of Documents.

Van Hees, Giles and C. Dale Hendricks. 1987. Summer cutting workshop. Presented at the Perennial Plant Association Meeting, Baltimore, Maryland.

Weiler, T. 1995. Forcing perennials. *Greenhouse Business* (August): 30–32.

Whitman, C., R. Heins, A. Cameron, and W. Carlson. 1996a. Forcing perennials crop by crop. *Greenhouse Grower* (August, September series).

Whitman, C., R. Heins, A. Cameron and W. Carlson. 1996b. Perennial flower induction—the light you use can make a difference. *GrowerTalks* (July): 80–84.

Wilcox, L. V. 1955. *Classification and use of irrigation waters.* Circular 969. Washington, DC: U.S. Department of Agriculture.

Yantorno, P. 1997. Perennial plugs—the sensible solution. *GrowerTalks* (February): 62–66.

Yuan, M., V. H. Carlson, R. D. Heins, and A. C. Cameron. 1995. Effect of temperature on time to flower of *Coreopsis grandiflora, Chrysanthemum superbum, Gaillardia grandiflora,* and *Rudbeckia fulgida. HortScience* 30 (4): 861. Abstract 723.

Yuan, M., V. H. Carlson, R. D. Heins, and A. C. Cameron. 1996. Forcing perennials crop by crop. *Greenhouse Grower* (June): 57–58.

Zhang, D, A. Armitage, J. Affolter, and M. Dirr. 1996. Environmental control of flowering and growth of *Achillea millefolium* 'Summer Pastels'. *HortScience* 31 (3): 364–365.

Glossary

Absorbent — A material such as silica gel or cornmeal that absorbs moisture from air and is used in seed storage to keep low moisture levels in containers.

Acclimatization — Also called acclimation; the process of plants adapting to another climate or environment, such as to winter cold.

Adventitious — Describes new growing points arising from vegetative plant parts, often in unusual places, such as roots from stems or shoots from roots.

Aeration — Characteristic of good soils with adequate air space and content for roots.

Air prune — Using air movement, as under benches, to "prune" roots or keep them from growing out bottoms of pots.

Alkalinity — A measure of water's capacity to neutralize acids; is related to pH but not the same as alkaline (low pH) or basic (high pH). Alkalinity is measured in milligrams per liter of calcium carbonate equivalents (mg/L $CaCO_3$).

Annual — A plant that completes its growth cycle in one season; often a function of climate, as many subtropical perennials such as salvias and verbenas may be grown as annuals in the North.

Asexual — Vegetative type of propagation.

Azalea pot — A short pot; its height is $3/4$ of its width.

Bacteria (singular bacterium) — A unicellular, microscopic plant that lacks chlorophyll and multiplies by fission. Some bacteria cause plant diseases.

Bactericide — A pesticide used to kill bacteria.

Bare root — A plant or plant division not in a field or container, generally with the soil removed from its roots.

Bedding plant — An ornamental flower or foliage plant used to "bed out" or plant in flower beds; they are usually sold in the spring in garden centers in small packs and are usually (but not always) annuals.

Biennial — A plant that requires two growing seasons to complete its life cycle, often flowering only in the second year; many self sow, such as hollyhock.

Biological control — Controlling pests by use of natural enemies such as predators, parasites, and disease-producing organisms to reduce damage caused by pests to tolerable levels. Selective chemical use can be compatible with biological control, either to treat hot spots or to reduce pest numbers before releasing predators.

Blight — A disease characterized by a general and rapid killing of leaves, flowers, and stems.

Bracts — Modified leaves, often brightly colored, and often mistaken for flowers as in many *Euphorbia* or spurges.

Bud blast — Death of a flower bud without opening; main causes are water stress, pollution, and insect damage.

Buffer — In the context of land, an area with no buildings or use that is set aside to use for potential future expansion, or to protect a facility against external impacts, such as nearby development.

Buffering — The ability of a growing medium to prevent large nutrient imbalances while holding onto excess nutrients.

Bulb — An underground, shortened stem or modified bud with scales; serves as a storage organ.

Bulbils — Also known as bulblets; small bulbs produced by plants as offsets to bulbs or even on some stems for the plant's self-propagation.

Bushel — Volume of media containing 1.25 cubic feet or 35.7 liters.

Calcined clay — Clay mineral heated to high temperatures to harden, then ground into small granules; absorbs and holds water, as in kitty litter.

Capillary mat — Type of bottom watering system; a fiber mat is used to distribute water to the bottoms of pots.

Capillary tubes — Small water-conducting tubes found naturally in soils; or the small tubes in some irrigation systems.

Cation exchange capacity (CEC) — The ability and activity of organic matter and clays that holds and releases nutrients with positive charges (such as calcium and potassium).

Cell — In relation to containers, a small individual unit of a tray or flat containing many such units; in relation to plant structure, the small microscopic component of living tissue, the basic unit of life.

Chimera — A plant with tissue of more than one genetic type, often seen with variegated plants.

Chlorophyll — Green pigment in cells responsible for photosynthesis.

Chlorosis — Yellowing, usually of leaves, indicative of nutrient deficiency or other stress such as pests or root diseases.

Clay — A type of soil consisting of the smallest soil particles (0.0002–0.002 millimeters in diameter); often has high water and low air porosity.

Coir — Coconut husk fiber, it is recently being reinvestigated as a medium amendment.

Coldframes — Structures similar to hotbeds but usually without heat and often deeper and larger; used to provide frost protection for tender plants.

Cold storage — Holding plants at cool temperatures to prevent growth or to enable forcing into flower.

Complete fertilizer — A fertilizer containing the three major elements of nitrogen, phosphorus, and potassium.

Constant fertilization — The application of a small amount of fertilizer at each watering.

Controlled-release fertilizer (CRF) — Often called slow release; a fertilizer in which the nutrients are released gradually over a predetermined time.

Corm — An annual, solid bulb.

Cover crop — A crop used to help control weeds, protect soil from erosion, and sometimes add nutrients; is usually planted to a fallow field.

Critical daylength — The number of hours daily of light or dark needed for a plant to change from vegetative to flowering.

Crown — The main growing center of perennials, usually at soil level, from which new roots and stems arise.

Cultivar — A "cultivated variety"; a group of plants that are roughly identical, arising from or maintained in cultivation, and, when reproduced, maintain their similarities.

Cyclic — Applying either light or irrigation water repeatedly, usually at uniform intervals.

Deciduous — Losing its leaves in winter.

Desiccation — Drying out, such as from leaves losing moisture from excess temperature or wind.

Dicot — Short for dicotyledonous, which describes plants having more than one seed leaf, nonparallel veins, and other traits; includes most perennials.

DIF — Refers to the DIFference in day and night temperatures, a new concept of growth regulation. A positive DIF is when the night temperature is less than the day temperature; a negative DIF is when the day temperature is less than the night temperature and is usually applied around sunrise to retard growth.

Dioecious — Unisexual, with male and female flowers on separate plants, as in hops.

Direct costs — Costs for tangible items such as pots, potting mix, and plants.

Disease — Any disturbance of the plant that interferes with its normal structure, function, or economic value. Diseases can be caused by pathogens, including bacteria, fungi, viruses, and other related organisms.

Disinfest — To eliminate the disease potential on tools, on work surfaces, and in pots; often done with labeled chemicals or a solution of one part bleach to nine parts water by volume (the latter is a non-registered use).

Dormancy — A resting phase during which plants may have no leaves or flowers. "Apparent" or "quiescent" dormancy is not true dormancy, as plants are capable of regrowth in a matter of days (given the proper environment), and is typical for most herbaceous perennials.

Electrical conductivity (EC) — A measure of transmission of weak electrical current through a solution in order to determine the amount of dissolved salts.

Entomopathogenic — An organism, usually a disease, used to control specific insect pests.

Ethylene — The gas produced by decaying flowers and ripening fruit, which can cause growing tips to be injured or deformed, twisting and curling, and flowers on sensitive ornamentals to close or even fall off.

Evapotranspiration — The loss of water from the soil by both evaporation and uptake followed by transpiration by the plant.

Eye — A unit of division referring to a basal growing point of some perennials such as hosta and peony.

Family — The grouping of plants between order and genus; Latin family names end in -aceae.

Fan — A unit of division for some perennials such as daylily and iris.

Fixed-asset loans — Long-term loans, usually for a period of years, that are used for purchases of equipment and capital such as greenhouses.

Flat — A tray with sides, usually about 11 by 21 by 3/4 inches, for growing plants or holding plant containers or plugs.

Flood bench — A bench used for growing crops which can hold water for subirrigation — the bench is flooded, then drained.

Fog — Fine water droplets (much finer than mist) used in propagation areas and to cool greenhouses.

Foot-candle (ft-c) — The amount of light 1 foot from a candle; a common unit for measuring the amount of light (a normal reading lamp provides 40–75 ft-c).

Forcing — Controlling the environment to make plants bloom when they normally would not.

Free-standing greenhouse — A greenhouse not connected to another or to another structure.

Fungicide — A pesticide used to kill fungi.

Fungus (plural fungi) — An organism lacking chlorophyll and conductive tissue. Although fungi are microscopic, their spores can be seen with a hand lens. Many plant diseases are caused by fungi.

Genus — Grouping of plants below family and above species that unites a group of species with distinctive characteristics in common; it is the first name in Latin plant names and is capitalized and italicized.

Germination — The emergence of the root or appearance above the soil of a seedling from a seed.

Grades — Classes or designations of plants based on factors such as size and number of growing points or buds.

Green manure — A cover crop turned back into the soil to add nutrients and organic matter.

Growth retardant — Anything (a chemical, water, temperature, or other agent) used to control or restrict plant growth.

Gutter-connected greenhouse — A greenhouse connected to another by means of a common gutter, usually without a wall between them; useful for increasing space efficiency.

Hardiness zones — Geographic zones shown on maps that share the same range of average annual minimum winter temperatures.

Headhouse — Structure attached to greenhouses for propagating, potting, storage, etc.

Herb — A (horticultural) plant used by humans for its culinary, medicinal, functional, or other properties.

Herbicide — A pesticide used to kill or inhibit plant growth.

HID — Refers to High Intensity Discharge, a type of bright lighting found in some greenhouses and large stores.

Horizontal air flow (HAF) — Moving air gently in greenhouses at plant level by means of low-velocity fans; HAF is employed to minimize disease, among other reasons.

Hormone — A chemical (such as IBA — indole butyric acid) that promotes specific plant processes such as rooting.

Hotbeds — Small structures, usually square or rectangular, about 1 foot high, and 2-3 feet wide, often with heating cables on the bottom and sashes or other clear covering on top, used to start or hold small plants outdoors.

Hydrogel — A type of water-absorbing compound that absorbs many times its weight in water and is used to keep media moist and reduce watering.

IBA — Indole butyric acid, a growth hormone used in the rooting of cuttings, often in the form of a powder applied to cutting bases.

Indirect costs — Overhead costs; nonspecific items such as utility costs, property-related costs, or marketing costs.

Inorganic — Not organic; the part of growing media not containing carbon, such as sand, perlite, or vermiculite.

Insecticide — A pesticide used to kill insects.

Integrated Pest Management (IPM) — The use of a variety of pest control methods to produce high-quality plants. IPM aims to use a number of control techniques (cultural, biological, physical, and chemical) in an integrated fashion to maximize the use of natural mortality factors and to apply chemical control measures only when necessary.

Ions — Elements (as in nutrients) with either a positive or negative charge.

Juvenile — The young stage of growth, which in some plants is pronounced and different from more mature growth, during which some processes, such as flowering, will not occur and others, such as rooting, occur more easily.

Layering — Methods of propagation that produce new roots and plants on stems while they are still attached to the mother plant.

Leach — To water heavily until water runs out the bottom of pots; used to prevent soluble salt buildup.

Liner — A plant grown from a seed or cutting and grown in a plug, flat, or bed.

Lines of credit — Short-term loans from banks, usually for six to twelve months, that are used for temporary and extra and immediate cash for purchases and operating expenses.

Liverwort — Flat, scaly leaves 1–2 inches long and the thickness of paper that grow in different directions and creep over damp soil and rocks; primitive — among the first land plants; sometimes grow on container media.

Long day (LD) — Describes a plant needing long days (anywhere from 12–16 hours usually) to bloom or complete another process; actually, it needs short nights. Long days are often provided by night interruption.

Luxury consumption — The absorption of nutrients from the soil by plants at a level higher than what is actually needed for growth; most often seen with potassium.

Macroelements — Nutrient elements needed in largest amounts by plants. These are nitrogen (N), phosphorus (P), and potassium (K).

Market — The act of selling, including advertising, or the target group one is selling to.

Market pack — A small container for growing plants, roughly 3 inches by 5 inches by 2 inches deep.

Market share — Portion of your overall market audience that actually buys your goods or services.

Medium — Growing mix, with or without soil, used to provide water, support, nutrients, and oxygen to the roots.

Merchandise — The in-store or on-premise selling of products, as well as how they are displayed.

Mho — Unit of measurement of electrical conductance; used in reporting soluble salts.

Microclimate — Local conditions that determine plant growth in a particular site, such as proximity to buildings, slope, wind, and sun.

Microelements — Nutrient elements needed in small amounts by plants; may be called trace or minor elements.

Mist — A fine spray of water applied frequently to propagation beds to prevent water loss from plants.

Mites — Tiny arthropods closely related to ticks; not true insects.

Mobile — Moves easily, usually used in relation to the ability of nutrient elements to move within a plant.

Monocot — Short for monocotyledon, a type of plant having a single seed leaf and other characteristics such as parallel veins; examples include lilies, iris, and grasses.

Monoecious — Having male and female flowers on the same plant.

Mycelium (plural mycelia) — The mass of threadlike filaments that form fungi "roots."

Nematode — A tiny wormlike organism that may feed on or in plants, including roots; they may be referred to as roundworms, threadworms, or eelworms.

Niche — A thing, or a place in the market, that is unique to a business and that can be attractive to customers such as native plants or alpine perennials.

Night interruption — The process of interrupting night darkness with light in order to control flowering; usually done by providing a 4-hour light break from about 10 A.M. to 2 P.M. with incandescent bulbs to provide 10–25 foot-candles or more.

Nomenclature — Plant names and the process of naming them.

Obligate — "Must have," such as an obligate long-day plant (must have long days to bloom).

Organic — In relation to growing media and fertilizers, those ingredients containing carbon, such as peat moss and manure.

Overwinter — The process of protecting perennials in the hopes that they will survive winter cold.

Parasite — An organism that lives and feeds in or on a plant (the host) and obtains all its nutrients from the host.

Pathogen — A disease-producing organism.

Pearlwort — A mosslike evergreen perennial only 1–2 inches high that forms a dense mat of foliage.

Peat-lite — A type of growing mix containing no soil; primarily peat moss and other components such as vermiculite or perlite.

Pelleted seed — Those seeds that are often small or difficult to germinate and are encased in an outer shell that makes them larger and easier to handle or contains starter nutrients; also known as coated seed.

Perennial — A plant with an overwintering structure (perennating organ) that lives more than two years. The plant completes its life cycle each year, but may not begin blooming until the second year. Can apply to woody plants, but the term is often used for nonwoody or herbaceous plants.

Perlite — White granules formed from heating volcanic silicate ore to 1,400°F; is added to growing media for additional air and water porosity, is dusty, and can "float" to the top of the media surface and blow around.

Pest — Any unwanted organism that is destructive to crops.

pH — The potential acidity or alkalinity of a solution or medium. A pH of 7 is the value for pure distilled water and is considered neutral; a lower pH is more acid, a higher pH more alkaline. Plants grow best in media of pH 5–7.

Photodermititis — A skin rash or irritation from certain plants in sunlight.

Photosynthates — Those sugars and compounds produced with photosynthesis; they are needed for a plant to grow and used up when plants respire.

Photosynthesis — The process of a plant using chlorophyll to trap the sun's energy in the form of sugars and producing sugars and oxygen from carbon dioxide and water.

Phytoplasma — A disease, similar to bacteria, that causes foliage to yellow and flowers to stay green.

Phytotoxic — Harmful to plants, such as leaf injury or even death from pesticides.

Plug — A small individual compartment or unit in a flat of many units (36–300 or more) for small plant production.

Porosity — The amount of space in a soil or growing medium for air and water.

Postemergence — Something, usually an herbicide, that is applied after seedlings have emerged.

Precharged — Refers to a growing medium with nutrients — a nutrient "charge" — already incorporated.

Preemergence — Something, usually an herbicide, that is applied prior to seedlings emerging.

Propagule — Parts naturally produced on plants for their propagation and reproduction, such as spores from ferns, seeds, and bulbils.

Quonset — Type of greenhouse generally made of metal hoops over which plastic is fastened.

Radicle — The first root stage or embryonic root.

Rastral pattern — Bristles on the backs of some beetle larvae, usually in distinct patterns, such as "V" or "C" shapes or parallel lines, and used in identification.

Respiration — The process by which a plant exchanges oxygen and carbon dioxide through the stomata.

Retail — A store, or the act of selling directly to consumers.

Revegetation — Replanting a site from which, for some reason, plants have been removed.

Rewholesale — A firm, or the act of buying from a wholesaler and then reselling to a retailer or landscaper.

Rhizome — A specialized stem lying on or under the soil surface from which aerial parts arise.

Rockwool — A growing medium amendment composed of finely spun fibers of rock that are formed when rock is heated to extremely high temperatures; used for soilless culture, as a substitute for peat moss, or as an amendment to add porosity.

Rooting hormone — A root-stimulating substance, usually a powder, applied to the base of cuttings to promote better and faster rooting; often available in several strengths.

Root initials — Buds on crowns or mature roots that will form new roots.

Rootstock — In grafting, the host or "mother" plant onto which the desirable plant part (usually type of cutting or bud) — the scion — is attached.

Root zone heating — Heat provided to the root zone of plants, usually as bottom heat from heating cables or small tubes filled with hot water.

Rose — In reference to watering, another name for a water breaker.

Salt burn — A "burned" appearance to edges of leaves, browning, and death; is due to excess salts in the soil holding water and keeping the plant from absorbing water, which results in leaves drying out.

Sand — The type of soil with the largest particles (0.05–1.0 millimeter in diameter); sand has high air and low water porosity.

Sanitation — Any activity carried out to eliminate or reduce the numbers of a pest or pests; may include removing diseased plants and weeds, pasteurizing soil, and disinfesting propagation tools and areas.

Scarification — Abrading the seed coat, especially of hard seeds such as legumes, in order to allow water and air to penetrate. This is usually done by rubbing the seeds on sandpaper, nicking the seed coat with a knife, or soaking seeds in hot water or even sulfuric acid. (If using the latter, use extreme caution and consult germination references before attempting.)

Scion — In grafting, the desirable plant part placed onto the rootstock.

Sclerotium (plural sclerotia) — A resting mass of fungus tissue usually without spores on or in it, often sphere-shaped.

Seeder — A machine that automatically sows seeds, often by picking them up by vacuum and releasing them in cells, plugs, or trays of media.

Shelter belts — Usually consist of rows of trees used to provide protection from wind; also called windbreaks.

Short day (SD) — A plant needing short days (often less than 12 hours) to bloom; actually, the plant needs long nights.

Silt — The type of soil with particles intermediate in size; between sand and clay.

Soaker hose — A hose, usually porous, through which water flows slowly to water crops or beds.

Softened water — Water in which the calcium and magnesium ions and the carbonates are exchanged chemically with sodium ions.

Softwood bark — Bark from conifers such as fir, pine, or redwood; a mulch from this contains less than 85% lignin (main wood tissue that decomposes slowly).

Soluble salts — Chemical compounds dissolved in the soil solution that may build to harmful levels and precipitate out as a white crust on the soil surface or inside rims of pots. They usually come from fertilizer residues left in the growing medium, or from other sources such as manures.

Species — The grouping of plants below a genus of closely related, morphologically similar plants from a distinct geographical region; usually the second word in a plant's Latin name that is not capitalized but is italicized.

Sphagnum — A particular type of moss from which most common peat moss is derived.

Standards — Guidelines for quality factors, such as plant size, or for processes, such as transplanting and potting, agreed to by key organizations such as national plant organizations.

Sticking — Pushing a cutting into a rooting medium.

Stock — To a business, an inventory of goods; to a grower, a plant used to provide propagation material.

Stock plant — A plant used to propagate more plants, such as from cuttings.

Stoloniferous — Spreading by means of stolons — prostrate branches from a plant base along or just under the soil surface, which root at nodes and form new plants. Stolons are often called "runners." A common example is the strawberry.

Stomate (plural stomata) — A minute pore-like opening in plant leaves for the exchange of gases.

Structure — In relation to soil, refers to the arrangement of the soil particles.

Subirrigation — Watering from below, such as with capillary mats or with ebb and flow or flood benches.

Swale — A runoff ditch or holding area for surface water.

Synthetic — Non-organic.

Systemic — Moves throughout the system of a plant, including roots and shoots; often used in relation to pesticides.

Taxonomy — The identification, classification, and naming of plants.

Terminals — New tip growth, either on roots or shoots.

Texture — In relation to soil, refers to the relative size of soil particles; sand has the largest and clay the smallest particles, with loam in between.

Thermoblanket — An insulated cover applied to perennials, usually directly, for overwintering.

Threshold — The number or level of a pest that can be tolerated or accepted before applying control measures.

Toning — Hardening plants for planting out, or plugs for shipping, often by subjecting them to cooler temperatures or slight stresses such as from lack of water or fertility.

Topdress — To apply to the top of the soil or medium surface, such as with fertilizers.

Toxicity — How poisonous a pesticide is to an organism; the ability of a pesticide to produce injury; the ability of a poisonous plant to produce injury.

Trace elements — See *microelements*

Transpiration — The loss of water vapor by a plant through the stomata.

Transplant — A rooted seedling or rooted cutting that has been transplanted at least once.

Tuber — A specialized stem without scales that is usually underground and serves to store food for the plant; dahlia is a common example.

Variety — A further subcategory under species, often used incorrectly but interchangeably with cultivar.

Vector — To carry a pathogen, or an insect or other animal that carries a pathogen.

Vegetative — Nonflowering; in propagation, refers to asexual methods such as cuttings.

Vermiculite — Gray, expanded mica ore heated to 1,800°F in its creation; added to growing media for additional water and air porosity; compacts and loses this feature over time.

Vernalization— Cold treatment needed to get many perennials to flower; usually the minimum period is six to twelve weeks at 40°F or below.

Vernalize — To expose a plant to an environmental condition or signal, such as cold, to induce flowering or other growth response.

Virus — A submicroscopic pathogen that consists of nucleic acid and protein and that needs living cells to grow.

Water breaker — A type of nozzle put on the end of a hose to break a forceful stream into a "shower"; less injurious to small plants and results in more even watering.

Wetting agent — A substance added to water or a growing medium to help hydrophobic media (especially some peat-lite ones) absorb water easier.

Wholesale — A firm, or the act of selling to a retailer or other firm, not directly to the consumer.

Winter kill — Death during winter of plant parts from freezing.

Recommended Reading and Other Sources of Information

Publications from Cornell University

The references below are available from the Cornell University Resource Center. Before ordering, contact the center for current prices and availability. A complete publications catalog is available.

Cornell University Resource Center
7 Business and Technology Park
Ithaca, New York 14850
Phone (607) 255-2080
Fax (607) 255-9946
E-mail DIST_CENTER@CCE.CORNELL.EDU
Web site: WWW.CCE.CORNELL.EDU/PUBLICATIONS

- *Cornell Peat-Lite Mixes for Commercial Plant Growing.* Information Bulletin 43. 1982.
- *1996 Pest Management Recommendations for Commercial Production and Maintenance of Trees and Shrubs*
- *1997 Pest Management Recommendation for the Production of Herbaceous Perennials.* (This document is available on the Internet at <http://pmep.cce.cornell.edu/recommends/herbperen/index.html>.)
- *1995 Recommendations for the Integrated Management of Greenhouse Florist Crops: Management of Pests and Crop Growth*
- *Sequence of Bloom of Perennials, Biennials, and Bulbs.* Information Bulletin 196. 1992.
- *Weed Management Guide for Herbaceous Ornamentals* by A. Senesac and J. Neal. Weed Management Series No. 1, WeedFacts. 1995.

Publications from NRAES

The references listed below are available from NRAES, the Northeast Regional Agricultural Engineering Service (see inside back cover for a description of NRAES). Before ordering, please contact NRAES for current prices and shipping and handling charges. NRAES has over 120 publications; call for a free catalog.

NRAES
Cooperative Extension, 152 Riley-Robb Hall
Ithaca, New York 14853-5701
Phone: (607) 255-7654
Fax: (607) 254-8770
E-mail: NRAES@CORNELL.EDU
Web site: HTTP://RCWPSUN.CAS.PSU.EDU/NRAES

- *Designing Facilities for Pesticide and Fertilizer Containment,* MWPS–37. 1991. This 113-page reference compiles the best available information on storing, handling, and using pesticides and fertilizers.
- *Greenhouse Engineering,* NRAES–33. 1994. This 212-page manual contains current information needed to plan, construct, and control the commercial greenhouse. Major sections describe structures, materials handling, the greenhouse environment, and energy conservation.
- *Greenhouse Systems: Automation, Culture, and Environment,* NRAES–72. 1994. This proceedings from an international conference provides in-depth information on the engineering principles of greenhouse system design and management. 306 pages
- *Herbaceous Perennials: Diseases and Insect Pests,* IB–207. 1987. This 25-page publication outlines strategies for the prevention and control of diseases and

pests that attack herbaceous perennials. Forty-four color photos help in identifying insects and diseases.

- *On-Farm Agrichemical Handling Facilities,* NRAES–78. 1995. This publication discusses considerations regarding agrichemical storage, principal parts of a facility, storage environmental requirements, safety requirements, and storage alternatives. 22 pages

- *On-Farm Composting Handbook,* NRAES–54. 1992. Topics covered in this comprehensive publication include the composting process, raw materials, composting methods, operations, management, site and environmental considerations, using compost, marketing, economics, and other options for waste management. 186 pages

- *Trickle Irrigation in the Eastern United States,* NRAES–4. 1985. This handbook was developed for humid climates and is an excellent planning and installation guide for growers considering a trickle irrigation system. 24 pages

- *Water and Nutrient Management for Greenhouses,* NRAES–56. 1996. This 110-page publication includes discussions about general crop needs, balancing nutrient applications with crop demand, water, fertilizer, substrates, temperature, and the biotic environment.

Publications from Other Sources (Categorized by Topic)

General

- *Alan Bloom's Hardy Perennials: New Plants Raised and Introduced by a Lifelong Plantsman.* Alan Bloom. London: B. T. Batsford Ltd. 1992.

- *All About Perennials.* Chevron Chemical Company. Ortho Books. 1996.

- *The American Horticultural Society A-Z Encyclopedia of Garden Plants.* Christopher Brickell and Judith Zuk, eds. DK Publishing. 1997.

- *American Standards for Perennial Plants.* Perennial Plant Association. (see "Societies" listing on page 207)

- *America's Garden Book.* Louise Bush-Brown and James Bush-Brown (Howard Irwin, ed.). Macmillan General. 1996.

- *Andersen Horticultural Library's Source List of Plants and Seeds.* 1996. (see "Plant Sources and Supplies" on page 208)

- *The Art of Perennial Gardening: Creative Ways with Hardy Flowers.* Patrick Lima. Firefly Books. 1998.

- *Ball Red Book.* Vic Ball. Batavia, Illinois: Ball Publishing Company. 1998.

- *Bedding Plants IV: A Manual on the Culture of Bedding Plants as a Greenhouse Crop.* E. Jay Holcomb. Batavia, Illinois: Ball Publishing Company. 1994.

- *Blooms of Bressingham Garden Plants: Choosing the Best Hardy Plants for Your Garden.* Alan and Adrian Bloom. London: Harper Collins. 1992.

- *Designing with Perennials.* Pamela J. Harper. New York: Macmillan. 1991.

- *Hardy Herbaceous Perennials* (two-volume set). Wilhelm Schacht and Alfred Fessler. Portland, Oregon: Timber Press. 1990.

- *The Harrowsmith Perennial Garden.* Patrick Lima. Camden East, Ontario: Camden House. 1987.

- *Herbaceous Perennial Plants: A Treatise on Their Identification, Culture, and Garden Attributes.* 2nd edition. Allan M. Armitage. Stipes Publishing Co. 1997.

- *Hortus Third: A Concise Dictionary of Plants Cultivated in the United States and Canada.* Liberty Hyde Bailey. New York: MacMillan. 1976.

- *Index Hortensis: Perennials.* Volume 1. Piers Trehane. Timber Press. 1990.

- *International Code of Botanical Nomenclature.* Greuter et al. Konigstein, Germany: Koeltz Scientific Books. 1994.

- *Manual of Herbaceous Ornamental Plants.* Steven M. Still. Stipes Publishing Company. 1993.

- *Naamlijst van Vaste Planten* (Dutch *Namelist).* H. J. van de Laar and I. G. Fortgens. Boskoop, Holland: Proefstation voor de Boomkwekerij. 1995.

- *National Garden Book.* Editors of Sunset Books and *Sunset* Magazine. Menlo Park, California: Sunset Publishing Company. 1997.

- *New Royal Horticulture Society Dictionary of Gardening* (four-volume set). Anthony J. Huxley and Mark Griffiths. MacMillan Pr. Ltd. 1992.

- *The Perennial Garden: Color Harmonies Through the Seasons.* Jeff Cox and Marilyn Cox. Emmaus, Pennsylvania: Rodale Press. 1992.

- *Perennial Gardening.* Michael Ruggiero. New York: Pantheon Books. 1994.

- *Perennial Garden Plants: Or the Modern Florilegium: A Concise Account of Herbaceous Plants, Including Bulbs, for General Garden Use.* Graham Stuart Thomas. Oregon: Timber Press. 1990.

- *Perennial Plant Symposium Proceedings.* Perennial Plant Association. 1983– . (see "Societies" listing on page 207)

- *Perennials.* Pamela Harper. H.P. Books. 1985.

- *Perennials for American Gardens.* Ruth Rogers Clausen, Nicolas H. Ekstrom, Kassie Evashevski, and Jason Epstein. New York: Random House. 1989.

- *The Plant Finder.* Yearly. (see "Plant Sources and Supplies" on page 208)
- *The Random House Book of Perennials: Early Perennials.* Volume 1. Roger Phillips and Martyn Rix. Random House. 1992.
- *The Random House Book of Perennials: Late Perennials.* Volume 2. Roger Phillips and Martyn Rix. Random House. 1992.
- *Successful Perennial Gardening: A Practical Guide.* Lewis Hill and Nancy Hill. Storey Books. 1988.
- *Taylor's Pocket Guide to Perennials for Shade.* Ann Reilly (ed.) and Norman Taylor. Houghton Mifflin Co. 1989.
- *Taylor's Pocket Guide to Perennials for Sun.* Maggie Oster (ed.) and Norman Taylor. Houghton Mifflin Co. 1989.

General Production/Greenhouses

- *Fertilization of Container-Grown Nursery Stock.* C. Gilliam and E. Smith. Extension Bulletin 658. Ohio State University Extension. 1980.
- *Greenhouse Management: A Guide to Structures, Environmental Control, Materials Handling, Crop Programming, and Business Analysis.* 3rd edition. Robert W. Langhans. Ithaca, New York: Halcyon Press. 1990.
- *Kieff's Growing Manual.* C. Kieff. Blokker, Holland: Kieff Bloenzadan. 1989.
- *Overwintering Woody and Herbaceous Ornamental Plants (L'hivernage des Plantes Ligneuses et des Vivaces Ornementales).* Proceedings (English and French) from a conference held February 9-10, 1995 at Trois-Rivieres, Quebec. Available from IQDHO, (Institut québécois du développement de l'horticulture ornementale), 3230 rue Sicotte, B219, St. Hyacinth, Quebec J252M2.
- *Perennial Production (Les Vivaces la Production).* Proceedings (English and French) from a conference held February 9-10, 1994 at Trois-Rivieres, Quebec. Available from IQDHO (Institut québécois du développement de l'horticulture ornementale), 3230 rue Sicotte, B219, St. Hyacinth, Quebec J252M2.
- *Principles, Practices, and Comparative Costs of Overwintering Container-Grown Landscape Plants.* David J. Beattie, ed. Southern Cooperative Series Bulletin 313. Pennsylvania Nurserymen's Association, 1924 North Second Street, Harrisburg, PA 17102. 1986.
- *Requirements and Costs of Establishing and Operating a Three-Acre Herbaceous Perennial Container Nursery.* R. D. Taylor, E. M. Smith, D. J. Beattie, and G. P. Pealer. Southern Cooperative Series Bulletin 354.

OARDC Special Circular 136. Ohio Agricultural Research and Development Center (OARDC), Wooster, Ohio 44691-6900. 1990.
- *Tips on Growing Potted Perennials and Biennials.* Harry Tayama, ed. Second edition #107. Ohio Florists Association, 2130 Stella Court, Suite 200, Columbus, Ohio 43215-1033.

Propagation

- *Ball Perennial Manual: Propagation and Production.* Jim Nau. Ball Publishing Company. 1996.
- *Hardy Perennials from Seed.* Ernst Benary. Hann, Münden, Germany. 1988.
- *Park's Success with Seeds.* Anne Reilly. George W. Park Seed Co., Inc., Greenwood, South Carolina 29646. 1978.
- *Seed Germination Theory and Practice.* Self-published and distributed by the author, Norman C. Deno, Professor Emeritus of Chemistry. Ordering address is 139 Lenor Drive, State College, Pennsylvania 16801 USA. Two supplements are also available. The book is $20.00 U.S., and the supplements are $15.00 U.S. each. Prepayment is requested. Checks drawn on a U.S. bank or a foreign bank with a U.S. affiliate are accepted.

Specific Plants

- *Alliums: The Ornamental Onions.* Dilys Davies. Timber Press. 1994.
- *Border Pinks.* Richard Bird. Timber Press. 1995.
- *Classic Roses: An Illustrated Encyclopedia and Grower's Manual of Old Roses, Shrub Roses, and Climbers.* Peter Beales. Henry Holt and Company, Inc. 1997.
- *Clematis as Companion Plants.* Barry Fretwell. Timber Press. 1995.
- *Daylilies.* 1991. Lewis and Nancy Hill. Garden Way Publ.
- *Daylilies: The Wild Species and Garden Clones, Both Old and New, of the Genus Hemerocallis.* A. B. Stout. Sagapress. 1986.
- *Encyclopedia of Ferns.* David L. Jones. Timber Press. 1987.
- *Encyclopedia of Ornamental Grasses: How to Grow and Use over 250 Beautiful and Versatile Plants.* John Greenlee and Derek Fell. Emmaus, Pennsylvania: Rodale Press. 1992.
- *Euphorbias: A Gardeners' Guide.* Roger Turner. Timber Press. 1996.
- *Ferns to Know and Grow.* F. Gordon Foster. Timber Press. 1993.

- *The Gardener's Guide to Growing Hardy Geraniums.* Trevor Bath and Joy Jones. Timber Press. 1994.
- *The Gardener's Guide to Growing Hellebores.* Graham Rice and Elizabeth Strangman. Timber Press. 1993.
- *The Gardener's Guide to Growing Hostas.* Diana Grenfell. Timber Press. 1996.
- *The Gardener's Guide to Growing Irises.* Geoff Stebbings. Timber Press. 1997.
- *The Gardener's Guide to Growing Lilies.* Michael Jefferson-Brown and Harris Howland. Timber Press. 1995.
- *The Gardener's Guide to Growing Peonies.* Martin Page. Timber Press. 1997.
- *The Genus Primula.* Josef Halda. Tethys Pub. 1992.
- *Graham Stuart Thomas' Rose Book.* Graham Stuart Thomas. Books Britain. 1994.
- *Growing and Propagating Wildflowers.* Harry R. Phillips and Charlotte A. Jones-Roe. University of North Carolina Press. 1985.
- *Hardy Geraniums.* Peter F. Yeo. Timber Press. 1992.
- *Hemerocallis: Daylilies.* Walter Erhardt. Timber Press. 1994.
- *Hemerocallis, the Daylily.* R. W. Munson, Jr. Timber Press. 1993.
- *The Hosta Book.* Paul Aden, ed. Timber Press. 1992.
- *Iris (Gardener's Handbook,* Vol. 2). Fritz Kohlein and Molly Comerford Peters. Timber Press. 1988.
- *Japanese Iris.* Currier McEwen. University Press of New England. 1990.
- *Manual of Alpine Plants.* Will Ingwersen. Timber Press. 1986.
- *Manual of Grasses.* Rick Darke and Mark Griffiths, eds. Timber Press. 1995.
- *Modern Roses 10.* Thomas Cairns, ed. American Rose Society. 1993.
- *Ornamental Grasses.* Roger Grounds. Christopher Helm Publishing Ltd. 1990.
- *Ornamental Grasses: The Amber Wave.* Carole Ottesen. McGraw-Hill. 1995.
- *Ornamental Grasses for Cold Climates.* M. H. Meyer, R. B. White, and H. Pellett. NC Regional Extension Publication 573, University of Minnesota Distribution Center, 1420 Eckles Avenue, St. Paul, MN 55108. 1995.
- *Ornamental Grass Gardening: Design Ideas, Functions, and Effects.* Thomas A. Reinhardt, Martina Reinhardt, and Mark Moscowitz. New York: Michael Friedman Publishing Group. 1989.
- *Peonies.* Allan Rogers. Timber Press. 1995.
- *The Peony: Alice Harding's Peonies in the Little Garden and the Book of the Peony.* Alice Harding. Sagapress. 1993.
- *Perennials* (Eyewitness Handbooks). DK Publishing. 1996.
- *Poppies: A Guide to the Poppy Family in the Wild and in Cultivation.* Christopher Grey-Wilson. Timber Press. 1993.
- *Primula.* John Richards. Timber Press. 1993.
- *Rock Gardening: A Guide to Growing Alpines and Other Wildflowers in the American Garden.* H. Lincoln Foster. Timber Press. 1982.
- *Rock Garden Plants of North America: An Anthology from the Bulletin of the North American Rock Garden Society.* Jane McGary. Timber Press. 1996.
- *Sedum: Cultivated Stonecrops.* Ray Stephenson. Timber Press. 1994.
- *The Siberian Iris.* Currier McEwan. Timber Press. 1996.
- *Succulents: The Illustrated Dictionary.* Maurizio Sajeva and Mariangela Constanzo. Timber Press. 1997.
- *The World of Irises.* Bee Warburton. American Iris Society. 1986.

Pests, Diseases, Weeds, and Other Problems

- *Ball Pest and Disease Manual: Disease, Insect, and Mite Control on Flower and Foliage Crops.* 2nd edition. Charles C. Powell and Richard Kenneth Lindquist. Batavia, Illinois: Ball Publishing. 1997.
- *A Color Atlas of Pests of Ornamental Trees, Shrubs, and Flowers.* David V. Alford. New York: John Wiley and Sons. 1995.
- *Common Weeds of the United States.* U.S. Agricultural Research Service. Dover Publishing. 1972.
- *Diseases and Pests of Ornamental Plants.* 5th ed. Pascal Pirone. John Wiley and Sons. 1978.
- *Diseases of Annuals and Perennials: A Ball Guide: Identification and Control.* A. R. Chase, Margery Daughtrey, and Gary W. Simone. Batavia, Illinois: Ball Publishing. 1995.
- *A Field Guide to Wildflowers of Northeastern and North-Central North America* (Peterson Field Guide Series, 17). Roger Tory Peterson. Houghton Mifflin Co. 1975.
- *Floriculture Crops: Chemical Use Handbook — A Guide for Insecticide, Miticide, Fungicide, Growth Regulator, and Herbicide Application.* S. A. Carver, R. K. Lindquist, J. C. Peterson, C. C. Powell, and H. K. Tayama. Bulletin no. 735. Ohio Florists Association,

2130 Stella Court, Suite 200, Columbus, Ohio 43215-1033. 1997.

- *Fungi on Plants and Plant Products in the United States.* David F. Farr, Gerald F. Bills, George P. Chamuris, and Amy Y. Rossman. APS Press. 1989.
- *The Gardener's Guide to Common-Sense Pest Control.* William Olkowski, Shelia Daar, and Helga Olkowski. Newton, Connecticut: Taunton Press. 1996.
- *Guide to the Identification of Grasses.* O.M. Scotts & Sons. 1985.
- *Herbaceous Perennial Insect, Disease, Weeds, and Fertility Guidelines.* University of Maryland Cooperative Extension.
- *Insect Pests of Farm, Garden, and Orchard.* Ralph Howard Davidson and William F. Lyon. New York: John Wiley and Sons. 1987.
- *National Audubon Society Field Guide to North American Wildflowers: Eastern Region.* William A. Niering and Nancy C. Olmstead. Knopf Publishing. 1979.
- *National Audubon Society Field Guide to North American Wildflowers: Western Region.* Richard Spellenberg. Knopf Publishing. 1979.
- *Newcomb's Wildflower Guide: An Ingenious New Key System for Quick, Positive Field Identification of Wildflowers, Flowering Shrubs, and Vines.* Lawrence Newcomb. Little Brown & Co. 1989.
- *The New England Greenhouse Floricultural Recommendations: A Management Guide for Insects, Diseases, Weeds, and Growth Regulators*, 1997-1998. Bulletin FLOR1000NF78. Available from Bulletin Distribution Center, Draper Hall, Box 32010, University of Massachusetts, Amherst, MA 01003-2010.
- *The Ortho Problem Solver.* 4th ed. Michael D. Smith, ed. Ortho Books. 1994.
- *Weeds.* Alexander C. Martin. Golden Books Publishing Co. 1972.
- *Weeds of the Northeast.* Richard H. Uva, Joseph C. Neal, and Joseph M. Ditomaso. Cornell University Press. 1997.
- *Westcott's Plant Disease Handbook.* 5th ed. R. Kenneth Horst. New York: Chapman and Hall. 1990.

Societies

Note: These society addresses may change periodically due to a change in officers. The most current contacts can usually be found on the Internet under one of the garden gates on "Perry's Perennial Pages" (see page 208 for the web site address).

- American Hemerocallis Society, 1454 Rebel Drive, Jackson, MS 39211
- American Horticultural Society, 7931 East Boulevard Drive, Alexandria, VA 22308-1300
- American Hosta Society, 7802 NE 63rd Street, Vancouver, WA 98662
- American Iris Society, P.O. Box 8455, San Jose, CA 95155-8455
- American Penstemon Society, 1569 South Holland Ct., Lakewood, CO 80232
- American Peony Society, 250 Interlachen Road, Hopkins, MN 55343
- American Rock Garden Society, P.O. Box 67, Millwood, NY 10546
- American Rose Society, P.O. Box 30000, Shreveport, LA 71130-0030
- Bedding Plants International, P.O. Box 27517, Lansing, MI 48909; newsletter, meetings, directory
- Dwarf Iris Society of America, 3167 E. U.S. 224, Ossian, IN 46777
- Hardy Fern Foundation, P.O. Box 166, Medina, WA 98039-0166
- Hardy Plant Society, 11907 Nevers Road, Snohomish, WA 98290
- Herb Society of America, 9019 Kirtland Chardon Road, Kirtland, OH 44094
- Heritage Roses Group, R.D. 1 Box 299, Clinton Corners, NY 12514
- International Bulb Society, P.O. Box 4928, Culver City, CA 90230-4928
- International Clematis Society, Burford House, Tenbury Wells, Worcester WR15 8HQ, England
- International Herb Association, 1202 Allanson Road, Mundelein, IL 60060
- International Water Lily Society, P.O. Box 104, Buckeystown, MD 21717-0104
- Median Iris Society, 682 Huntley Heights Drive, Baldwin, MO 63021
- Mid-Atlantic Hardy Plant Society, 225 Green Street, Emmaus, PA 18049
- National Chrysanthemum Society, 5012 Kingston Drive, Annandale, VA 22003
- New England Wildflower Society, Garden in the Woods, Hemenway Road, Framingham, MA 01701
- North American Gladiolus Council, 2624 Spurgin, Missoula, MT 59801
- North American Heather Society, 502 Haskel Hill Road, Shelton, WA 98584
- North American Lily Society, P.O. Box 272, Owatonna, MN 55060
- Perennial Plant Association, 3383 Schirtzinger Road, Hilliard, OH 43026; newsletter, meetings, directory,

annual proceedings, plant of the year, marketing materials, *American Standards for Perennial Plants*

- Reblooming Iris Society, N75 W14257 North Point Drive, Menomonee Falls, WI 53051-4325
- Seed Savers Exchange, 203 Rural Avenue, Decorah, IA 52101
- Society for Japanese Irises, 9823 East Michigan Avenue, Galesburg, MI 49053
- Society for Louisiana Irises, P.O. Box 40175, University of Southwestern Louisiana, Lafayette, LA 70504
- Society for Siberian Irises, 802 Camellia Drive, Anderson, SC 29625
- Species Iris Group of North America, 486 Skiff Street, North Haven, CT 06473
- Spuria Iris Group, 3342 West Orangewood, Phoenix, AZ 85051

Trade Publications

- American Nurseryman, 77 West Washington Street, Suite 2100, Chicago, IL 60602; twice/month
- Greenhouse Grower, 37733 Euclid Avenue, Willoughby, OH 44904; monthly
- Grower Talks, P. O. Box 9, Batavia, IL 60510-0009; monthly
- GM Pro and NM Pro, P.O. Box 1868, Fort Worth, TX 76101; monthly
- Herb Growing and Marketing, P.O. Box 245, Silver Springs, PA 17575; monthly

Perennial Information on the Internet

Perry's Perennial Pages
http://www.uvm.edu/~pass/perry/

This is a one-stop shop for the latest perennial information and links on the Internet. Updated at least monthly, often more frequently, it contains listings of perennial leaflets, dates, and more for consumers and the commercial industry; information about perennial research at the University of Vermont; featured perennials, with descriptions and photos; references; hundreds of links to other perennial sites on the Internet, with hot links and grouped by category; and fun perennial activities such as cartoons and quizzes. References are both written and electronic — electronic ones include interactive CD-ROMs about plant selection, plant names, sources, and poisonous plants.

At the above site, under the "links" page, visit the garden gates for information on discussion groups. These are interactive lists one can subscribe to easily for free. They provide the chance to learn and discuss questions and issues with others who have interests similar to yours — perhaps alpine and rock gardens or a specific plant group such as iris or daylilies.

Plant Sources and Supplies

There are too many sources to list them all, but the following list may be helpful.

- *Andersen Horticultural Library's Source List of Plants and Seeds*. 1996. Andersen Horticultural Library, Minnesota Landscape Arboretum, 3675 Arboretum Drive, P.O. Box 39, Chanhassen, Minnesota 55317-0039. Please call (612) 443-2440 for current prices.
- *Canadian Plant Sourcebook*. 1996. Anne and Peter Ashley, 93 Fentiman Avenue, Ottawa, Ontario K1S 0T7 Canada.
- *Gardening by Mail*. Barbara Barton. Houghton Mifflin Company. (Also available on the interactive CD-ROM version of *The Plant Finder* — see below.)
- Perennial Plant Association directory of members by specialty (see "Societies" listing on page 207)
- *The Plant Finder* (British sources). Available from Moorland Publishing, Moor Farm Road, Airfield Estate, Ashbourne, Derbyshire DEG1HD England. (An interactive CD-ROM version is also available that includes other plant databases, book store lists, and other information.) Contact Moorland Publishing for current prices.
- *PPP Index: The European Plant Finder,* 3rd edition. Anne and Walter Erhardt. Eugen Ulmer Gmbh and Co., Wollgrasweg 41, 70599 Stuttgart, Germany. 1997. A comprehensive listing of plants and sources from 19 countries, with notes in six languages and much descriptive information on each nursery. Book includes a CD-ROM version that is easily installed on most recent computers and easily searchable.

Also see:

- Seed lists from the American Rock Garden Society and Hardy Plant Society (see "Societies" listing on page 207)
- Annual supplier directories from trade journals (see "Trade Publications" on this page)
- Lists at trade shows — check your local, state, regional, and national organizations